ELECTRICAL ENGINEERING
A History of the Men and and the Ideas

ELECTRICAL ENGINEERING

A History of the Men and the Ideas

By P. W. KINGSFORD

NEW YORK
ST. MARTIN'S PRESS

First published in Great Britain by
Edward Arnold (Publishers) Ltd.

First Published in
the United States of America in 1970 by
St. Martin's Press, Inc.,
175 Fifth Avenue, New York, New York

Library of Congress Catalog Card Number
75–106373

Printed in Great Britain by
Cox and Wyman Ltd., London, Fakenham and Reading

Preface

This book is about the contribution which scientists, electrical technologists and workers of all sorts have made to the present industrial society.

When Britain was the workshop of the world her wealth rested on steam power and mechanical engineering. When she lost that position the source of power in industry and of communication in society moved to electricity. Scientists and inventors all over Europe and America made this possible. Of the men whose work is described in this book, five were American, eleven were English, two Scottish, three Italian, one German and one French. Some discovered secrets of nature, some found out how to use electricity in machines. From these there came light in darkness, enormous power, communication between nations, and instant communication with masses of people.

This change gave rise to new kinds of work and new occupations – the electricians and technicians of all kinds. They worked in the power station, the factories, the shipyards, the building sites, people's homes, throughout the countryside, and at sea. The rapid advance of electrical technology meant that more knowledge and more skill were continually required of them. They formed themselves into trade unions to protect their interests.

The combined efforts of all these men, whether scientist or technician, have played a great part in shaping the society we live in.

P.W.K.

1968.

Acknowledgments

My grateful thanks are due to the following sources in England: to the Research Departments of the Electrical Trades Union and of the Post Office Engineering Union for permission to examine their records; to the staff of the library of The Hatfield Polytechnic and of the Royal Television Society, and to Mr. J. H. Savage, F.I.E.E. Eric Gilman and my colleagues encouraged me when I was slighted in my profession. Miss Susan Kitson helped with the typing.

Acknowledgement is gratefully made to the following for permission to include various extracts from the sources given:

Alfred Knopf: C. Mabee, *The American Leonardo*.

Cambridge University Press: Lord Rayleigh, *The Life of J. J. Thomson*.

Ernest Benn Ltd: G. Z. de Ferranti, *S. Z. de Ferranti. M.E.S. & K.R.S., Sir Joseph Swan*.

Faber & Faber Ltd: P. Dunsheath, *History of Electrical Engineering*.

G. Bell & Sons Ltd: J. J. Thomson, *Recollections and Reflections*.

George Allen & Unwin Ltd: S. W. Lerner, *Breakaway Unions and the Small Trades Union*.

Hamish Hamilton Ltd: J. Dugan, *The Great Iron Ship*.

Hodder & Stoughton Ltd: S. A. G. King, *Kelvin the Man*.

Hughes Massie Ltd: M. Josephson, *Edison*.

McGraw-Hill Book Co. Inc: D. Marconi, *My Father Marconi*.

Macmillan & Co. Ltd: E. T. King (ed.), *Lord Kelvin's Early Home*. W. K. Burlingame, *Out of Silence into Sound*.

Marshall, Morgan & Scott Ltd: Sir Ambrose Fleming, *Memories of a Scientific Life*.

Odhams Press Ltd: S. Moseley, *John Baird*. Sir R. Watson-Watt, *Three Steps to Victory*.

Routledge & Kegan Paul Ltd: G. Hubbard, *Cooke & Wheatstone.*

Royal Institution: Faraday MSS.

Royal Society: Faraday MSS.

Follett Publishing Company, Chicago: Lee de Forest, *Father of Radio.*

The author is also indebted to the following for permission to reproduce illustrations from the sources quoted:

Chapman & Hall Ltd: L. P. Williams, *Michael Faraday.* F. G. S. Baldwin, *History of the Telephone in the United Kingdom.*

Electrical Trades Union (Photograph of Banner).

Faber & Faber Ltd: P. Dunsheath, *History of Electrical Engineering.*

Ferranti Ltd: *Centenary Book.*

Marshal, Morgan & Scott Ltd: Sir Ambrose Fleming, *Memories of a Scientific Life.*

Odhams Press Ltd: Sir R. Watson-Watt, *Three Steps to Victory.*

Post Office Engineering Union: *75 Years – a Short History of the P.O.E.U.*

Radio Times Hulton Picture Library.

Royal Institution: Photograph of exhibit.

Royal Television Society: J. D. Percy, John L. Baird.

The Director of the Science Museum, London: photographs of exhibits in the Museum (Plates 3, 8 & 14 – Crown copyright).

List of Plates

between pages 128 and 129

Contents

CHAPTER ONE

The Beginnings of Electrical Science

ELECTRICAL engineering is not more than a hundred years old but magnetism and electricity, on which it is based, have been known and observed for thousands of years. The need to use electricity for light and power did not arise until the nineteenth century but many centuries before that the lodestone and the magnetized needle were used for navigation. There was an enormous gap over the years during which very slowly men came to understand these two elementary forces and to control them for practical use.

Magnetism had obvious uses far back in antiquity. The Chinese emperors about 2000 B.C. had a 'south-pointing chariot' in which, by means of a lodestone, a figure pointed always to the south. Later the Greeks and the Romans described the lodestone and its power of attracting iron. As trading by sea developed sailors learned to use the magnetic compass. In the thirteenth century an Italian writer gave detailed instructions how to make a mariner's compass. The Greeks had also known a great deal about amber and the way in which, when rubbed, it attracted light objects; the Greek word for amber was 'elektron'. All this information was stored in the Latin and Greek writings and neglected until the Renaissance, centuries later, when the learning of the ancient world was revived and developed by the Western world.

Electricity was also known from early times as lightning, the aurora borealis, and the mysterious light, known as St. Elmo's Fire, which seamen saw playing round the ships' mastheads. The ancient world may have known how to use conductors to divert lightning from buildings. The Greeks certainly described the torpedo fish that could stun its prey with an electric charge. But no one could explain all these things and say why they happened, and so they remained just curiosities of nature.

Magnetism, however, was much more than merely a curiosity; it became necessary to understand it as much longer sea voyages were made and better navigation became necessary. From 1499 onwards the Portuguese, Spaniards, Italians and English began to discover the new worlds outside Europe. These bold navigators discovered new facts about the behaviour of their compasses. Christopher Columbus, using the magnetic compass on his famous voyage, found to his surprise that the deviation from the magnetic to the geographic pole increased as he went ever westward, and his pilots grew afraid that their compasses had become useless. These discoveries made men want to know more about magnetism.

At about the same time as the navigators were discovering the new world the scholars of western Europe were rediscovering the old Greek and Latin writings about science and mathematics and beginning to challenge traditional ideas. Copernicus challenged the age-old belief that the earth was the centre of the universe and stated that it revolved round the sun. The Church condemned the new ideas and there was a great division among scientists and writers between Copernicans and anti-Copernicans. The controversy spread to England where the group of Copernicans included a learned doctor called William Gilbert who could read the old classical writings about magnetism which had come to light. It is not surprising therefore that the first great book on magnetism was written by an English doctor at a time when England was becoming a great seafaring nation.

WILLIAM GILBERT (1540–1603)

William Gilbert was almost exactly a contemporary of Queen Elizabeth I. He was born seven years after her and died very soon after she had been succeeded by James I. He became physician to the queen, a great responsibility when the peace of the country depended on Elizabeth remaining head of the state. Gilbert was born in Colchester, where his monument can still be seen in Holy Trinity Church, the son of a Suffolk gentleman and recorder of that ancient town. He went to

Cambridge University, took his M.A., and then his M.D. In 1573, like many ambitious young men he moved to London, the centre of England's growing foreign trade and wealth. In that same year Francis Drake brought back to London £20,000 worth of Spanish treasure from his raid on Panama. He was to become a national hero by sailing the *Golden Hind* round the world. England's prosperity and safety were in the sea and above all it was navigation and seamanship which counted. In the meantime William Gilbert built up a large practice in London, climbed to the top of his profession and became President of the College of Physicians.

While England and Spain drifted towards war Gilbert began his research into magnetism for which the Queen had made him a grant. He published the results seventeen years later, in 1600, in his great book, written in Latin as was customary among scientists at that time, *De magnete, magneticisque corporibus, et de magno magnete tellure, physiologia nova*, or – in English – On the magnet, magnetic bodies, and the Great Magnet the Earth, a new physiology. This was the first great contribution to electrical science.

The main link between this learned work and the practical questions of the times was the problems of navigation. Dr. Gilbert had also a professional interest in amber which was supposed to have value for medicine. The problem of determining longitude at sea had puzzled mariners for centuries and it had become important to solve it. It was thought that a solution could be found by measuring the dip or inclination to the horizontal of a magnetized needle. The dip had been discovered by a Wapping compass maker, Robert Norman, and described by him in 1581 in his book *The Newe Attractive*. In fact he suggested that the attraction of the magnet was the earth itself. The scholarly physician Gilbert learned from Norman the practical compass maker and verified for himself the experimental results of Norman.

One of his chief experiments was to use a small-scale model of the earth. This was a large sphere of magnetic iron over which he moved a small compass needle on a pivot. He could then plot on the sphere the lines of direction in which the needle set and map out on its surface circles of variation and the poles. He also showed that, when the needle was moved about, its inclination to the surface varied according to its distance from the poles. At length he arrived at the explanation that the earth was one great magnet with its own magnetic field. This was a notable step forward in science.

Gilbert also investigated electricity, though not so thoroughly as magnetism, because it had no practical use. Much less was known about it and Gilbert had to go back to the ancient classical writers. He found that many other substances besides amber had electrical attraction, such as diamonds, sapphires, glass and sulphur. For these attracting substances he coined the word 'electrics'. He was the first man to show the differences between magnetic attraction and electrical attraction, although the connection between magnetism and electricity was not discovered until more than two hundred years later.

Gilbert never married. His priceless collection of papers and instruments was left to the College of Physicians, only to be destroyed in the great fire of London. His work was of great practical importance for navigation and it was also a landmark in science which many men were to follow. The great Galileo praised his research and it was used by Francis Bacon, the first Englishman to write a comprehensive account of scientific methods. The poet Dryden wrote: 'Gilbert shall live till lodestones cease to draw.'

LUIGI GALVANI (1737–1798) AND ALESSANDRO VOLTA (1745–1827)

There was a long gap of nearly two hundred years between Gilbert and the discoveries of Galvani and Volta from whom the words galvanometer and volt come. Electricity and magnetism continued to baffle men; moreover, apart from the demands from the seamen to improve instruments for navigation, there was no great need for their use.

However, men gradually came to know more about static electricity. A German, Otto von Guericke, invented the first frictional electrical machine out of a rotating globe of sulphur which gave off electrical sparks. An Englishman, Stephen Gray, was able to transmit electric charges over several hundred yards and discovered the principles of conduction and insulation. The most important discovery was the Leyden jar, the work of two scientists of Leyden University in the Netherlands in 1745. For the first time electric charges could be stored; this stimulated research into electricity all over Europe. Then came the first steps towards discovery of the steady electric current.

The equipment available to Galvani and Volta was simple. The generators were all frictional types producing static electricity in very small quantities. The electricity could be stored in capacitors, the Leyden jars, and measured by the force of repulsion between charged pith balls. Materials had been divided into conductors and non-conductors and it had been established that the production of electricity was the separation of dissimilar charges.

The first step was taken by Galvani, who was a professor of anatomy at the ancient University of Bologna, then in the Papal States. When experimenting with dead frogs and electricity he noticed that the frogs' legs twitched when two different metals, copper and zinc, were made to contact them. He explained this, wrongly, by saying that it was due to animal electricity, that is, the electricity in the frogs' nerves and muscles. The date was 1791. Galvani's real importance was that his mistake led to Volta finding the right explanation and, as a result, inventing in 1800 the Voltaic pile, the first electric battery.

Alessandro Volta was born at Como and became professor of physics there before he was thirty. He moved south to the University at Pavia, which was then in the Duchy of Milan, and was appointed professor of natural philosophy. He studied for some years Galvani's discovery of so-called 'animal electricity', which had made a great sensation. He was not convinced that Galvani was right. Eventually he found the correct explanation that the muscular twitchings in the frogs were caused by a current of electricity created by two different metals in contact in a moist body. Volta realized this was an entirely new kind of electricity and began to use the term 'current'. It was then a short step for him to add another pair of metals separated by a piece of moistened pasteboard and find that the current was increased. Then he went on adding more and more laid on top of each other vertically and thus created the first battery of cells called the Voltaic pile.

Volta, who was a Fellow of the Royal Society, immediately wrote to the President of the Society announcing his discovery:

Como,
March 20, 1800.

'After a long silence, for which I will not try to excuse my self, I have the pleasure of communicating to you, Sir, and through you to the Royal Society, some striking results which I have obtained in following up my experiments on the electricity developed by the mere contact of metals of different kinds which are liquids or contain moisture to which they owe their conductivity. The most important of these results, which really embraces them all is the construction of an apparatus which resembles the Leyden Jar in its effects, such as the shocks which it can give to the arms, etc., but which functions continuously, its charge being renewed after each discharge; it possesses in fine an inexhaustible charge and perpetual action upon the electric fluid.

'It consists of a long series of an alternate succession of three conducting substances, either copper, tin or water; or what is much preferable, silver, zinc and a solution of any neutral or alkaline salt. The mode of combining these substances consists in placing horizontally, first, a plate or disc of silver (half a crown, for instance) next a plate of zinc of the same dimensions; and, lastly, a similar piece of spongy matter, such as pasteboard or leather, fully impregnated with the saline solution. This set of threefold layers is to be repeated thirty or forty times, forming thus what the author calls his "columnar machine". It is to be observed that the metals must always be in the same order. That is if the silver is the lowermost in the first pair of metallic plates, it is to be so in all the successive ones, but that the effects will be the same if this order be inverted in all the pairs. As the fluid, either water or the saline solution, and not the spongy layer impregnated with it, is the substance that contributes to the effect, it follows that as soon as these layers are dry, no effect will be produced.'

Volta pointed out that his apparatus was like the structure of the electric eel which had layers of membrane surrounded by liquid. It, too, could rebuild its charge after giving a shock. There was no friction producing electricity in either and so both produced the new 'current' electricity.

This new source of electricity was a tremendous step forward. At last a source from which continuous current could be taken was available to all scientists. The electrostatic machines were quite incapable of producing more than a momentary current surge. The effect of Volta's discovery on science in England was immediate. Within a few years Humphrey Davy used it to separate chemical compounds, to discover many elements such as potassium and sodium, and to establish electrolysis. Davy employed Michael Faraday as his assistant and this led, in due course, to Faraday's great discoveries of electro-magnetism.

It is interesting to compare Galvani and Volta in the political upheaval of their time. It is called the age of the French Revolution and of Napoleon's empire because every country in Europe was deeply changed by these events. As well as a hot war between the struggling armies there was a cold war of ideas in which the new democratic ideas of liberty, equality and fraternity sought to overthrow the old system of rule by the nobility and the church. The scientists were affected like everyone else. Before the French Revolution of 1789, when Galvani was at Bologna and Volta at Pavia, the various small Italian states were under the sway of Austria. When Napoleon's armies spread over Europe and defeated Austria Napoleon re-organized Italy and set up in the north, under his control, the Cisalpine Republic. This new republic took Bologna and other cities away from the Pope, at their own request, and took over the Duchy of Milan which included Pavia.

Galvani and Volta reacted differently to these political changes by which they came under the modern rule of France instead of the old feudal government of Austria and the Pope. Galvani, who had lost in the controversy about electricity, remained a supporter of the old rule of the Pope, refused to take the oath of allegiance to the new republic and was discharged from his post at Bologna. Volta, who had discovered the new electricity, accepted the new political system. He was invited to describe his discoveries to Napoleon himself, was awarded the cross of the Legion of Honour and was made a Count of the French Empire.

GEORG SIMON OHM (1787–1854)

Every student knows about Ohm's Law, but who was the man who gave his name to it, and how did he come to discover the Law? Georg Ohm was born at Erlangen in Bavaria which was an independent kingdom, with its capital at Munich, before Germany became a nation. His father was a locksmith and a skilled metal worker, and he taught his son mathematics as well as his own skills. This was important to Ohm because he became a notable experimenter and his father's training enabled him to make all the apparatus he needed.

After attending the University of Erlangen for eighteen months Ohm became a teacher and until he was thirty he earned a meagre living as a tutor of mathematics and physics, travelling from job to job throughout Germany and Switzerland. After the peace of 1815 he eventually obtained a permanent post as teacher of mathematics at the Jesuits' College in Cologne in the Rhineland. The Jesuits had a great deal of power and in fact, a few years later, they controlled the government of catholic Bavaria.

While Ohm was at Cologne he carried out the experiments which resulted in the statement of his Law. He was inspired to do this work by a famous French mathematician, Fourier, and this was not surprising because, since the French Revolution, the ideas of France had spread all over Europe and particularly into those parts near France, such as the Rhineland.

When he announced the first results of his experiments Ohm expressed the famous Law incorrectly. After the error had been pointed out he published in 1827 the book *The Galvanic Circuit Treated Mathematically*, which contained Ohm's Law as we know it today. On the strength of his discovery he went to Berlin, then the capital of Prussia, with great hopes of obtaining an important post. But unfortunately for Ohm it took some years for his discovery to be accepted. His methods were attacked and his work was ignored. The reason for this was that the leading German philosophers of the day, and particularly in Prussia, did not believe in the need for experiment in science, and consequently they could not understand Ohm's work.

In disgust, Ohm resigned himself to obscurity as a private tutor in Berlin, until six years later he was appointed as a teacher at the Nuremberg Polytechnic. This was in his native land of Bavaria where the conservative German philosophers had less influence. From that time on he gained more recognition. His fame spread abroad and in England the Royal Society awarded him the Copley Medal, for 'establishing the laws of the electric circuit'.

Meanwhile in Bavaria there was a political upheaval which brought Ohm final recognition in his own country. Throughout Europe the middle-class liberals had been getting ready to revolt for their freedom against the royalist conservative governments; in 1848 revolutions took place in almost every country of Europe. In Bavaria the revolution forced the king to abdicate, ended the power of the Jesuits, and brought in a liberal government. Immediately afterwards the new government made Ohm a professor at the University of Munich. The value of his work and of modern scientific method was thus at last recognized in his own country, but he did not enjoy this long, for he died in 1854.

MICHAEL FARADAY (1791–1867)

Michael Faraday was one of the greatest scientists of all time. He has been compared in greatness with Galileo and Isaac Newton. Until his day the only important source of electricity was voltaic current. What Faraday did was to bring electricity and magnetism together and discover a new source of current. He discovered electromagnetic induction, the principle of the electric motor, and he laid down the laws of electrolysis. Yet his parents were poor and he had little education. He himself said, 'My education was of the most ordinary description, consisting of little more than the rudiments of reading, writing and arithmetic at a common day-school. My hours out of school were passed at home and in the streets.'

He was born at Newington, then in the Surrey outskirts of London, on 22nd September, 1791. His father was a blacksmith, a craftsman like Ohm's father, who had migrated from

Yorkshire, and his mother was a farmer's daughter from the same county. When Faraday was five the family moved to rooms over a coach-house in Marylebone and, because of his father's ill-health, they were reduced to receiving public relief under the poor law. When he was thirteen he started work in the shop of a bookseller and newsagent called Riebau, first as an errand-boy and then as an apprentice in book-binding. The errand-boy had to deliver and collect the news-papers loaned by Riebau to his customers. His elder brother became a blacksmith. While Faraday was still in his apprenticeship his father died and his mother kept the family going by taking in lodgers.

Faraday was lucky, in several ways, to be employed by Riebau, the bookseller. Learning the trade of bookbinding, sewing the pages, preparing the binding, binding the book, meant that he had to become quick and clever with his hands. This stood him in good stead later on when he had to make and arrange apparatus and carry out the experiments of others as well as his own. He liked reading; 'there were plenty of books there and I read them', he wrote. He kept notebooks of his reading and particularly of anything scientific. Many of Riebau's customers were men of science, and one of them noticed that Faraday was studying an article on electricity in an encyclopaedia which he was binding and found that he knew a good deal about it. This was Faraday's introduction to his life-long work. The article in question condemned the old theory that electricity was a kind of fluid and suggested that it was some sort of vibration.

During his leisure he continued to educate himself. Riebau gives us a vivid picture of this:

'. . . after the regular hours of Business, he was chiefly employed in Drawing and Copying from the Artists Repository a work published in Numbers which he took in weekly – also Electrical Machines from the Dicty. of Arts and Sciences and other works which came in to bind . . . he went an early morning walk in the Morning Visiting always some Works of Art or searching for some Mineral or Vegitable curiosity – Holloway Water Works Highgate Archway, W Middlesex Water Works – Strand Bridge – Junction Water Works etc. etc. . . .

his mind ever engaged, besides attending to Bookbinding which he executed in a proper manner. . . .

If I had any curious book from my Customers to bind, with Plates, he would copy such as he thought Singular or Clever, which I advised him to Keep by him. Irelands Hogarth and other Graphic Works, he much admired (Thomson's) Chemistry in 4 vols. he bought and interleaved great part of it, Occasionally adding Notes with Drawings and Observations.'

He made friends and was introduced to one of the societies which existed for people who were interested in science, the City Philosophical Society. There he attended some popular evening lectures on science given by the leading light of the group of young men who had formed the society; the fee of one shilling per lecture was paid by his brother. Faraday describes what he did at these lectures which opened a new world for him:

'My method was to take with me a sheet or two of paper stitched or pinned up the middle so as to form something like a book. I usually got a front seat and there placing my hat on my knees and my paper on the hat I as Mr. Tatum proceeded on his lecture set down the most prominent words, short but important sentences, titles of the experiments names of what substances came under consideration and many other hints that would tend to bring what had passed to my mind. . . .

On leaving the lecture room I proceeded immediately homewards and in that and the next night had generally drawn up a second set of notes from the first. These second notes were more copious, more connection and more legible than the first. . . .

These second set of notes were my guide whilst writing out the lecture in a rough manner. They gave me the order in which the different parts came under consideration and in which the experiments were performed and they called to mind the most important subjects that were discussed.'

Next he began to carry out simple experiments at home and made for himself a small Voltaic pile, as he humbly described in a letter to a friend:

'I, Sir, my own self, cut out seven discs of the size of halfpennies each! I, Sir, covered them with seven half pence, and I interposed between seven, or rather six, pieces of paper soaked in a solution of muriate of soda! But laugh no longer, dear A; rather wonder at the effects this trivial power produced. It was sufficient to produce the decomposition of sulphate of magnesia – an effect which extremely surprised me; for I did not, could not, have any idea that the agent was competent to the purpose.'

(Dear A was Benjamin Abbot, a young Quaker, better educated than Faraday but religious like him, whom he had met at the society and with whom he became close friends.)

He continued experimenting and observing and wrote again:

'Ideas and thoughts often spring up in my mind, and are again irrevocably lost for want of noting at the time. Several of the metals, when rubbed, emit a peculiar smell, and more particularly tin. Now smells are generally supposed to be caused by particles of the body that are given off. If so, then it introduced to our notice a very volatile property of these metals. But I suspect their electric states are concerned.'

Faraday was conscious that his English was not as good as it might be and he hoped that writing his correspondence would help him to improve it.

Soon he found that chemistry was the science which he must serve first. This change came about when he read a popular science book of the time called *Conversations on Chemistry*, by Mrs. Marcet. Much of it was based on the famous and fashionable lectures on the wonders of chemistry given by Humphrey Davy at the Royal Institution. Mrs. Marcet wrote:

'Mr. Davy . . . whose important discoveries have opened such improved views on chemistry, has suggested an hypothesis which may throw light upon that science. He supposes that there are two kinds of electricity with one or other of which all bodies are united. These we distinguish by the names of *positive* and *negative* electricity; those bodies are disposed to combine which possess opposite electricities, as they are brought together by the attraction which these electricities have for each other. But whether this hypothesis be altogether founded on truth or not, it is impossible to question the great influence of electricity in chemical combinations.'

After reading this Faraday realized he must study chemistry in order to understand electricity. The opportunity came when one of the customers at the shop, who was a member of the Royal Institution, gave Faraday tickets for a course of lectures by Davy in which Davy, among other things, defended his new theory that chlorine was an element. These lectures so inspired Faraday that, in his own words, 'The desire to be engaged in scientific occupation, even though of the lowest kind, induced me, whilst an apprentice, to write, in my ignorance of the world and simplicity of my mind, to Sir Joseph Banks, then President of the Royal Society. Naturally enough, "No answer", was the reply left with the porter.'

Rebuffed, but not discouraged, he took a job as a journeyman bookbinder, his apprenticeship having finished in 1812 when he was twenty-one. However, he was unsatisfied and unhappy in his work and he had far less time and leisure than before for science. It so happened that Humphrey Davy had had an accident to his eye during an experiment and, Faraday being recommended through the Royal Institution, he engaged him as his secretary for a few days, though at the same time he tried to persuade him to stick to bookbinding because a career in science was so uncertain. Faraday, however, decided to try again, and he sent his complete notes of Davy's lectures, bound by himself, a volume of 386 pages, as a gift to Davy, and asked for a job with him.

Davy, now president of the Royal Society, was quite a different kind of man from Sir Joseph Banks. From humble beginnings he had gained a European reputation as professor of chemistry at the Royal Institution. The Institution, which was devoted to research in technology, had been on the decline but Davy had put it on its feet with his own research and his brilliant lectures. A great scientist, he laid the basis for electrochemistry. The famous man, busy with many projects, did not ignore the unknown journeyman bookbinder; instead he sent him an encouraging reply:

December 12th, 1812.

Sir,

I am far from displeased with the proof you have given me of your confidence, and which displays great zeal, power of memory and attention. I am obliged to go out of town, and shall not be settled in town until the end of January. I will then see you at any time you wish.

It would gratify me to be of any service to you. I wish it may be in my power.

I am, Sir, your obedient humble servant,

H. Davy.

Faraday was lucky again; when Davy had to sack his laboratory assistant for disorderly conduct and offered the job to Faraday he eagerly accepted it, at a guinea a week, with two rooms over the Royal Institution, and fuel and candles. In the laboratory he soon became extremely useful in the experiments on chlorides which Davy was making.

So far his social life had been very limited, and he had hardly been outside London. Soon, however, he was asked by Davy to accompany him on a tour of Europe. The extraordinary thing was that England and France were at war during the whole eighteen months of the tour, a period between Napoleon's retreat from Moscow in 1812 and the battle of Waterloo in 1815. But the men of science did not consider themselves at war even if their governments were, and the French scientists welcomed the travellers.

The party set out in October 1813. The journey from London to Paris took eleven days. In Paris Faraday met Ampère, and saw Napoleon, and the Chappe system of semaphore telegraphs sending and receiving messages from the city. He met Volta in Milan. All the time he was learning from Davy, and while in Paris he watched Davy as he discovered a new element, iodine. The only blot on his pleasure was that Lady Davy, who was an extreme snob, tried to treat him as a servant, but he was too proud and refused to be treated in such a manner. 'This at first,' he wrote to Benjamin Abbott, 'was a source of great uneasiness to me and often times made me feel very dull and discontented and if I could have come home again at that time you should have seen me before I had left

England six months. As I became more acquainted with the manners of the world and those things necessary in my station and understood better her true character I learned to despise her taunts and resist her power and this kind of determined conduct added to a little polishing which the friction of the world had naturally produced in your friend made her restrain her spleen from its full course to a more moderate degree.'

When he returned to London in 1815 Faraday's restricted and poverty-stricken background had been widened by contact with a new social life. He had learnt to read French and Italian, the languages of Coulomb, Ampère, Galvani and Volta. He had met many scientists and had learnt about society, but had refused to be taken in by its glamour. Back at the Royal Institution, at an increased salary of thirty shillings a week, he developed Davy's work on chlorine, discovered two chlorides of carbon, and helped Davy with his safety lamp. He also worked on a project to find steel alloys for cutting instruments. These were practical technical projects required by the policy of the Institution. His duties included helping with the regular lectures, and he began to take pupils himself. In the meantime he began to build up a reputation as a consultant chemist; young men with his knowledge of chemistry were rare and by 1820 he had begun to make a name for himself. He was asked to analyse drinking water and to test the drying of food for ships' provisions. The water supply of London was an ever-present problem because of the cholera, and the danger of scurvy among seamen was not dealt with until ships carried lime juice.

Faraday had become a busy man without the time to spare for research into electricity. Here is one week's diary:

'On Monday evening there is a scientific meeting of Members here and every other Monday a dinner, to both of which my company is requested. On Tuesday evening I have a Pupil who comes at 6 o'clk and stops till 9, engaged in private lessons. On Wednesday the City Philosophical Society requires my aid. Thursday is my only evening for accidental engagements. Friday, my pupil returns and stops his three hours; and on Saturday I have to arrange my little private business'.

He had never had much time to be sociable; he knew that if he was to be a scientist he needed all the time he had to overcome the handicap of lack of early education. He had had no time for women and had regarded marriage as a snare. But like most men he needed a wife and in 1821, he married Sarah Barnard, the daughter of an elder of his church. He was, in fact, much in love: 'You know me,' he wrote to her, 'as well or better than I do myself. You know my former prejudices, and my present thoughts – you know my weaknesses, my vanity, my whole mind; you have converted me from one erroneous way, let me hope you will attempt to correct what others are wrong.'

Faraday was fortunate in his wife. They never had children but she looked after him as he needed to be. She did not understand his work but when he was absorbed in it she brought his meals to the laboratory. When he was exhausted by mental concentration and had bad headaches she gave him comfort and companionship on their long walks. His life alternated between periods of intense concentration and complete relaxation. He built himself a velocipede and amazed visitors by careering along the corridors of the Royal Institution. Even in the laboratory there were sometimes lighter moments. Faraday would take his favourite nieces there to watch the making of soda lozenges or the brewing of ginger beer, the behaviour of frog spawn or Planaria worms.

Faraday did not make his first major discovery in electricity until he was thirty. Until then it had taken him all his time to become a chemist. Then his interest in electricity was re-awakened by a request that he should write a short history of this new science for a journal. To do this he had to repeat for himself the recent experiments of Oersted and Ampère. Hans Christian Oersted, the Danish scientist, had just announced his discovery that an electric current produced magnetic effects and that the magnetic force was circular. Faraday noticed certain new facts which led to his famous experiment in which current-carrying wire was made to rotate round a magnet, or the magnet round the wire. This was his discovery of electromagnetic force, upon which the principle of the electric motor is based. He wrote: 'I have succeeded not only in showing the existence of the motion theoretically, but experimentally, and have been able to make the wire revolve round a magnetic pole, or a magnetic pole round the wire.' It was an exciting moment. Faraday's brother-in-law described the scene: 'All at once he exclaimed, "Do you see, do you see, do you see, George?", as the wire began to revolve. One end I recollect was in the cup of quicksilver, the other attached above to the centre. I shall never forget the enthusiasm expressed in his face and the sparkling in his eyes.'

After this Faraday made no further discovery in electrical science for ten years. This was not because he lost interest; on the contrary he made many experiments and thought a great deal about the connection between magnetism and electricity, and he noted down the ideas that came to him to be tried out when the time was available. It was rather that he felt it his duty to give his time to the research which the Royal Institution, where he was now director of the laboratory, was asked to do. It was the various branches of chemistry which were of practical importance to industry at a time when the industrial revolution was developing fast and demanding new processes and new materials, whereas electricity had little practical application. So Faraday worked on chemical research during these years and made useful discoveries in sulphur and its acids, the chemistry of rubber, chlorides, benzene, all of great use for industry. One particular research project, which took many years, was on improvement in glass; this was to be important for lighthouses and the safety of shipping.

Much of his time during this period was spent on getting wider support for the Royal Institution and improving its finances which were at a low ebb. He began his Friday Evening Discourses in order to popularize science. 'They are intended,' he explained, 'as meetings of an easy and agreeable nature to which members have the privilege of bringing friends and where all may feel at ease. It is desirable that all things of interest, large or small, be exhibited here either in the library or in the lecture-room. In the lecture-room the lecturer and the audience are relieved of all formalities except those essential to secure the attention and freedom of all. The lecture may be long or short, so it contain good matter, and afterwards everyone may adjourn for tea and talk.' He also appealed to young people with his Christmas Courses of Lectures adapted to a Juvenile Auditory. These were immensely popular with children and he continued them every Christmas until he retired. They have been maintained ever since.

As a lecturer he took great pains and conscientiously studied the art of lecturing. 'Those who will take the trouble of thinking, and the bees of business,' he wrote, 'wish for something they can comprehend . . . listeners expect reason and sense, whilst gazers only require a succession of words. . . . A lecturer should appear easy and collected, undaunted and unconcerned, his thoughts about him and his mind clear and free for the contemplation and description of his subject . . . His whole behaviour should evince respect from his audience, and he should in no case forget that he is in their presence . . . he should never, if possible, turn his back on them, but should give them full reason to believe that all his powers have been exerted for their pleasure and instruction.' Faraday could be an inspiring lecturer, as one of his admirers records:

'His instruments were never in his way, and his manipulation never interfered with his discourse. He was completely master of the situation; he had his audience at his command, as he had himself and all his belongings; he had nothing to fret him, and he could give his eloquence full sway. It was an irresistible eloquence, which compelled attention and insisted upon sympathy. It waked the young from their visions and the old from their dreams. There was a gleaming in his eyes which no painter could copy and no poet could describe. Their radiance seemed to send a strange light into the very heart of his congregation; and when he spoke, it was felt that the stir of his voice and the fervour of his words could belong only to the owner of those kindling eyes. His thought was rapid, and made itself a way in new phrases, if it found none ready, – as the mountaineer cuts steps in the most hazardous ascent with his own axe. His enthusiasm sometimes carried him to the point of ecstasy when he expatiated on the beauty of nature, and when he lifted the veil from her deep mysteries. His body then took motion from his mind; his hair streamed out from his head, his hands were full of nervous action, his light lithe body seemed to quiver with its eager life. His audience took fire with him, and every face was flushed.'

In 1827 he was offered the post of professor of chemistry at London University but he refused it because he felt that the Royal Institution, which had sheltered him and helped him so much, needed him for a few more years.

Faraday was happy at the Royal Institution and grateful to it. His pay there, at the age of forty was only '£100 per annum, house coals and candles' but, as an expert in many fields, he was frequently consulted by industry and the government, and his income as a consultant was about £1,000 a year. In fact, money meant little to him. In 1831 he decided to give up the consultancy and the very considerable income with it and devote himself to the research into electromagnetism which he had wanted to do for a long time. He asked to be relieved of the lengthy research on glass so that he could concentrate on his own research:

'With reference to the request which the Council of the Royal Society have done me the honour of making – namely that I should continue the investigation – I should, under circumstances of perfect freedom, assent to it at once; but obliged as I have been to devote the whole of my spare time to the experiments already described, and consequently to resign the pursuit of such philosophical inquiries as suggested themselves to my own mind, I would wish, under present circumstances, to lay the glass aside for a while, that I may enjoy the pleasure again of working out my own thoughts on other subjects.'

Oersted had produced magnetic attraction from an electric current. Faraday thought that electricity could be produced from magnetism and he had a burning desire to prove it. This was the subject of the 'philosophical inquiries' he wanted to pursue. Straight away, in the same year of 1831, between August and October, he achieved success in a series of experiments and discovered electromagnetic induction. His discoveries during these three months made possible later the transformer, the alternator, and the dynamo.

On 29th August he carried out the famous ring experiment. This is the record in his diary:

'Have had an iron ring made (soft iron), iron round and

$\frac{7}{8}$ inches thick and ring 6 inches in external diameter. Wound many coils of copper wire round one half, the coils being separated by twine and calico – there were 3 lengths of wire each about 24 feet long and they could be connected as one length or used as separate lengths. By trial with a trough each was insulated from the other. Will call this side of the ring A. On the other side but separated by an interval was wound wire in two pieces together amounting to about 60 feet in length, the direction being as with the former coils; this side call B. . . . Made the coil on B side one coil and connected its extremities by a copper wire passing to a distance and just over a magnetic needle (3 feet from iron ring). Then connected the ends of one of the pieces on A side with battery; immediately a sensible effect on needle. It oscillated and settled at last in original position. On *breaking* connection on A side with battery again a disturbance of the needle.

Made all the wires on A side one coil and sent current from battery through the whole. Effect on needle much stronger than before.'

After further experiments Faraday recorded: 'Hence here distinct conversion of Magnetism into Electricity.' The coil in these experiments, the first transformer, is still kept in the Royal Institution.

On 17th October he made the second major discovery. His diary records the experiment:

'O a cylinder, hollow, of paper, covered with 8 helices of copper wire going in the same direction . . . Expts with O. The 8 ends of the helices at one end of the cylinder were cleaned and fastened together as a bundle. So were the 8 other ends. These compound ends were then connected with the Galvanometer by long copper wires – then a cylindrical bar magnet $\frac{3}{4}$ inch in diameter and $8\frac{1}{2}$ inches in length had one end just inserted into the end of the helix cylinder – then it was quickly thrust in the whole length and *the galvanometer* needle moved – then pulled out and again the *needle moved but* in the opposite direction. This effect was repeated every time the magnet was put in or out and therefore a wave of Electricity was so produced from *mere approximation of a magnet* and not from its formation *in situ*.'

This was the second step in the induction of electrical currents. Pulsating currents, or what Faraday called waves of electricity, could be produced by pushing and pulling a magnet in and out of a helix.

The next step was to produce steady continuous currents. This Faraday achieved at the end of October. His apparatus was simply a circular copper plate on a horizontal brass axle which revolved between the poles of a magnet; two contacts, one on the brass axle and one on the edge of the plate, led to the galvanometer. Powerful currents lasted as long as the plate revolved. This was the origin of the dynamo. Faraday was not interested in developing this apparatus into a practical dynamo because he cared only for scientific discovery. Three years later the prime minister, Sir Robert Peel, is said to have visited him and asked him what was the use of the apparatus. Faraday's answer was, 'I know not, but I wager that one day your government will tax it.'

These marvellous discoveries were the basis of all future electrical technology. They were made during a period of only a few weeks but they were the result of ten years' deep thinking.

Faraday continued his research into the nature of electricity until his health broke down in 1839. This immense work included electrochemistry, induction, static electricity and its relation to current electricity. The strain caused complete mental exhaustion and he was unable to do any work for nearly two years; he referred to 'the ill health connected with my head'. His achievement had been made by sacrificing his personal and social life and by isolating himself from society. It so happened that his religious beliefs and activities also led him to this.

He belonged to a small nonconformist sect called the Sandemanians, which led a simple life and had strict rules of behaviour. They gathered in small congregations, without a priest but led by their own elders. When Faraday had been a member for twenty years he was elected an elder. He was then forty-nine and a world-famous scientist. As an elder he preached and read from the Bible at the meeting place. The Sandemanians followed the practices of the early Apostles, breaking bread together on the Lord's day, celebrating the

Lord's supper, and collecting money for charity and expenses. It was sinful to save money. They were a self-contained group, marrying among themselves and not mixing with the outside world.

Faraday's religion was the basis of his scientific discoveries. God had given man the natural world to understand and control, and it was man's highest duty to push that understanding as far as possible. He never thought that his discoveries showed more than a fragment of the truth; he marked in his Bible the passage from Job: 'If I justify myself mine own mouth shall condemn me: if I say I am perfect, it shall prove me perverse.' He was able to carry out an enormous amount of research because of the strength and confidence he got from his church. A friend said: 'I think that a great deal of Faraday's week-day strength and persistency might be referred to his Sunday Exercises. He drinks from a fountain on Sunday which refreshes his soul for the week.' Faraday's philosophy, as distinct from his religion, originated in Germany. Kant, the German philosopher, had put forward the view that physics could be based solely on the fundamental ideas of attraction and repulsion. All the forces of nature were unified and they could be converted into one another. Oersted, who discovered the unity between electricity and magnetism, was a follower of Kant. One can see how such a philosophy would drive Faraday to explore this unity and to establish electromagnetism. Kant's philosophy reached Faraday in this way. The poet, Samuel Taylor Coleridge, having travelled in Germany, brought it over to England and taught it to his friend Humphry Davy, and Davy was Faraday's teacher.

When Faraday's health broke down in 1839 he suffered from severe headaches and giddiness and his memory became unreliable. He frequently walked thirty miles a day, but it took long to recover from his nervous exhaustion; he wrote to a friend:

'I must begin to write you a letter, though feeling, as I do, in the midst of one of my low nervous attacks, with memory so treacherous, that I cannot remember the beginning of a sentence to the end – hand disobedient to the will, that I cannot form the letters, bent with a certain crampness, so I hardly know whether I shall bring it to a close with consistency or not.'

Although he never fully recovered his health, he became strong enough by 1844 to take up his research again. Between that year and 1860 he arrived at the fundamental ideas on which the whole future of electrical science was based.

During this last period of work Faraday withdrew from all social and professional engagements so as to husband his strength for it. His memory worsened and he became afraid that he would not be able to finish lectures at the Royal Institution. 'My memory wearies me greatly in working,' he wrote, 'for I cannot remember from day to day the conclusions I come to and all has to be thought out many times over.' In 1857 he refused the presidency of the Royal Society because he did not feel capable of the duties. Soon he had to resign all his appointments, one by one; as scientific adviser to Trinity House, his lectureship at Woolwich Arsenal, his professorship at the Royal Institution, and even his position as elder of his church. These changes left him with very little income, and Queen Victoria gave him a house near Hampton Court to live in for the rest of his life. There he died in 1867. Although world-famous, he was buried, not in Westminster Abbey, but according to his wish, privately and plainly in Highgate Cemetery, the grave bearing simply his name and the dates of his earthly life.

Faraday called himself a natural philosopher; he was hardly concerned at all with the problems of society. His views on politics were consistent with his religious beliefs and his self-contained life. When, on his tour of Europe with Davy, he learnt that Napoleon had escaped from Elba, a dramatic event which shook Europe, he merely noted in his diary that as he was no politician he did not trouble himself about it. During the revolutions of 1848 Faraday saw them, not as struggles for liberty and freedom, but only as fights between angry men, which should be avoided at all costs. Later, during the American Civil War when many writers and scientists debated hotly the pros and cons of slavery, the war seemed to him merely like the punishment which a naughty and disobedient child among the nations had brought upon itself. His only wish was for peace for scientific research. 'For me,' he wrote, 'who never meddle with politics and who think very little of them as one of the games of life, it seems sad that Scientific men should be so disturbed by them and so the progress of pure science and philosophy be much and so often disturbed by the passions of men.'

He was, however, passionately interested in education. As a self-educated man he believed that education was essentially the ability to criticize oneself, and so be able to develop one's ability. As a scientist he joined in the dispute whether science, as well as classics and mathematics, should be taught in schools. Education, he said, included 'the ability to discover and obey the laws of nature. Electricity is often called wonderful – beautiful – but it is so only in common with the other forces of nature. The beauty of electricity, or of any other force, is not that the power is mysterious and unexpected . . . but that it is under *law*, and that the taught intellect can now govern it largely'. When he was asked to give evidence to the Royal Commission on the public schools he argued strongly for science to be taught in them, though this was not done for many years. But, 'You want men who can teach,' he told the commissioners, 'and that class has to be created.' He himself had shown how to make science a fascinating and stimulating subject.

Additional Reading

P. Dunsheath, *History of Electrical Engineering*, Faber, 1962.
L. P. Williams, *Michael Faraday*, Chapman & Hall, 1965.

CHAPTER TWO

The Telegraph

THE word telegraphy means writing at a distance; it comes from the Greek words 'tele' meaning far and 'grapho' meaning write. Ever since the beginning of civilization man has had the problem of sending information faster and farther than the human voice alone could send it, and today he is still working on this problem.

Methods of communication over quite long distances go back to the Greeks and the Romans and even earlier to the Chinese. Julius Caesar set up a series of manned call posts by which messages could be relayed over intervals of a hundred yards by shouting from one post to the next. Beacon fires on hilltops were used by ancient man and for centuries after. Later on men used the sun and a mirror when they invented the heliograph. But if there was no sun, there was no message. The greatest advance, before the electric telegraph, was made when the semaphore was developed. In fact for nearly a hundred years the telegraph meant for everyone the semaphore system. It was during the eighteenth century, when the semaphore was being perfected by a Frenchman, Claude Chappe, that the word 'telegraph' was coined.

CLAUDE CHAPPE (1763–1805)

Chappe's semaphore telegraph gave Napoleon the best military intelligence system in Europe. It helped the French revolutionary government in Paris to control the provinces of France, and when it was extended to Italy it enabled Napoleon to maintain his conquests there. Chappe's father was a legal official of the royal government who had married a daughter of the local nobility. His family was, therefore, well known as a member of that political and social system which was over-thrown by the French revolution. He was sent to a college in Rouen and, as was customary for a second son, he was educated for the church. He qualified as an abbé but he never became a priest. When he was twenty-one his father died but he continued his studies within the church. They were now, however, more concerned with scientific experiments in physics and electricity.

Then occurred the great event which changed Europe. On 14th July, 1789, the people of Paris stormed the Bastille, and the revolution had begun. When the new government seized the wealth of the church Chappe's occupation came to an end and, then aged twenty-five, he was obliged to return to the family home at Brulon, near Le Mans. The government undertook a complete reorganization of the country. This included not only the church, but the legal system, the abolition of serfdom, and the wholesale reform of local government, dividing France into eighty-three departments instead of the old feudal provinces. In sweeping away the old France the government was faced with the immense task of unifying the new France, and to do this it had to keep in touch with the whole country. In such conditions any system of communication was very important.

Chappe and his brothers welcomed the revolution and they decided to make such a communication system as the new government needed. It was not a new problem. Many men throughout Europe had tried to devise a satisfactory method of telegraphing. A hundred years earlier Sir Robert Hook, the mathematician, had laid down the main principles. Chappe knew about the work already done; what he had to do was to combine it all into a practical working system.

At first he built equipment which was based on the operation of shutters. A large rectangular frame at each station was fitted with five shutters which were made to appear or disappear according to the code of the letter or word to be sent. His machines were set up in Paris and they worked successfully for a year. But in the meantime the turmoil of the revolution continued. Austria and Prussia took the side of the French king and invaded France. This danger provoked a revolt in Paris and there was a wholesale massacre of royalists. In the chaos Chappe's machines were destroyed by revolutionaries who thought that they were being used to signal to the king. This stimulated Chappe to construct a better system; it was the semaphore, which was eventually used all over France.

He had to decide which were the best and most visible shapes and materials to use. Eventually he found that the semaphore arms with the best visibility were long narrow parallelograms constructed so as to offer the least resistance to the wind and not to reflect the sunlight.

The revolution continued and by 1793 the left-wing Jacobins, led by Danton, had gained power in the National Convention, the king had been executed, and France was encircled by a ring of hostile countries. Then the Committee of Public Safety, which had become the supreme authority, began the reign of terror and of the guillotine. In such a crisis the need for a system of internal communication and control became even more important to the government. The National Convention agreed to investigate Chappe's system and as a result he was appointed Telegraph Engineer to the government. From August of that year the Committee of Public Safety issued decrees, signed by Robespierre and other members, for construction of the first telegraph line from Montmartre to Lille, a distance of some sixty miles. Because France was at war, money and labour were chronically scarce, but Chappe and his brothers worked so hard that by July 1794 they had built fifteen stations, and the line was working. The first message sent from Lille was to tell the National Convention in Paris that the French had recaptured a fortress on the Flemish frontier.

Chappe's telegraph was in great demand, for France was still at war with Britain and Austria. The government gave orders for two more lines; one north-west to Brest, the naval base which was under the watchful eye of the British navy, and the other eastward to Strasbourg, on the Rhine frontier. There were great difficulties in completing these lines. France was suffering from rapid inflation, there was still a chronic shortage of money available to the government, and the cost of each relay station was found to be very high. The stations on the Paris–Lille line had required large quantities of tin plate, iron plate, iron wire, copper wire, lead, iron and other materials. The government could not give Chappe money to pay wages or provisions to feed the labourers; on the north-west line they died of hunger. Chappe sent a telegram to his masters in Paris:

> 'Finance, finance and yet more finance, or else we can do nothing. Send it to Port Malo. Through lack of money we have lost eight precious days. Situation is desperate. Am doing all I can for success. Without money no line to Brest. Greetings and fraternity. Chappe, engineer.'

By superhuman efforts Chappe completed both lines within a year; from Paris via Arranches and St. Malo to Brest, and from Paris via Verdun and Metz to Strasbourg. The latter had no less than fifty stations.

The distance between the stations was limited by the range of the telescopes used by the operators, about six to eight miles on the level. The line could be operated by night if torches or lanterns were fixed to the arms. Chappe took great care to work out a foolproof drill and signal manual. Strict discipline was enforced; in revolutionary France imprisonment was the punishment for negligence. The operators were carefully selected from men who were reliable but also of sufficiently limited intelligence to be satisfied with the simple work of relaying signals.

During his remaining years Chappe's ceaseless efforts to get enough money to establish the telegraph on a sound basis wore him out. The government had too many other, and bigger, problems to grapple with. He drew up various schemes for the telegraph to raise money; to charge fees for commercial telegrams, for newspaper telegrams, to operate a national lottery, but only the last of these came to anything. Then he was challenged by other inventors who claimed to have made a working telegraph before him, and he became involved in lengthy disputes. Finally when he was instructed to build a new line from Paris to Milan the strain became too great.

When Napoleon made himself Emperor France became a military dictatorship with the ambition of conquering Europe, and Chappe was involved in it. When Napoleon was getting ready to invade England Chappe invented a system of secret communication between Calais and Dover. On the other side of Europe, Napoleon demanded a telegraph system from Paris to Milan via Lyons in order to control his conquests in Italy. This demand was the last straw for Chappe. Although the line was eventually finished with its fifty-eight stations, he did not see the end of it. Returning home to Paris from a station site near Lyons, he developed acute depression and in January 1805 he committed suicide.

Many years later, in 1829, his body was removed from its first burial place to the famous Père Lachaise cemetery in Paris where his tomb bears the simple inscription 'Chappe'. Two memorial stones were fixed at the entrance to the headquarters of the Posts and Telegraphs Department in Paris.

During Chappe's lifetime his telegraph was essentially a means of security against the foreign and internal enemies of the French state. He was evidently an enthusiastic supporter and servant of the new France created by the revolution. Early in his career the government secret service reported on the brothers Chappe as follows. 'The smallest, who is the eldest brother and known here as the engineer because he is the inventor of the machine, seems always to have used his great gifts with the utmost loyalty to the Republic.'

During the forty years after Chappe's death his telegraph was extended throughout France as far as the Pyrenees and the Mediterranean, and it was copied by England and other countries. It was the main means of communication by which Paris controlled France. From Calais a message could be received in four minutes five seconds, and from Toulon in thirteen minutes fifty seconds. The system became a very complete and effective one; before it gave way to the electric telegraph it had no less than 556 manned stations and a total length of 2,500 miles. It performed its last service in 1855 when, as in 1794, it sent news of a victory in another war, the fall of Sebastopol in the Crimea.

In the meantime the electric telegraph was being developed. Chappe himself experimented with electricity and he invented a simple system in which alphabetical messages could be sent along a single wire. Clockwork dials bearing the letters revolved at each end of the wire and as the letter to be sent passed a marker on the dial the sender transmitted a spark to the other end. But this depended on static electricity, and the semaphore was far more useful at that time. Volta had not yet discovered the battery. When that happened and a steady current was possible then scientists could make progress towards a practical electrical telegraph.

The electric telegraph was not far off. Twenty-five years after Chappe's death the American Samuel Morse saw the French semaphore system and it fired his imagination to think of a telegraph worked by electricity.

SIR CHARLES WHEATSTONE (1802–1875) AND SIR WILLIAM F. COOKE (1806–1879)

Charles Wheatstone, the scientist, was the main inventor of the first practical electrical telegraph in Britain. William Fothergill Cooke, his partner for many years, was the business-man who got the telegraph into practical use, eventually throughout the whole railway system, and himself invented some of the equipment necessary to bring that about. Before Wheatstone there were many men who worked on the telegraph and of these three pioneers stand out, an Englishman, Francis Ronalds, and two Germans, K. A. Steinheil and Paul Schilling von Canstatt.

Each of these men made a definite and different contribution. Ronald's telegraph was much more than a model; it was a working telegraph which sent messages over 500 feet of wire buried in his garden. It used synchronized clockwork dials marked with the alphabet. When the sender discharged the line, by earthing one end, two pith balls at the other end fell and all the receiver had to do was to note the letter indicated on his dial at that moment. It worked on static electricity generated by a friction machine. That was in 1816. Four years later the Danish physicist, Oersted, showed the magnetic property of electric current. Then came the contribution of Steinheil, a professor at Munich. He invented a receiver which was based on two pivoted magnets, only one of which was free to swing when current was sent through the coil in one direction, while the other magnet was free to swing when current went in the other direction. The contribution of the third man, Schilling, was to build a telegraph which was based on five magnetic needles, each of which could be deflected one way or the other by current flowing in five coils. Ten keys were used by the sender to reverse the current. Later this apparatus was developed into a single-needle instrument. Schilling demonstrated his working model to the Czar Nicholas of Russia in 1832.

It so happened that in 1836 William Fothergill Cooke, then in Heidelberg, was taken to a lecture at which a model of Schilling's telegraph was demonstrated. This impressed him tremendously: 'I was so much struck with the wonderful power of electricity, and so strongly impressed with its applicability to the practical transmission of telegraphic intelligence, that from that very day I entirely abandoned my former pursuits, and devoted myself thenceforth with equal ardour, as all who know me can testify, to the practical realization of the Electric Telegraph.'

But let us look first at Charles Wheatstone. His father was a musician, a performer on, and teacher of the flute. When Wheatstone was four the family moved up from Gloucester to London and his father took a shop in Pall Mall, where he made musical instruments. Wheatstone himself was apprenticed at the age of fourteen to the craft of musical instrument making. He was naturally curious about sound and he began to investigate it scientifically; this was the way he became a scientist. At the same time his training gave him manual dexterity and the ability to judge if mechanical apparatus would work or not. He was thus well equipped to become an inventor.

In his teens he became interested in the way sound was conducted and in acoustics, the science of hearing. He carried out experiments in sound when he should have been making musical instruments. When he was nineteen he made an instrument which he called the Enchanted Lyre, and which drew many people to the shop. It was, in fact, merely two sounding boards, one in an upper room, the other, shaped like a lyre, in a lower room, the two connected by a rod through the floor. When music was played near the upper board it appeared to come from the lower one. This simple device attracted much attention; a contemporary magazine referred to the possibility of 'the sound travelling, like gas, through snug conductors, from the main laboratory . . . to distant parts of the metropolis'. Simple though it was, it was important as the first of Wheatstone's many practical demonstrations of scientific principle – in this case the general principle of conducting or transmitting sound.

Oersted, the Danish physicist, visited the shop and saw his experiments. Wheatstone had learnt about the basic wave theory of light. This was to be his guide in science, and because of his grasp of the idea of wave motion he was able to go on from acoustics to optics and then to electricity. In 1827, when he was twenty-five, he invented the 'Kaleidophone, or Phonic Kaleidoscope, a new Philosophical Toy for the Illustration of several Interesting and Amusing Acoustical and Optical Phenomena'. It was a steel rod fixed at one end, with a white bead at the other, and the purpose was to show how vibrations of the rod caused the bead to make corresponding patterns of movement. A description of it was published by the Royal Institution. Michael Faraday was now director of the laboratory at the Institution and Wheatstone began a life-long friendship with the great man.

Continuing his experiments, Wheatstone prepared lectures for the Institution on different kinds of musical sound, for instance those coming from the mouth organ and the jew's harp. He prepared them but did not give them, for he was so shy and nervous in public that he could not face a large audience. It was therefore Faraday, who was responsible for the lectures at the Institution, who delivered Wheatstone's, as only he knew how.

Wheatstone, the musical instrument maker, was by now well known among men of science. He used scientific principles to produce musical instruments and in 1829 he patented several unusual ones, among them the original concertina, a gas-jet organ and a speaking machine which was meant to imitate the human voice. Two years later he was still busy investigating the transmission of sound through solid rods. He followed up his Enchanted Lyre with another paper to the Royal Institution in which he discussed the problem in detail and speculated about future possibilities:

'. . . as the velocity of sound is much greater in solid substances than in air, it is not improbable that the transmission of sound through solid conductors, and its subsequent reciprocation, may hereafter be applied to many useful purposes.

The transmission to distant places, and the multiplication of musical performances, are objects of far less importance than the conveyance of the articulations of speech. . . . I have found by experiment that all these articulations . . . may be perfectly, though feebly transmitted.'

It is easy to imagine that it was this interest in transmitting sound and in communicating over a distance that led Wheatstone to the study of electricity and his main achievement.

During the next two years while he went on with his study of acoustics he began to investigate electricity. As a result he wrote a paper called 'An account of some experiments to measure the Velocity of Electricity and the Duration of the Electric Light'. Electric light at that time meant the electric spark. Scientists had long been curious about the speed of electricity and some had tried, unsuccessfully, to discover it. The problem was how could the velocity be measured. Wheatstone, in a series of experiments, showed how it could be done. His result was inaccurate, since it gave a velocity of 288,000 miles a second, higher than the speed of light, but he had, for the first time, shown the correct experimental method.

This was an extremely clever piece of work and it so increased his reputation that in 1834, at the age of thirty-two, Wheatstone, the musical instrument maker, was appointed professor of experimental philosophy at King's College, London. With the facilities now at his disposal he experimented with another aspect of 'electric light'. In experiments with the effects of an electric discharge on metals he laid the foundations of the spectrum analysis of the future. Prophetically he wrote: 'We have here a mode of discriminating metallic bodies more readily than by chemical analysis and which may hereafter be employed for useful purposes.' In 1836, he was elected a Fellow of the Royal Society.

Wheatstone's thoughts then turned to the practical uses of electricity and particularly to the telegraph. He knew about the earlier work of Francis Ronalds. During the next year or two he invented several telegraph instruments, of which the most important was his keyboard transmitter, and he operated them over four miles of wire laid out in the basement of King's College. He was, however, only interested in them as scientific models and had no idea of their becoming of world-wide commercial importance.

Now it is necessary to return to Cooke, Wheatstone's partner. Cooke's personality was completely different from that of the shy scientist; he was an optimistic, persuasive and imaginative man with great energy and drive. He was the son of a surgeon who, while Cooke was still young, was appointed professor of anatomy at Durham University. His family was a comfortably off middle-class one. He went to Edinburgh University but only for a short time, for at the age of nineteen he shook off the family ties and went out to Madras as an officer cadet in the East India Company. When he was twenty-seven, while on leave in England, he resigned because of ill-health.

At home with his parents he took up an occupation which came from his father's profession. This was the modelling in wax of different sections of the human body, for use in teaching. He went to Heidelberg in 1834 to study anatomy in order to equip himself for what he called 'the interesting and by no means unprofitable profession of anatomical modelling; a self-taught pursuit to which I have been devoting myself with incessant and unabated ardour, working frequently fourteen or fifteen hours a day'.

This second career also was short-lived. A year later he went to see a demonstration of Schilling's electric telegraph, a chance event which started the process by which England became covered in a network of telegraph wires. He made a crude copy of Schilling's instrument, with some modifications of his own; it was a three-needle instrument. Then, having picked up some knowledge of the subject, he decided to change to the type of instrument made by Chappe and Ronalds in which two synchronized dials bearing the alphabet were turned by electromagnets by means of a clockwork mechanism.

He hurried back to England to get a skilled mechanic in London to make the instrument for him, but it would not go. Throughout 1836 he struggled with it but he did not really know what he was doing for he knew nothing about the discoveries in electricity made by Oersted and Ohm. He consulted the great Michael Faraday and received some encouragement from him. He still had no idea whether the telegraph which he had seen sending messages across a room in Heidelberg could send them over a long line. In spite of this, and with unbounded confidence even at this stage, he tried to sell his idea to a railway company.

There were very few railways in existence in 1837 and the one he approached, the Liverpool and Manchester company, was only the second public railway to have been built. Cooke was able to interest the directors sufficiently to get facilities to experiment in the Lime Street tunnel at Liverpool.

Still unsuccessful he nearly gave the whole thing up. 'In truth,' he wrote to his mother, 'I have given the telegraph up since Thursday evening and only sought proof of my being right to do so ere announcing it to you. This day's enquiries partly revive my hopes but I am far from sanguine. The scientific men know little or nothing absolute on the subject, Wheatstone is the only man near the mark.'

He decided to see Wheatstone and after the meeting he described what took place:

'. . . yet I felt less satisfied than ever, and called upon a Mr. Wheatstone, at the London University, and repeated my queries. Imagine my satisfaction at hearing from him that he had four miles of wire in readiness, and imagine my dismay on hearing that he had been employed for months in the construction of a telegraph, and had actually invented two or three with a view to bringing them into practical use. We had a long conference and I am to see his arrangement of wire tomorrow and we are to converse upon the project of uniting our plans and following them out together. From what passed my plan, if practicable, will, I think, have advantage over any of his, but this remains to be proved.'

This was the beginning of the partnership between the two men which launched the electric telegraph. Wheatstone had the necessary scientific knowledge and skill, and Cooke thought he had, but they soon agreed to share their resources and become partners. Cooke, who kept his mother informed of everything (he relied on the family finances), wrote to her:

'At 4 yesterday I went to King's College to meet Professor Wheatstone and try my instruments which have nearly received their last touch. . . . I had hoped to have our experiments made public today but dare not until the patent is out, as one day's impatience may ruin all. The King's health is still so precarious that he can transact no business. A report was very prevalent yesterday that he was dead, but contradicted in the eveng. . . .

P.S. Hurrah for the 10th of June. On the back I send you good news, this moment (5 minutes to 10 o'clock, 10th June) obtained. All is now safe. In haste. Cooke's and Wheatstone's Patent signed by His Majesty and receiving the Great Seal this day June 10th!!! 1837 for Electric Telegraphs Alarums. I had intended to send you some small present but now send this instead.'

Although Cooke wrote of 'his instruments' all the instruments covered by the patent were designed by Wheatstone. It included the transmitter and receiver, the method of running the five cables used, the five-needle indicator, the alarum to call the attendant, and the fault detector. Wheatstone used astatic needles, that is, a system not influenced by the earth's magnetic field. The telegraph was simple to operate and could be used by any person after a few minutes' instruction.

Cooke lost no time in negotiating with the railway again; this time it was a new railway, not yet opened, the London and Birmingham of which the young Robert Stephenson was the chief engineer. At that time it was necessary for trains from the terminus at Euston to be hauled by rope up a long incline and the directors wanted a signalling system on that section. Cooke and Wheatstone gave a successful demonstration over a line between Euston and Camden Town, a distance of about one and a half miles.

This was a turning point for it was shown beyond doubt that the electric telegraph was a practical commercial instrument of communication. Cooke, at the Camden Town end, recorded the great event:

'Yesterday Mr. Stevenson [*sic*] witnessed our experiments through 19 miles of wire, extending from Euston Square to Camden Town, and declared himself so satisfied with the result that he begged me to lay down my wires permanently between these two points on my best plan. . . . He seemed quite delighted at the correspondence we carried on at so great a distance from each other, requesting me to send the word "Bravo" along the line more than once. It ended by his desiring me to send an invitation to Mr. Wheatstone to join us, which he politely replied to by saying "he would do himself the honor".'

Wheatstone, in a little office lit by a candle at Euston, was, for him, unusually excited. 'Never did I feel such a tumultuous sensation before,' he wrote, 'as when, all alone in the still room I heard the needles click, and as I spelled the words, I felt all the magnitude of the invention pronounced to be practicable beyond cavil or dispute.'

In spite of this success the London and Birmingham did not want the telegraph because it was too expensive to install, and it adopted pneumatic tube signalling instead. Cooke turned to the Great Western Railway, which was soon to be opened. I. K. Brunel, the engineer in charge, was a man of great imagination and he saw the possibilities of the telegraph, although there was no need then to use it for railway working. It was agreed that Cooke should lay a telegraph from Paddington to West Drayton, a distance of thirteen miles. He described his preparations to his mother:

'I am very busily occupied so very well and very cheerful, and only want six hours more daylight per diem to be very contented. I do not anticipate coming on the road before Monday week at the soonest. I am going to drill two gangs of workmen in Lord Hill's Garden which is lent me for a day or two and when they are all au fait I shall make my appearance on the road. I look upon this drilling as a jewel of a plan 1st because this will in consequence be no experimental trying of plans on the permanent line 2nd no interference from lookers on and no awkwardness or misunderstanding when under the eyes of the engineers and other men. Besides the plan is a novel one which Brunel has decided upon and I have thought less upon it than on any other. I mean to lay down about a quarter of a mile in the garden over and over again till each knows his duty. The materials will do again on the main line except the wires which will have their jackets worn out, and even these can be burnt clean and recovered. It will only cost me £4 or £5 and the expense to Drayton is £3,159.'

From July to September, 1839, this telegraph was used by the Great Western Railway to send to Paddington the passing times of trains at West Drayton and Hanwell. It was the first in the world. It was Wheatstone's telegraph but it would not have been laid without Cooke.

While Cooke was busy promoting more lines, Wheatstone continued his scientific work and his inventions which ranged over a wide field, including a printing telegraph which was to be an important development in the future. At about this time his name was given to the device for measuring resistances which became known as Wheatstone's Bridge. In fact this device was invented by Samuel Christie, as Wheatstone was careful to point out; all Wheatstone did was to make it well known.

Cooke soon found that the Great Western Railway did not really need the telegraph. Railway operating at that time was based simply on admitting one train at a time to each block of railway. He therefore extended the telegraph line at his own cost to Slough, another four miles, in the hope that it would be used as a link between the government in Whitehall and the queen at Windsor Castle. He had improved the instruments himself, now using only two needles instead of five. To reduce the cost, for he was still short of money, he suspended the wires from iron posts instead of putting them underground in iron pipes as before. To raise money he opened offices at Paddington and Slough where for the first time the public could send telegrams at a flat rate of one shilling. Another way of raising money was as shown in the following notice:

'Under the Patronage of Her Majesty and H.R.H. Prince Albert, the Public are respectfully informed that this Interesting and Extraordinary Apparatus may be seen in operation Daily (excepting Sundays) from 9.00 am. to 8.0 pm. at the Telegraph Cottage, near the Slough Station. Admission 1s.'

In 1844 the telegraph sent the news of a royal birth from Windsor Castle. It was a great wonder that it took a mere eleven minutes for this news to be taken by horse from the Castle to Slough Station, flashed to Paddington and acknowledged.

Although this was useful publicity the telegraph was too slow in getting public interest and support for Cooke's liking. In the same month as the royal birth, however, he was able to rejoice in a contract from the Admiralty. He sent the news to his sister-in-law:

'My dear Betsy,

Telegraphic Despatch from the Admiralty

Director of Works, Admiralty

My Lords are pleased to approve of the arrangements you have made with Messrs. Cooke & Wheatstone for the use of the Electric Telegraph between the Admiralty and the Commander in Chief's residence at Portsmouth, and have directed their solicitor to communicate with you with a view to making a contract.

By command of their Lordships,
Sidney Herbert"

When I left you I promised to transmit, at the earliest possible moment, the long expected fiat from the Admiralty; this I have done, with a heart overflowing with gratitude to the Dispenser of all good . . .

I remain yrs
Ever Affc.
W.F.C.'

It took a murder trial to arouse sufficient public interest in the telegraph to make its future sure. A respectable middle-aged married citizen of Berkhampstead, John Tawell, was in the habit of visiting his mistress Sarah Hart, living near Slough. On the evening of 1st January 1845, he was seen leaving Sarah Hart's cottage and shortly after the woman was found dying in agony. After Tawell had been seen to catch the 7.42 p.m. train from Slough the telegraph clerk sent the following message to Paddington: 'A murder has just been committed at Salt Hill and the suspected murderer was seen to take a first-class ticket for London by the train which left Slough at 7h. 42m. p.m. He is in the garb of a Quaker, with a brown coat on which reaches nearly down to his feet; he is in the last compartment of the second first-class carriage.' When Tawell arrived at Paddington the railway police sergeant, who had been alerted, followed him on to an omnibus and arrested him at the Jerusalem Coffee House. He was tried and hanged, in public, in front of Aylesbury Town Hall. The case was a sensation in the press, and particularly the way in which the electric telegraph had led to the arrest. What struck the public was that the telegraph clerk had to send the word Quaker as Kwaker because there was no letter Q in the code.

The publicity created a demand for the telegraph and made people ready to invest in it. Tawell was hanged in March 1845; by the end of the same year financiers in the City had formed the Electric Telegraph Company. It bought from Wheatstone and Cooke their patents and the line to Slough, and quickly went ahead with extending the system. Two of the men who formed the new company were also railway directors. Before long the government compelled the railways to have the telegraph in the interests of safety, and the system of block signalling was brought in, with the signalman using the telegraph to signal trains ahead. By 1848 the new Company had supplied half the railways in Britain with the telegraph. Six years later it had seventeen offices in London alone, three of which were open day and night to meet public demand.

The Company had a monopoly for four years and charged the public high rates, but then competition developed. Other companies were formed and finally the whole system was bought by the Post Office for ten and a half million pounds in 1869.

Wheatstone and Cooke did well out of this. Wheatstone received £30,000 for his patents, and Cooke became a director of the telegraph company and, for a time, a wealthy man. The partnership was finished and it was just as well, for there had always been friction between the two men. The dispute as to which man could claim to be the inventor continued for many years and there was much bitterness. Each of them wrote pamphlets claiming the invention and Cooke finally published a two-volume book called *The Electric Telegraph, was it invented by Professor Wheatstone?* The answer is clearly yes, but the long quarrel was not made up until near the end of Wheatstone's life. He was knighted in 1868 but Cooke had to wait another year for that honour.

Wheatstone remained professor until his retirement and continued to make many other inventions of importance, among them a dynamo and a typewriter. He married and had five daughters. In spite of this expense he left the considerable sum of £70,000, not the legacy of an absent-minded professor.

Cooke was out of a job when the telegraphs were nationalized. He lost his money and soon became so hard up that he was awarded a government pension of £100 a year, the maximum that could be given. At the age of sixty-five he was practically penniless. 'I am really in a desperate position,' he wrote, 'having parted with everything that I can do without to appear tolerably decent and people are calling daily for rates, taxes, water and coal bills . . . besides the tradesmen whom we have always paid weekly, and we have been without money for many days. I only see one alternative, the ruinous nature of which I am fully aware, namely our application to money lenders. I know it will only postpone the evil for a few weeks, and I am morally certain that the wreck that remains to me of commercial property, properly and fairly treated would restore us to permanent comfort. But all that must disappear if the securities are to fall into the hands of money lenders or bill discounters. But a man will put off the actual distress of his family so long as he can. I do not see what good this letter can do but I feel after writing it that I have brought my position within a more definite scope.'

He spent his last years in comfort, cared for by his son-in-law at whose home he died.

SAMUEL FINLEY BREESE MORSE (1791–1872)

At almost the same time as Wheatstone and Cooke patented their telegraph in London, on the other side of the Atlantic an American also invented the telegraph and the code which were to become universal and to make his name famous throughout the world.

Like Cooke, Morse was neither a scientist nor an engineer. He was an artist, well known as a painter who earned considerable sums from his portraits. He was born on 27th April,

1791, at Charlestown, near Boston, Massachusetts. His father was a Congregationalist minister, a scholar from Yale University who was also the author of the first geography book published in America. On his mother's side he was descended from the president of the college which became Princeton University. Morse received a comfortable but strictly religious upbringing, warm affection and a good education. He was sent to a Calvinist boarding school at the age of seven and when he was fourteen to Yale. There he made little progress but spent much of his time painting and this earned him a little money. However he did learn about electricity for the first time. The subject was already taught at Yale and he was much impressed by the mystery of the 'electrical fluid'. He wrote home:

'My studies are at present, Optics in philosophy, Dialling, Homer, beside disputing, composing, attending lectures, etc. etc., all which I find very interesting, and especially Mr. Day's lectures who is now lecturing on Electricity.'

After Yale his parents did not know what to do with him and for a time he became a clerk in a publishing firm which handled some of his father's books. But soon they agreed that he should study to be a painter and sent him, in the care of a respectable Boston painter, to London, to enter the Royal Academy school. Three weeks from New York he landed at Liverpool, in a country soon to be at war with America, smuggled his supply of cigars through the customs and found lodgings in London. After several months' hard work he was accepted in the Academy school. He was then twenty.

By the end of four years' training, all the time financed by his parents, he was a more than competent painter. In 1815 he returned home, supremely confident of a career in America. 'My ambition,' he wrote, 'is to be among those who shall rival the splendor of the fifteenth century; to rival the genius of a Raphael, a Michelangelo, or a Titian; my ambition is to be enlisted in the constellation of genius now rising in this country; I wish to shine, not by a light borrowed from them, but to strive to shine the brightest.'

He soon began to earn from portrait painting and courted the girl who was to be his first wife. On a visit to her, he wrote home: 'Charles Walker Esq. son of Judge W., has two daughters, the eldest very beautiful, amiable, and of an excellent disposition. This is her character in town. I have enquired particularly of Dr. McFarland respecting the family, and his answer is in every way satisfactory except that they are no professors of religion. He is a man of family and great wealth; this last you know I never made a principal object, but it is somewhat satisfactory to know that in my profession. I may flatter myself, but I think I might be a successful suitor.' He went south to Carolina and quickly found patrons among the wealthy slave-owning planters. Within a few months he made three thousand dollars, returned home and got married. In Charlestown, however, the supply of patrons was limited and for four years he had to struggle. At last he made his name in Washington with a large painting of Congress in session and an outstanding portrait of Lafayette, the republican statesman of France and the popular hero of America, which had been commissioned by the New York council. He was now moving in the highest political and social circles. Then just when he had been able to provide a home for his family his wife died.

He decided to return to Europe to study the great Italian masters. Leaving his three children in the care of relatives, he sailed with commissions for pictures to be painted. He was now thirty-eight, but still determined to become a better painter. However, he had continued his earlier interest in science and had heard lectures about the recent discovery from England, electromagnetism.

The visit to Europe set him on the path to the electric telegraph. He spent eighteen months in Rome. He was very happy with his painting, although he hated the political régime and the power exercised by the Catholic church. On his way back through Paris he saw the French semaphore telegraph system which had been started by Chappe, and was impressed by its advantages over the postal system at home. Before he left France he continued to think about the telegraph and the possibility of an electric spark being used for it. Then on the voyage home in 1832, he developed the basic ideas for his electromagnetic telegraph and his code. Among some of the passengers there was much discussion about electricity and electromagnetism; Ampère had made his great discoveries in Paris, and Faraday his in London. When Morse learnt, to his surprise, that the length of wire made virtually no difference to the speed of transmission the great idea came to him. 'If this be so,' he said, 'and the presence of electricity can be made visible in any desired part of the circuit, I see no reason why intelligence might not be instantaneously transmitted by electricity to any distance.'

By the time the ship reached New York, six weeks later, he had sketched in his notebook the device which became his pen recorder. It was based on a strong electromagnet and a weak permanent magnet, a marker and a moving strip of paper. Amateur as he was, he believed he was the first to think of an electric telegraph.

Morse was then appointed professor of the arts of design in the new University of New York. For a time he was divided between two ambitions, to be a great painter and to be a famous inventor, but gradually all his efforts were absorbed in developing the telegraph. Because of his ignorance of science he soon found he needed help and he got it from a colleague, a professor of geology and mineralogy, who became his partner. This man showed him that what he needed for his experiments was increased voltage rather than increased current and that he could get it by using a larger battery. He also introduced him to the work of the famous American physicist, Joseph Henry. With Henry's help Morse was able to solve the problem which was holding him up – making a relay based on switches moved by an electromagnet.

Finally, in September 1837, after learning with dismay of Wheatstone and Cooke's telegraph in England, he gave a successful demonstration of his telegraph with 1,700 feet of wire. He was invited to show his invention to the president and cabinet ministers of the United States. He acquired two other partners, one to help with engineering and the other to provide finance, a congressman who proved to be the kind of politician who merely wanted to use Morse to make a fortune for himself. Then he left for Europe again to sell his invention.

Morse arrived in London in time to see the coronation of Queen Victoria. He applied for an English patent only to find his application opposed by Wheatstone and Cooke. Wheatstone invited Morse to see his telegraph at King's College. Morse was impressed by what he saw but he was confident that his own quite different instruments were better. He wrote to his brother: 'His Telegraph is truly an ingenious and beautiful piece of mechanism, but it is not so simple as mine, and unless my opponents here have discovered my mode from those who have seen it in America, and who may be able to describe it to them (and of which they are manifestly ignorant) and thus shall adopt mine into their new patent, I shall instantly supersede them. At any rate I shall have the gratification of knowing that my invention is *the one of all other which will prevail, and be generally adopted*; whether I shall be pecuniarily profited by it here, or whether I shall get the credit of it, is as yet uncertainty.'

He was unsuccessful in England and so he went on to Paris and there he was granted a French patent. But although his telegraph was highly praised by the scientists the French government was satisfied with the Chappe semaphore, and he returned to America empty-handed.

He secured his patent in America in June 1840 but it was to be nearly three years before Congress could be persuaded to build a telegraph line. He spent all his money in preparing a bill for the approval of Congress and in arranging demonstrations for influential politicians. He was often hard up. 'For nearly two years past,' he wrote, 'I have devoted all my time and scanty means, living on a mere pittance, denying myself all pleasures, and even necessary food, that I might have a sum to put my Telegraph into such a position before Congress as to insure success to the common enterprise.' Joseph Henry wrote encouragement from Princeton:

'At about the same time with yourself Professor Wheatstone, of London, and Dr. Steinheil, of Germany, proposed plans of the electromagnetic telegraph but these differ as much from yours as the nature of the common principle would well permit; and unless some essential improvements have lately been made in these European plans, I would prefer the one invented by yourself. With my best wishes . . .'

At last thirty thousand dollars was approved for construction of a telegraph, to connect the Capitol at Washington and

Baltimore, forty miles away. It was just in time, for Morse had spent his last cent.

He was appointed Superintendent of the United States Telegraphs at a salary of two thousand dollars a year. Although he was no businessman he was now to spend most of the remainder of his life and energies in organizing and financing the construction of the telegraph, something completely new in America. It was all-important that the first line should be a success but it nearly ended in failure. When most of the money had been spent the lead pipes for laying the wires were found to be defective. Morse switched to chestnut poles which could be quickly put up. Just at that time the political parties were holding their conventions at Baltimore in order to nominate candidates for the election of a new president of the United States. Morse wanted to finish the line in time to send the news to the Capitol where it would be eagerly awaited by the Senate. He was successful and in May 1845, Washington learnt on the telegraph the name of the Democratic candidate, who was, in fact, soon to be president. This event was a sensation and Morse and his telegraph were famous at last.

The question then arose whether the government would take over the telegraph and run it as a state service or whether it would be developed for private profit. Morse himself had always believed that the telegraph should be owned by the government, and he now tried to persuade Congress to accept responsibility for building more lines. But Congress refused and the telegraph was left to speculative financiers. Soon company after company had been formed to make lines to other cities, New York, Boston, Philadelphia, Buffalo. By 1847 there were already over 1,200 miles in operation, whereas England had only about 200.

Even at that time Morse still hankered after painting and half intended to take it up again. Only when Congress refused to give him the commission he hoped for, a large painting in the Capitol, did he finally give up, at the age of fifty-five, the idea of being a great painter.

During the next few years Morse spent a great deal of his time and energy in a long and complicated defence of his patents against competitors. Eventually the supreme court decided in his favour. At the same time, in the year 1854, when his patent of 1840 was due to expire, he succeeded in getting it extended for another seven years, as the authorities thought he was entitled to more income from his invention. A few years earlier he had bought himself a hundred-acre estate near Poughkeepsie where he settled down with his second wife.

In the eighteen fifties the great project for an Atlantic cable was begun. More than ten years earlier Morse had prophesied that a telegraph across the Atlantic would be made, and now he became actively engaged in it. He sailed with the Anglo-American fleet which made the first but unsuccessful attempt to lay the cable. He became friends with Cyrus Field, the man who persisted with the project and who eventually triumphed when in 1865 Brunel's *Great Eastern* laid the cable from coast to coast.

Before that however, the United States went through the greatest crisis in its history, the long-drawn-out and bloody civil war of 1861–65. Although a civilian, Morse was deeply involved. He believed that slavery must be accepted because it was ordained by God, as revealed in the Old Testament, and was president of a pro-slavery society. During the war he actively campaigned in the presidential election to defeat Abraham Lincoln, who was determined to subdue the South, and to bring in a president who would negotiate a compromise peace. These views were a fundamental part of the religion which governed his life, and he maintained them although they made him unpopular. All the time, however, the telegraph was helping the North to win, and his income from it in those years was about thirty thousand dollars a year.

In his old age Morse was a rich man. He gave away large sums to colleges, churches and religious societies. His fame now was immense. A statue of him was erected, during his lifetime, in Central Park, New York. At the last banquet in his honour the president of the National Academy which Morse had founded said:

'Morse, the painter, invented the electric telegraph, Fulton, the painter, discovered steam navigation; Daguerre, an artist, gave us the photographic process . . . The studio of my beloved master, in whose honour we have met tonight, was indeed a laboratory . . . I can never forget the occasion when he called his pupils together to witness one of the first, if not the first, successful experiment with the new electric telegraph. It was in the winter of 1835–36. I can see now that rude instrument, constructed with an old stretching frame, a wooden clock, a home-made battery, and the wire stretched many times around the walls of the studio. With eager interest we gather about it, as our master explained its operation, while with a click, click, the pencil, with a succession of dots and lines, recorded the message in cypher. The idea was born. The words circled that upper chamber as they do now the globe.'

The modern teleprinter is a development from Morse's telegraph. The telegraph key is replaced by a typewriter key, and the Morse code by a Band code employing five digits. The depressing of a transmitter key produces the code corresponding to a letter or symbol and this is transmitted over the telegraph lines. The receiver converts the received pulses to the transmitted letter and prints it. The result is, in effect, typing at a distance, and the speed at which information is conveyed depends largely on the skill of the key-board operator and can easily reach forty to fifty words per minute. The European Telex service (the new name for telegraphy) is now available to any who wish to install the apparatus. The station to be contacted is dialled in the same way as with the telephone.

CHAPTER THREE

Spanning the Atlantic

IT IS only just over a hundred years ago that the first successful Atlantic cable was laid. The year when this took place, 1866, was during the lifetime of Faraday and of Wheatstone and both these men had something to do with it. But it was two other men who were chiefly responsible for the great achievement. They were Cyrus W. Field, the American businessman, and William Thomson, Lord Kelvin, the Scottish scientist. There was also a third party, but that was a ship, the *Great Eastern*, the monster vessel of its day, built by the railway engineer, I. K. Brunel.

The project of laying the cable took an enormous amount of effort and money, and a long stretch of nine years between the first attempt and final success. Why then was it started? There were two main reasons. The fact that it was now possible to telegraph overland led people to ask whether it could not be done across the oceans, and the new technical problems involved inspired scientists and engineers to tackle them. Secondly, there was the desire, particularly in the United States, to receive commercial and political news more quickly across the Atlantic. The trade between Britain and America was very important; it was said that Liverpool was closer to New York than it was to London.

Before the Atlantic cable was mooted quite a number of submarine cables had been laid. A colonel in the Royal Engineers had transmitted signals along a cable under the river Medway, and the year after that, in India, signals were sent across the river Hooghly. By 1840 there was so much public interest that the House of Commons appointed a committee to inquire whether a cable from Dover to Calais was possible.

Many people wanted to have a hand in the project. One competitor laid a rubber-insulated cable in Portsmouth Harbour. Then the important discovery was made of a new gum from forest trees, gutta-percha. Singapore had been founded by Stamford Raffles, Malaya had been explored, and in 1842 a Scottish surveyor employed by the East India Company brought the new raw material to England. It could be moulded when warmed, and so it was quickly tried out as a cable dielectric in the sea near Dover. The German inventor, Werner Siemens, also used gutta-percha as a coating for his experimental cables across the Rhine and in Kiel harbour.

In the meantime financiers in London had a Channel cable manufactured. It consisted only of one strand of no. 14 gauge copper with a coating of gutta-percha half an inch thick. Leaden weights were bolted to the cable to ensure that it would lie on the sea bed. It was made in one-hundred-yard lengths which were joined together by twisting and soldering the copper wire and covering the join with hot gutta-percha.

The operation of laying the cable took place in August 1850. It was a great event; from a hut on Dover beach a message of greetings was sent to Louis Napoleon, the newly elected president of France. But it was also a short-lived triumph. Almost immediately communication broke down. The most likely explanation is that a Boulogne trawler picked up the cable and cut out a length of copper for its own use.

The next year another, much stronger, cable was laid. Four no. 16 gauge copper wires were covered with gutta-percha, tarred hemp and tarred spun yarn, and protected by an armouring of ten no. 1 gauge galvanized iron wires. This cable was quite successful. Other cables followed quickly and as soon as the problems of laying in deeper water had been overcome England was linked with Ireland and Ireland with Scotland. The next step was to cross the ocean.

Meanwhile on the other side of the Atlantic American engineers and businessmen had made progress.

CYRUS W. FIELD (1819–1892)

Field was the businessman who, by his determination and enthusiasm, made the Atlantic cable possible. Born in Massachusetts, he was the son of a congregational minister. His grandfather had served under George Washington against the English. The family was large, he was the eighth child, and never well off. The children were brought up strictly according to religious principles. The family led a quiet life in the village.

At sixteen he left home for New York to make his fortune, with eight dollars from his father in his pocket. He took a job as errand-boy in the warehouse of a large dry goods merchant at a salary of fifty dollars a year. Then he served a three-year apprenticeship as a clerk. Field was conscientious and ambitious. 'I always made it a point to be there before the partners came,' he wrote, 'and never to leave before the partners left. My ambition was to make myself a thoroughly good merchant. I tried to learn in every department all I could, knowing that I had to depend entirely on myself.'

He was determined to equip himself for a successful career. He read a good deal; he was deeply impressed by Bunyan's *Pilgrim's Progress*. He learned book-keeping at evening classes in order to earn more, for he wanted to repay the loan from his father, including interest. Field obviously made an impression on his fellow clerks and on his employers. The custom was that when the clerks arrived late they were fined and the employer gave the fines to charity. The clerks, all twenty-seven of them, asked for the fines to be received by Field, and he spent the money on a feast for all of them. When he left the firm, having completed his apprenticeship, the firm gave him a diamond tie pin and the clerks gave him a farewell supper.

He was determined to launch out on his own, though he was still only nineteen. For a while he worked as assistant to his brother who had his own paper factory in Massachusetts. Then he joined a firm of wholesale paper merchants in New York.

A year later the firm went bankrupt and Field had to deal with the creditors to whom the firm owed money. He undertook to pay them everything owed them although he was not legally bound to. Once again he started a new business with his brother-in-law, the firm of Cyrus W. Field & Co., wholesale paper dealers, with offices near the East River docks, New York. Driven on by the debts hanging over him, he worked all hours of the day and night and built up a flourishing trade. He wrote:

'In 1841 I was not worth a dollar. What money I had made had gone to pay the debts of the old firm. My business was conducted on long credit; we did a general business all over the country. I built up a first rate credit everywhere. All business entrusted to me was done quickly and promptly. I attended to every detail of the business and made a point of answering every letter on the day it was received.'

He had now been over-working for several years and he was forced to take a long holiday. He spent six months in Europe, much of it in England. However, by 1853 his fortune was made and he was worth over a quarter of a million dollars. He paid off all the creditors of the old firm, plus interest at seven per cent. No doubt the general prosperity caused by the California gold discoveries of 1849 helped him to become rich, but he himself explained his success as follows:

'There was no luck about my success which was remarkable. It was not due to the control or use of large capital, to the help of friends, to speculations, or to fortunate turns of events, it was by constant labour and with the ambition to be a successful merchant; and I was rewarded by seeing a steady, even growth of business.'

Field, now thirty-four, retired from business, leaving 100,000 dollars in the firm, and he looked around for another interest. But first he went travelling and exploring in South America for six months. With a painter friend he made some of the most difficult journeys in the world, including a crossing of the Andes, in remote parts of Colombia and Peru.

Why was it that such a man as Field, a shrewd, hard-headed New Englander, seized on the adventurous and risky idea of laying a cable across the Atlantic? He knew very little, if anything, about the technical difficulties. In fact it was after the success of the English Channel cable and the heavy use to which it was put that he began to be interested. Then one day early in 1854 an English engineer, who was working on a project to lay a cable between Nova Scotia and Newfoundland, called on Field to discuss the project with him. This suggested to Field immediately that the next step would have to be a cable from Newfoundland to Ireland, and that this too could be done. So the great idea was born, and the more he thought about it the better the idea became. From the business point of view he felt sure that the traffic on the cable would be heavy once it was established. As a paper merchant he had knowledge of the newspaper world and he knew that the New York papers were hungry for news from Europe. When the telegraph wires from New York reached Halifax in Nova Scotia the newspapers had set up their agent there to send them the news brought by the incoming ships. This scramble for news showed Field that there was a need for the cable to England. He saw that it was bound to come and that the old era of horse express, pilot boat and pigeon news service was over.

Once Field was interested in the project it was inevitable that he should join up with Samuel Morse who was already famous (see Chapter Two). Years before Morse had prophesied that a cable would cross the Atlantic. He himself had carried out experiments under water. As early as 1842 he had rowed across New York harbour paying out a wire coated with pitch, tar and rubber from the Battery to Governor's Island, and had sent signals along it. Unfortunately when a crowd assembled to watch a demonstration the cable went dead. Like the first Channel cable it had been caught up, not by a fisherman's trawl, but by a ship's anchor, and cut in two.

First of all Field got the opinion of an expert of that time about the Atlantic sea bed. 'The plateau is neither too deep nor too shallow,' he explained, 'yet it is so deep that the wires once being landed will remain forever beyond the reach of vessels, anchors, icebergs and drift of any kind; and so shallow that the wires may be readily lodged upon the bottom.' Field then gathered round him a powerful group of supporters – bankers, merchants, lawyers – and formed a company with the ambitious name, the New York, Newfoundland and London Telegraph Company. Samuel Morse was vice-president.

The company started with the job of linking Nova Scotia and Newfoundland. As the telegraph poles gradually crept across Newfoundland, Morse told everyone that within three years he would be able to telegraph to the cities of Europe.

In the summer of 1854 Field's company attempted to lay the cable from the mainland to Newfoundland. A sailing vessel which had brought the 85-mile long cable from England was towed from Nova Scotia across Cabot Strait by a paddle steamer. Field and Morse were on board. But there was confusion about the course to be followed, a storm blew up, and the attempt was abandoned. In the following year, however, another attempt was successful, and St. Johns, Newfoundland, could signal to New York. The main task, to link Newfoundland with Ireland, could now be started.

As a million dollars had already been spent, and money was scarce just then in America, Field went to England in 1856 in order to raise capital and talk to the technical experts there. England had just brought the Crimean War to a victorious end, and Field soon found support for his project. He discussed it with Michael Faraday and Robert Stephenson. I. K. Brunel took him down to Millwall where the giant ship, the *Great Eastern*, was being built, and said, 'There is the ship to lay your cable.' And so it was, ten years later.

Accompanied by Morse he had an interview with the British foreign secretary who said to him, 'Suppose you do not succeed, that you make the attempt and fail, your cable lost at the bottom of the ocean, then what will you do?' Field's reply was typical: 'Charge it to profit and loss and go to work to lay another.' The British government offered a subsidy of £14,000 a year in return for future use of the cable. This was a great encouragement and as a result Field won the support of leading merchants and bankers of London and Liverpool. He formed a company, the Atlantic Telegraph Company, and its shares, 350 of £1,000 each, were quickly sold. A notable member of the board of this new company was the great scientist, William Thomson, the future Lord Kelvin.

The first attempt to lay the cable in 1857 was unsuccessful. Field tried to hurry on too fast. In his enthusiasm he had announced that the cable would be ready for use in that year. The result was that little thought was given to its design and it was manufactured too quickly. After 300 miles had been laid the cable snapped and the ships returned to England.

At the second attempt in June 1858 the cable again broke and the time taken in splicing it forced the ships to return to

Ireland for coal and stores. At the third attempt, in the same year, success was achieved. The two ships, the *Niagara* which was the latest American steam frigate, and the *Agamemnon* which was one of the old English wooden warships, each with half of the cable on board, met in mid-Atlantic and spliced the cable. Then the *Niagara* steamed westward and landed her end of the cable at Newfoundland on 5th August while the *Agamemnon* sailed eastward and landed her end in Ireland on the same day.

There was tremendous enthusiasm in America and England. Field was a hero in New York. This was a placard displayed in the town:

Lightning
Caught and tamed by
Franklin
taught to read & write and go on errands by
Morse
started in foreign trade by
Field
with
Johnny Bull
and
Jonathan
as
special partners

The first official message sent through the Atlantic cable was – 'Glory to God in the highest, on earth peace, good-will towards men'. The first press message, sent in response to the demand from New York for news from Europe, ran:

'Emperor of France returned to Paris Saturday. King of Prussia too ill to visit Queen Victoria. Her Majesty returns to England August 31. Settlement of Chinese question. Chinese empire open to trade; Christian religion allowed; foreign diplomatic agents admitted; indemnity to England and France. Gwalior insurgent army broken up. All India becomes tranquil.'

Queen Victoria herself sent a message of congratulations to the president of the United States.

But the triumph was short-lived. The cable went silent four weeks after it was laid and no more messages ever passed. There was a great uproar; it was even suggested that the whole thing was a hoax. Though the failure was never fully explained there were probably two main causes. It was not a sudden failure; communication had gradually got worse. The cable must have been in poor condition before it was laid; it had been lying about in the heat of the sun for long periods, and it had been coiled and uncoiled many times. Added to this, the chief electrician in charge had insisted on using high voltages to test the cable, and these two things probably destroyed the insulation. At any rate nearly £500,000 had been lost, and it was to be eight years before another cable was laid.

In the meantime a thorough inquiry was made to find out what was needed to make a successful transatlantic cable. In due course there came out the 'Report of the Joint Committee appointed by the Lord of the Committee of Privy Council for Trade and the Atlantic Telegraph Company to inquire into the Construction of Submarine Telegraph Cables.' The report said that provided the standards it laid down for manufacture and laying were kept the cable could be a success.

Much encouraged by this, Cyrus Field again set out to raise capital.

He had a difficult time. The American civil war between north and south raged between 1861 and 1865 and it was no wonder that Field could raise only a little money in the United States. There was little friendship between the American and British governments because Britain had declared her neutrality and this gave the Confederacy, the southern states, belligerent rights equal to those of the north. And yet the mere fact that there was a war increased the need for a cable so that news of the war could be had more quickly. Field travelled continually between England and America and during the civil war he made over thirty crossings, no mean feat in those days. In 1863, for example, he was in New York and Boston but he could get only £70,000, and the American merchants told him that because of the shortage of capital he would have to postpone the cable until the war was over.

In fact only one-tenth of the £600,000 required came from America. Field succeeded in raising another £215,000 from capitalists in England, making a total of £285,000. There was still £315,000 to find. Then the Telcon Company was formed to manufacture cables. It made an agreement with Field's Atlantic Telegraph Company to make and lay the cable, and it was so confident in its ability and in the future of the cable that it contributed the rest of the capital required. The financial problem had been solved for the time being.

The new cable was to be the strongest and heaviest yet made. The core was a 7-wire strand with four coverings of gutta-percha. This was covered with tarred jute yarn and then armoured with ten ungalvanized soft iron wires, each of which was covered with five tarred strands of manila hemp. The cable weighed 1¾ tons per mile in air, and 14 cwt in water and its diameter was 1·1 inch. This was, then, a big manufacturing job.

The main problem was transport. How was the cable to be carried at sea? It seemed that a cable of such bulk would need at least three ships. Two ships had been used in 1857 and 1858 and this had complicated the laying operation. But now, by one of the lucky coincidences of history there was one ship big enough to do the job alone. This was Brunel's masterpiece, the *Great Eastern*, which he had shown to Cyrus Field ten years earlier.

THE 'GREAT EASTERN'

In the eighteen-fifties and sixties the *Great Eastern* steamship was a tremendous sensation. The thing which made such an impression on the Victorians was her sheer size. Everything about her was far bigger than anything before on the sea. Five times bigger than any other ship afloat, she was designed to carry four thousand passengers, twice the number of even a modern liner. She was six hundred and ninety-two feet long, and one hundred and twenty feet wide; her displacement of 22,500 tons was to be the highest for fifty years. Thirty thousand iron plates and three million rivets were used to build her. The first ship to be built without ribs, she was so strong, with her two hulls one inside the other and, inside these, watertight bulkheads, that she was practically unsinkable.

Her power and speed were just as impressive. Two sets of engines supplied 11,000 horse-power, enough, it was said, 'to run all the cotton mills in Manchester'. One set drove the enormous twenty-four-foot screw, the other turned the paddle wheels. The two together gave her a small turning circle and made her very manœuvrable. Designed to sail to Ceylon and back without refuelling she could take 15,000 tons of coal in her bunkers. With her five funnels and six masts she was an unforgettable sight for thousands of people; pictures of her of all kinds, engravings, lithographs, photographs, and even *Great Eastern* pottery, were very popular.

How was it that this ship, such a monster for those days, was built? Her designer, I. K. Brunel, the most famous engineer in Britain, nicknamed the Little Giant, already had a great reputation for his railways, bridges and ships. He had built the Great Western Railway and two very large ships, the *Great Western* and the *Great Britain*. The *Great Britain* was the first iron-built ocean-going vessel and the first to use only screw propulsion. With this reputation Brunel convinced a group of financiers that there would be large profits from a bigger ship than ever before. The *Great Eastern* was to make the 22,000-mile round trip to Trincomalee, Ceylon, without refuelling, and secure all the trade with the East. The sum of £600,000 was raised to build her.

The ship took three years to build, at Millwall, and after three months' effort she was launched, broadside on, in the Thames in 1858. She had now cost £800,000 and required another £120,000 to fit out. The company which had financed her went bankrupt and a new company bought her for a mere £160,000. She was mistakenly put on the Atlantic run and never made enough money to cover her costs. After six years she had lost so much money that she was put up for auction. At the first auction the bids did not reach even the reserve price of £100,000. The second time the *Great Eastern* was knocked down for a mere £25,000 to Daniel Gooch, friend of Brunel. Gooch had already invested a large sum in the Atlantic cable.

Now Cyrus Field and the *Great Eastern* came together. Field, busy raising money in London, had discussed the ship with Gooch and on hearing the news of his purchase sent him a telegram:

> 'I shall be truly glad to have the *Great Eastern* used in laying the Atlantic cable.'

Gooch offered the use of the ship in return for shares to the value of £50,000 in Field's Atlantic Telegraph Company; if the cable venture was a failure he would ask for nothing. This offer was gladly accepted by Field.

The great ship now began the only really useful period of her life – cable laying. First of all certain modifications had to be carried out. She had five boiler-rooms, with a funnel to each. However one funnel which passed through the hold had to be removed to make room for the cable. This meant putting one boiler-room out of action. The cable was coiled in three great water-filled tanks.

By May 1865, the cable of 2,300 nautical miles, which had taken eight months to make, was now lying stored in water-filled tanks at Greenwich, ready for shipment. The *Great Eastern* was too big to tie up at Greenwich and so the cable was brought down in barges from the wharf to Sheerness where the ship lay.

The great ship loaded up. She took on 8,000 tons of coal, provisions for the crew of 500 and the parties of technicians and experts, including a cow, a dozen oxen, twenty pigs, one hundred and twenty sheep, and poultry, 5,000 tons of cable and the massive machinery for laying it. Altogether her full load came to 21,000 tons. All was now ready for the 1865 expedition.

At this point all three of the chief parties in the venture came together, for William Thomson and Cyrus Field were both on board the great ship. Field was the only American present. Thomson's invention, the mirror galvanometer, which was the key instrument for testing the cable, was installed on the ship. With them were Daniel Gooch and the famous correspondent of *The Times*, W. H. Russell, who had made his name with his dispatches from the Crimean War.

WILLIAM THOMSON, LORD KELVIN (1824–1907)

William Thomson was born in Belfast where his father was professor of mathematics and also lecturer in geography. His mother's family were country gentry with a comfortable private income. Thomson's mother died when he was only six, and the family of seven children was brought up by their father and a nurse and their grandparents.

Thomson's father, Dr. James Thomson, was Scottish by origin, although Belfast was his home. He was an extraordinary man. Starting as a labourer on his father's farm, he taught himself so that he could get entrance to Glasgow University. That university was famous as a place where no religious tests were imposed, unlike Oxford, Cambridge and Dublin. Later he became professor of mathematics at Glasgow. He was a tremendously hard worker; he used to get up at four o'clock to write textbooks before doing his teaching during the day, so that he could spend the evening with his children who had no mother.

Young Thomson was taught by his father from a very early age. When he was only three he joined in the family lessons in geography and arithmetic and by the time he was six he knew a good deal of these subjects. When he was seven he went to school for a year and won a first prize. Apart from that period, all his education until he was ten came from his father's lessons. On Sundays, morning and evening, his father read chapters of the Bible with the children.

When Dr. Thomson became professor at Glasgow University young Thomson, then aged eight, and his brother were allowed to attend his lectures. At the age of ten he matriculated and became a student at the university – exceptionally early even allowing for the custom of those days. It was also the custom at Glasgow for the students to decide by vote the prizewinners in each class. As a result young Thomson and his brother James won the prizes available for Latin, Greek, mathematics, astronomy and natural philosophy (which included electricity) every year at the university.

Young Thomson's studies were not only theoretical or wholly based on book learning. He and his brother were given a room at home in which to make apparatus and experiments. When he was twelve they each made an electrical friction machine, storing the current in Leyden jars, and supplied electric shocks to the family. They made themselves voltaic piles and galvanic batteries and experimented with metals and fluids. At this same period Faraday was making his great discoveries in electromagnetism at the Royal Institution in London (see Chapter Two).

When he was fourteen Thomson was sent by his father to Paris for two months to improve his conversational French. He passed the examination for the B.A. degree of Glasgow University when he was nearly fifteen, and the M.A. degree a year later. But he did not actually receive the degrees because he intended to go to Cambridge University and felt that he would be more acceptable there without the degree of another University. And so when writing to his brother he signed himself B.A.T.A.I. (B.A. to all intents and purposes). Though he was a brilliant student he was not a dull bookworm. He had an irreverent sense of humour. On one occasion at a revivalist religious service in the Highlands he was so overcome with laughter at the enthusiasm expressed by the congregation that the minister pointed a warning finger at him and exclaimed: 'Ye'll no laugh when ye're in hell!'

He was not quite seventeen when he was entered as a student at St. Peter's College, Cambridge, in April 1841. When his father took him to the University it was quite a journey. They went by mail coach from Glasgow to Carlisle, slept there, took another coach to Hull, ferried across the Humber and, not liking the look of the boat that was to take them from Hull to Ely, took a third coach to Cambridge. He wrote to his sister:

'St Peter's College
Friday evening

'My dear Elizabeth,

I am now fairly settled in my rooms at College. I was exceedingly fortunate in getting comfortable rooms at once, as most of the students do not get them till the second year . . . My suite of apartments consists of a parlour, a bedroom, and a gyp's room . . . after chapel – which is at eight for a few days till lectures begin – I made my first attempt at preparing breakfast. I got on very well except that I forgot whether to put the coffee in after or before the water was boiling, and also whether I should keep it any time boiling after the water is put in. . . .

Great numbers of tradesmen have been calling upon me and leaving their cards. One fashionable young man was particularly anxious to get me to put down my name as a subscriber to get my hair dressed – subscription 2/6 a term – very cheap. I however declined the tempting and advantageous offer, considering that previously my hair dressing has cost me only 2d. the half year hitherto.

My breakfast and tea, besides coffee or tea, consist of a small loaf left by the gyp, and two or three cylinders of butter. He always comes in and lays the things, takes them away, and cleans them, etc. . . . The dinner at the hall is nothing remarkable, consisting of substantial joints, and, if you pay sixpence, about, additional, you can get sizings (i.e. puddings, or apple pie, or something of that sort). . . .

I have got no time to be dull, as I have got as much to do as I can possibly accomplish and a great deal more besides; that is, I may do as much as I please, as the quicker I get through what I have to read the better. Lectures have now commenced, which take up some time both for preparation and the time of attendance, this is an hour a day. We have classics and mathematics day about.

I don't know whether I told you yet that I have joined the Union Society, which is for a joint stock library and reading-room. . . . The Union is also a debating society, but I have not gone to any of the debates yet, and I do not anticipate much interest in them. . . .

In this college, and in all the others there is a boat-club. I have not joined the club, however, as rowing for the races is too hard work for getting on well with reading, and, besides, the men connected with the club are generally rather an idle set.'

Thomson finished as the best mathematician of his year, and he also won the silver sculls trophy. (When money was scarce and books were expensive he still managed to buy himself a second-hand boat.) Immediately after his final examination he was elected to a fellowship worth £200 a year and his money difficulties were over. Then in the following year, at the age of twenty-two, he was elected professor of natural history at Glasgow University and returned to his home city.

Although at first he was embarrassed by the presence at his lectures of students older than himself, he soon became popular. This was partly because he became famous for his discoveries but also because he was an inspiring teacher. Some of his methods of teaching were unorthodox and they became well known in the University. When teaching acoustics he brought out the French horn he had used at Cambridge and played on it to illustrate a point in his lecture. A shot from his rifle at a lead pendulum was used to illustrate his lectures on ballistics. These events were loudly cheered by the students. With them he maintained a friendly spirit of fellowship, and in fact always called himself a student. One of his greatest improvements as a teacher was to insist that students should have the use of a physics laboratory. This was unheard of when he started teaching but he took over an empty wine cellar adjoining the lecture-room and converted it to a physics laboratory.

Thomson remained professor at Glasgow for fifty-three years, refusing three times a professorship in physics at Cambridge University where the subject at that time was not so well advanced. During his first years as professor he concentrated on studies of heat and energy. His most important discovery was the concept of an absolute zero of temperature, on which he based the absolute scale named after him. He also worked with the great Lancashire-born physicist James Joule. Then just about the time that Thomson and Joule published their work on the new scale Thomson first became interested in submarine cables. This was in 1854 when he was thirty. It was a turning point in his life because it led him away from scientific research to a career as an engineer.

Thomson was on both the cable-laying expeditions in 1857 and 1858. They were unsuccessful and this was largely because he was not in charge of the design and testing of the cables. A retired physician and amateur electrician had been appointed chief electrician and his methods were truly amateur. The cable specification had already been accepted and it was too late when Thomson urged that the cable should be several times larger. When the first cable parted during laying he wrote a paper 'On Machinery for Laying Submarine Cables' and designed paying-out brakes. These were put on the cable ships the next year. He also invented his mirror galvanometer and it was used on the 1858 expedition. But the chief electrician in charge was determined to use his own faulty equipment and methods instead of Thomson's. After the failure of the 1858 cable he was no longer employed and Thomson now had the last say on cable design. For instance, Thomson insisted, against opposition, that a certain minimum quality of copper must be used in all future specifications of cables. He carried out experiments with his mirror galvanometer at the Greenwich works of the cable manufacturers. When the *Great Eastern* sailed with the cable he controlled all the electrical measurements.

On Saturday, 14th July, 1865, the great ship sailed for Valentia on the west coast of Ireland where the shore end of the cable was laid by the steamer *Caroline*. As soon as this was spliced to the main cable the great ship began to pay out. Russell described the scene; it was Sunday, 23rd July.

'The bight of the cable was slipped from the *Caroline* at 7.15 p.m. and the *Great Eastern* stood slowly on her course N.W. by West. . . . The brake was eased, and as the *Great Eastern* moved ahead the machinery of the paying-out apparatus began to work, drums rolled, wheels whirled, and out spun the black line of the cable, and dropped in a graceful curve into the sea over the stern wheel. The cable came up with ease from the after tank, and was payed out with the utmost regularity from the apparatus. The system of signals to and from the ship was at once in play between the electricians on board and those at Foilhummerum.'

During the first night out the mirror galvanometer showed a fault in the cable, and the ship's alarm rang. It was necessary to re-wind the cable on board until the fault was found. This was a difficult and slow operation because the cable could not be reeled back over the stern but had to be transferred from the stern to the bow and back again the whole length of the ship. Only after ten miles had been picked up was it found that a broken wire had driven into the core. Five days later the same thing happened. Again the weary task of picking up had to be done and again the same cause of the fault was found. This time sabotage by men in the cable tanks below deck was suspected.

All then went well for four days. Then on 2nd August Gooch wrote in his diary: 'All is over, I fear, for this year, and our cable is gone.' Cyrus Field himself was on watch in the cable tank, a faulty section of cable was noticed but passed overboard. As the cable was being wound in it became chafed against the ship and parted. The Atlantic cable, 1,186 miles of it, was lying 2,000 fathoms down on the ocean bed. It was decided to grapple for the cable, although it had never been done before at such a depth, and the gear on board was not suitable. For eight days the ship moved slowly around. Several times the cable was hooked by the grapnel but never raised to the surface. The tackle parted repeatedly; two cable-men were badly cut in the face by flying ropes. Only after all the tackle, and miles of wire, manila and hemp rope had been lost was the struggle given up. The spot was marked with a buoy. It had at least been shown that it was possible to raise a cable in 2,000 fathoms and that the cable could be recovered.

'How one short hour has buried all our hopes!' Gooch confessed in his diary. 'This one thing, upon which I had set my heart more than any other work I was ever engaged in, is dead. . . . I must now return to England to receive the sympathy of my friends not their congratulations, as I had so fondly hoped. . . . The day has been foggy, wet and dreary, and the night is no better. I have just had a solitary ramble for half an hour on deck, and I shall get to bed. Every one on board, since our accident, has been very low in spirits . . . nor do any of them seem inclined for a rubber of whist.' Cyrus Field had other things to think about. He was busy with Professor Thomson and the financiers on board making plans to form another company to raise the money for yet another cable.

As soon as he arrived back in England Field organized the new Anglo American Telegraph Company while the Telcon company began to make the cable which was to be laid in the following year, 1866. To do this and to find and complete the lost cable £600,000 more was required. About 1,600 miles of new cable was manufactured. The main improvement was that in order to make the armouring less brittle the wires composing it were of milder iron and were now galvanized. The *Great Eastern* herself received some attention. She was cleared of a heavy coat of barnacles and seaweed, which added a knot to her speed. The powerful cable machinery on board was improved so that cable could be picked up, as well as let out, at the stern, and proper tackle for grappling was provided.

Once again, on 30th June, the great ship sailed, the shore end at Valentia was spliced and on 13th July, in a thick fog, she started paying out; H.M.S. *Terrible* in the lead, the *Medway* and the *Albany* on either side. This year it was fair weather and plain sailing all the way. On board everything proceeded according to plan. There was still a suspicion of sabotage of the cable and so the men in the tanks were dressed in special overalls without pockets so that tools could not be carried down below. The days were monotonous and trying while everyone waited for the accidents which did not happen. Gooch wrote: 'This stretch of the nerves day after day is hard work, and the mind has no change; morning, noon, and night it is all the same – cable, cable, cable.'

The whole time the instrument-room on board was in communication with Valentia. Nine days out Field sent a message: 'The *Great Eastern* has passed the place where the cable was lost last year and all is going well.' As the work moved from one cable tank to another it interfered with Gooch's customary evening walk along the 600 feet of lighted deck, which was nicknamed Oxford Street. 'It will be my last walk in Oxford Street,' he noted, 'as two-thirds of it will be cut off when we are paying out of the middle tank.' Ten days' out Field, with one eye to business, and full of confidence, sent another message:

'Please obtain the latest news from Egypt China India and distant places for us to forward to the United States on our arrival at Hearts Content.'

Egypt and India were large producers of raw cotton, which

competed with the American South for the Lancashire market. The China tea trade had always been important for America. News from these countries was commercially valuable. On the eleventh day Field telegraphed joyfully:

> 'We are within four hundred miles of Hearts Content and expect to be there on Friday when shall the Atlantic cable be open for business.'

A return for the vast sums spent was at last in sight.

After penetrating dense fog off Newfoundland the great ship and her attendants at last arrived at Hearts Content, Trinity Bay, where the relay station was ready to receive the cable. Gooch described the scene as the cable end was taken ashore:

> 'There was the wildest excitement I have ever witnessed. All seemed mad with joy, jumping into the water and shouting as though they wished the sound to be heard in Washington. . . . The old cable hands seemed as though they could eat the end; one even actually put it in his mouth and sucked it. They held it up and danced round it, cheering at the top of their voices. It was a strange sight – nay, a sight that filled our eyes with tears. Yes, I felt not less than they did. I did cheer, but I could better have silently cried.'

It was the end of ten years' struggle. The captain of the *Great Eastern* wrote to Mrs Field in New York: 'Mr Field, at least, never gave out. He never ceased to say "It would come all right" even when his looks hardly bore out the assertion. But at last it did.' Field began to see some tangible reward straight away. There was a queue of applications to send messages before the cable was open for business. One of the first messages from Ireland announced the end of the Austro-Prussian war. Queen Victoria sent greetings to President Johnson. On the first day the revenue was £1,000 at a minimum charge of £20 for the first twenty words plus £1 for each additional word.

But Field was not yet finished with the Atlantic cable, nor were the *Great Eastern* and Professor Thomson. They now had the difficult task of finding the 1865 cable in mid-ocean. The great ship sailed again after taking on 8,000 tons of coal which had been brought in five ships from South Wales, and met her escorts in mid-Atlantic, 600 miles from Newfoundland, on 11th August. Grappling went on throughout that month often in bad weather; the cable was repeatedly hooked, surfaced and then lost again. The coal and provisions were nearly used up and the men were exhausted. Then on 31st August, a clear calm day, when the grapnel was lowered for the thirtieth time the cable was secured on board. The question was whether it was in order after lying in the sea for a year. It so happened that an operator had continually manned the instruments at Valentia in order to test the cable. When the Great Eastern electrician sent a trial message the operator replied, as soon as he had recovered from his surprise. Cyrus Field was overcome. 'One of the most interesting scenes I have ever witnessed,' he wrote, 'was the moment when, after the cable was recovered, it was brought to the electrician's room to see whether it was alive or dead . . . I left the room on hearing those six memorable letters "Both O.K.", went to my cabin and locked the door; I could no longer restrain my tears, crying like a child . . .'

No sooner had the cable been tested than it was spliced to the new cable on the ship which safely landed the end of the salvaged cable at Newfoundland on 7th September. There were great celebrations, and honours were bestowed on the men responsible. Queen Victoria conferred knighthoods on Professor Thomson and on the managing director and engineer of the Telcon Company, as well as making Daniel Gooch a baronet for his part in making the *Great Eastern* available. Cyrus Field had the rare honour of a Vote of Thanks from the Congress of the United States 'for his foresight, courage and determination in establishing telegraphic communication by means of the Atlantic cable traversing mid ocean and connecting the Old World with the New'.

Thomson, who knew better than anyone, put Field's achievement on record when he wrote to him: 'I am sorry I had not the opportunity of saying in public how much I value your energy and perseverance in carrying through this great enterprise, and how clearly you stand out in its history as its originator, and its mainspring from beginning to end.'

Important though the Atlantic cables were for their own usefulness – they had after all cost the sum of 2½ million pounds – they were just as important because they led to many more: their success encouraged plans to lay cables, step by step, all over the world. For one thing it was now easier to raise the money required. The policy was to link the main points of the British Empire. First India was reached four years after the Atlantic cable, and only a year later this route had reached Australia. Many other Atlantic cables were laid; by the end of the century there were fifteen of them, twelve in working order. It was, however, nearly forty years after 1866 before the Pacific Ocean was crossed. The Pacific cable, jointly owned by the governments of Australia, Canada, New Zealand and the United Kingdom, was the first to be sponsored by the State instead of private enterprise. Every place of real importance could be reached by cable, overland or submarine. The world had shrunk into a single market. Britain lived by its trade 'in the middle of this shrunken world, whispering along its copper wire news about the goods that slid along its lines of iron and steel to the sea'.

Cyrus Field, William Thomson and the *Great Eastern* all had long and useful lives after 1866. Thomson, now Sir William Thomson, continued to be professor at Glasgow and gave his last lecture there at the age of seventy-five. Throughout the years he poured out a stream of inventions, mainly electrical. Although he was a great theorist his main interest was in the practical applications of science. He insisted that his scientific work should be useful to society. He said: 'I see no use in a new discovery until it is applied to the use of mankind.' It was typical of his interests that he introduced Bell's telephone into Britain.

The year after the success of the Atlantic cable he invented his siphon recorder. By means of this instrument incoming signals were made to record themselves automatically on paper tape. It was a sequel to his mirror galvanometer and it was equally useful as a means of recording impulses through long cables but it had some important advantages. The galvanometer had required highly skilled 'mirror clerks', who had to watch intensively the rapid movements of a beam of light, and writers to record the movements. It had imposed a great strain on clerks and operators so that they became irritable and quarrelsome, with the result that the steady watch required was often interrupted. This problem was solved by the siphon recorder which also meant that only one clerk instead of two was necessary.

By 1870 Thomson began to make a good deal of money from his patents, and bought a yacht called *Lalla Rookh.* His keen interest in the sea and yachting led him to other inventions. Among these was his improvement to the mariner's compass, which was adopted by the Royal Navy and used widely for forty years, and his machine for taking deep-sea soundings.

Because he was both a great scientist and a practical engineer he became very famous throughout the world. When he became Lord Kelvin he was the first scientist to receive a peerage. In politics he was a Liberal and was invited to stand for Parliament but he refused because he would not give the time. He was a religious man, without being rigid. He said: 'If you think strongly enough, you will be forced by Science to a belief in God, which is the foundation of all religion.' All who knew him emphasized his kindness and his modesty. Not long before he died he wrote:

'One word characterizes the efforts I have made during fifty-five years: that word is failure. I know no more of electric and magnetic force, or of the relation between ether, electricity and ponderable matter than I knew and tried to teach to my students of natural philosophy fifty years ago in my first session as professor.'

He married, when he was twenty-eight, a cousin and childhood friend. After she died childless he married again, at the age of fifty, but again there were no children. At his funeral in Westminster Abbey in 1907 the pall bearers included the presidents of the Royal Society and of the Institution of Civil Engineers and a past president of the Institution of Electrical Engineers. Thus both science and technology paid homage.

In the United States Cyrus Field did nothing more as remarkable as the Atlantic cable. He remained a wealthy man until near the end of his life and invested his money in railways and newspapers. But he became heavily involved in railway speculation and in consequence lost most of his money when he was nearly seventy. He died in 1892 at the age of seventy-three. He was too visionary and chivalrous and not ruthless enough to be a great leader of the business world.

The *Great Eastern* still had twenty years' life, some of it very useful. Three years after Field's triumph she laid a French cable from Brest to the French island of Miquelon off Newfoundland, the longest yet laid. The following year, painted white to lessen the tropical heat, she laid the long length from Bombay to Aden, thus completing the route to India. But very soon cables had become such big business that it was worth building the first ship specially designed for cable work, the *Faraday*. This made the *Great Eastern* obsolete and her days were numbered.

No one knew what to do with the great ship for the rest of her life. In 1885 she was auctioned for £26,000, chartered to Lewis's the big drapers of Liverpool. She lay in the Mersey acting as a great poster hoarding with enormous advertisements for Lewis's along her sides. She was turned into a fairground complete with circus, trapeze artists and sideshows. Hundreds of thousands paid a shilling for admission. She was hauled to Dublin and then to the Clyde to attract sightseers. Finally a firm of metal dealers bought her for £16,000 for breaking up. The aged Gooch wrote in his diary:

'It looks like the last of the grand old ship, the *Great Eastern*. I would much rather the ship was broken up than turned to base uses. Poor old ship, you deserved a better fate.'

But the ship still had to be taken apart and this was almost as tough a problem as her launching had been. Beginning on the first day of 1889 it took the breakers more than eighteen months to finish the job.

THE CABLE MAKERS

By 1866, when the first successful Atlantic cable was laid, more than 5,000 miles of submarine cable had been manufactured. In fact all the cable used was made in Britain, and this was to be so for many years to come. Although this amount was insignificant compared with the vast mileage required when a cable network covered the whole world, yet it was a big achievement for the Britain of that day. Britain was still only half industrialized, agriculture and domestic service were still much the largest occupations, and factories and steam power had not spread far outside the textile industries.

Who were the men who made the cables, who did they work for, what conditions did they work in, what kind of lives did they lead, what was the price of their achievement?

A hundred years ago cable making was one of the new industries. A handful of enterprising businessmen had started it and soon there was keen competition between them. It was mainly a Thames-side industry. There were good reasons for this. The industry grew out of the old rope making which went back hundreds of years. The wharves at Millwall, Greenwich and Blackwall were ideal places for manufacture because they were close to the old naval dockyards at Deptford and Woolwich which used enormous amounts of rope. Hempen rope gradually gave way to wire rope as greater strength was needed by the iron ships and the collieries. In addition the river site enabled the long lengths of cable to be wound from the factories straight into the barges or the holds of the ships to be taken out to sea. Another reason was that London had the foremost engineering workshops in the world and so the machinery for cable making and laying could be made near by.

Of all the cable firms W. T. Henley's had the longest continual history until it was absorbed into Amalgamated Electrical Industries a few years ago.

WILLIAM THOMAS HENLEY (1814–1883)

W. T. Henley was the presiding genius of his firm for nearly fifty years. He and the world-famous firm he created are worthy of study as examples of the industry which made Britain, for a short time, the most wealthy and powerful nation in the world. A country boy, he was born at Midhurst in Sussex in 1814, a year before Waterloo. His father was a maker of buckskin breeches, a thriving trade in a farming and fox-hunting county. When Henley was four his family moved up to London where his father began business as a maker of sheepskin mats. Henley himself was left behind at Midhurst in the care of his grandfather who was a quite prosperous glover and fellmonger. From the age of six until he was eleven he went to school in the village. 'At eleven,' he wrote, 'I finished schooling and was set to work. I had learned all that was absolutely necessary. Reading, writing, arithmetic and history I had pretty well mastered.' Henley stayed in the leather business at Midhurst until he was sixteen. His time was spent in dressing leather, in riding about the county taking leather gaiters and gloves to the farmers' men and collecting sheepskins. Although his uncle, who had taken over the business, wanted to apprentice him, Henley did not take to the trade. He was fascinated by machinery; he used to stand by the razor-grinder's barrow, watching it with intense interest. When he reached sixteen he took the stage coach for London, with two pounds in his pocket, to join his mother.

Henley's mother must have been a woman of great determination. Her husband had died soon after moving to London and she had a hard time making a living for herself and the two children. Frequently their dinner consisted of a red herring between them. Originally she had been a domestic servant, then she became a straw bonnet maker and milliner and she continued at this in London. To supplement her wages she used to make ink and carry it round to the numerous pawnbrokers. Later she took up ladies' bootmaking. When Henley joined the family in their single room he took another room in the same house and furnished it with the basic necessity, a flock bed and bedding.

His first job was as light porter in Cheapside, carrying silk goods on his back to customers in various parts of London. He lived in and fed well. Each evening his bed was placed on the landing of the steps leading down to the stores in the cellar so as to prevent thieves breaking in. This job ended when he came to blows with the head porter.

He then went to St. Katherine's Dock and was taken on as an extra labourer at 2s. 6d. per day. There was work for only four days a week and as the hours were short (eight to four in summer and nine to four in winter) he had plenty of spare time. This he intended to use to teach himself a trade as mechanic and instrument maker. He was now seventeen. Having set himself up in a back room in the Cambridge Road,

Mile End, he bought an old lathe and a vice with which he taught himself turning in wood and brass. He also studied hard. 'In three years,' he wrote, 'I had got myself pretty well up in electricity and magnetizing optics, pneumatics, chemistry, mechanics and the laws of motion, as well as the use of tools.'

His ambition was to be a maker of 'philosophical instruments', that is scientific instruments. At that time the latest discoveries in electricity, magnetism and the early telegraphs were causing a great stir. Henley tried his hand at making electrical apparatus and made an electrical friction machine and a Leyden jar.

After his five years of working at the docks he felt competent to make scientific, and in particular electrical, apparatus – both the metal and the wooden parts. He had to live very economically. From his wage of 10s. 0d. a week he spent 7s. 6d. on rent, food and clothing, and the rest on books and materials. He ate sparingly, on week-days chiefly bread and butter or buttered toast and coffee, with an occasional half pint of beer for dinner. On Sundays he cooked pies, puddings and pancakes for himself.

His first opportunity came when a chemist in the Commercial Road gave him some orders for apparatus and allowed him to put his electrical machines for sale in his window. Then he received an order worth £5, and he felt it was time to leave the docks, although he had made progress there. He had been given a preference ticket which meant that when there was work on a ship he was among the first of the dockers waiting at the gates to be called on. This meant a full week's work as well as fourpence a day more pay. It was a rough struggle for existence which he had survived.

In 1836 Henley now started his own business as a scientific instrument maker. He rented a workshop with a living-room over a cook-shop in Red Lion Street, Whitechapel. He bought two more lathes and turned his old one into a wire-covering machine. With this machine he could earn a pound a day because there was an increasing demand for wire covered with silk and cotton which could be used in electromagnetic apparatus. Increasing business forced him to move to a house in the Minories where he employed three men and a boy.

He also had the satisfaction of having his mother to live with him and providing her with some comfort.

During all Wheatstone's first experiments with the electric telegraph Henley made most of his apparatus. As the telegraph was increasingly used by the railways in the 1840's so Henley's work grew. He moved again to a bigger house and workshop in St. John Street, Clerkenwell. 'There,' he wrote, 'I increased the number of my workmen to twenty-three and found I was obliged to leave off working at the lathe; as I had enough work to attend to, although I still did all the lacquering of the various pieces of brass work.' This was his advertisement in that year:

ELECTRIC TELEGRAPHS

OF ANY KIND, and of very Superior Workmanship, supplied by W. T. HENLEY, Telegraph Engineer, Magnet Manufacturer, and Mechanician, and patentee of the Magneto-Electric Telegraph, 46, St. John's-Street-Road, Clerkenwell, London.

W.T.H. undertakes to erect Telegraph Works, in this country or abroad, at a very reduced charge, and, if required, keep them in order; or when Railway Companies or other wish to erect their own Wires, he will supply them with Instruments of first-rate quality, as he has lately done (on Cook and Wheatstone's principle) to the South Eastern Railway Company, for the Reading, Reigate, and Guildford and Hastings and Ashford Lines – the Telegraph Company being paid for a Licence for using the Patent. W. T. HENLEY also calls attention to his Magneto-Electric Telegraph, the Patents for which he has assigned to the Magneto-Electric Telegraph Company. This Instrument requires no battery, and is the only Telegraph not affected by wet weather or bad weather of any kind.

W.T.H. also manufactures Magnets, Magnetic, Magneto-Electric, or other apparatus, of any dimensions; also all descriptions of Clock-work Trains and other Machinery.

Wire, covered with Silk, Cotton, Gutta Percha, or India-rubber, of any size or in any length.

Henley exhibited at the Great Exhibition at the Crystal Palace in Hyde Park in 1851 and he was awarded a gold medal for, in the words of the judges, 'his convenient and ingenious application of magnetic electricity to the purpose of electric telegraphs'. His main exhibit was a magneto-electric telegraph which was used by Wheatstone. Shortly after that he began making cables and by 1858 he had made several hundred miles, including one cable of 240 miles from Australia to Tasmania. He started a new factory at North Woolwich where many thousand miles of cable were to be made in the next twenty years. He described these events:

'I commenced business at North Woolwich in 1859. My capital when commencing there was about £8,000. I took 3½ acres of land on lease for 99 years, with option of purchase. Of the £8,900 I was obliged to spend £7,000 on buildings and removing machinery and making new. During the years 1860, 1862 and 1863 I executed several important cable contracts for the Spanish government and the Persian Gulf cable for the Indian government.'

He was on the flood-tide of a new industry. His growing reputation was shown when he was invited to give evidence to a government committee which had been set up to inquire into the numerous failures of submarine cables. The failure of the first Atlantic cable, and of others, had prompted the government to hold this inquiry.

Henley's business continued to grow. 'During this time,' he wrote, 'I erected some more buildings, and added the wire drawing and galvanizing to my other business of submarine cable and telegraph instrument making, which materially increased the profit attending the making of cables. I attended to the laying of cables myself where the cable contract included the laying, and succeeded in picking up a submarine cable at greater depth than had ever been done before – nearly a mile deep in the Mediterranean. In order that I might bestow as much attention to the Works as possible, I fitted up a bedroom in the factory, and used to live there, only going home once a week.'

He now comes into the story of the Atlantic cable, for in 1864 another company began to manufacture the cables laid in 1865 and 1866, and they sub-contracted to Henley the heavily armoured shore ends. Henley's own cable ship laid the shore end at Valentia on the south-west coast of Ireland. During the next few years he bought three more cable ships and made thousands of miles of cable, including those in the Behring Sea, Cook's Strait, and the Mediterranean.

The works grew rapidly until they spread over 13 acres, instead of the original three. Henley decided to make his own iron and steel rods and so he built a rolling mill and a Siemens furnace. He preferred to make his own cable-making machinery rather than buy it from outside and so he had to have an iron and brass foundry and fitting, smith's, boiler, and instrument maker's shops. But this rapid growth had dangers for a man like Henley who was an engineer and not a businessman. This is his own account of the expansion and the financial problems it brought with it:

'My net profits from April 1868 to December 1873, as shown by the accountants amounted to £560,000. Had I been a sensible man, no doubt I should have put at least half this amount in some safe investment outside of my business, but instead of doing so I went on extending my works. By the end of 1873 the 2½ acres of leasehold land had increased to 13 acres of freehold and 3 of leasehold (with power to purchase) all covered with buildings comprising cable factories, wire drawing and galvanizing works, rolling mills, steel works, wire rope works, puddling and ball furnaces – in short, everything requisite for the manufacture in every stage, both in iron and steel, from the pig iron to the finished article, either in the shape of submarine cables, telegraph or any other wire, wire ropes, steel for springs, tools, forgings, railway axles, points, crossings, or any castings either in steel or iron up to ten tons in one casting. Also engineering and boiler-making shops, so that all boilers, engines and every other sort of machinery is now made on the premises. I also bought three steamships for the purpose of laying cables, and extended the siding from the Great Eastern Railway into and all over my Works, as well as making a substantial wharf on the river side 400 feet long, where ships of 500 tons can lay alongside to load and unload. During the period mentioned, I manufactured upwards of

12,000 miles of submarine cable weighing about 60,000 tons, besides wire for the Maintenance Company, wire for land lines and other purposes to an amount of over 100,000 tons. By the end of 1873 a sum of £500,000 had been expended on the North Woolwich Works without taking into account the cost of maintenance, as that had always been charged to revenue. . . .

Notwithstanding all this outlay, had I been content to stop here, I believe everything would have gone right, but as I generally make all the wire used by the other cable makers in London (as I can undersell the country wire makers owing to the carriage they have to pay), and if I lose a contract for a cable, I get the wire to make, and knowing that when cable business is brisk such enormous quantities of wire are required, I was induced to purchase some wire works in South Wales for the purpose of manufacturing wire rods. This involved the locking up of about £100,000 more capital, and besides which, owing to the great distance away, I was not able to manage it myself, and the working resulted in very heavy losses.

'Thus the capital locked up at North Woolwich, including the stock-in-trade, amounted to £600,000, which, with £90,000 in steamships and over £100,000 in South Wales, made a total of £800,000, £200,000 of which was borrowed on mortgage.'

In his eagerness to invest all his profits in the works and thus continually expand Henley was always short of ready money or working capital for running the business from week to week. When trade slackened off, and with it the demand for cables, he was therefore in difficulties.

He began to realize that he had made a mistake in always insisting on being his own master, responsible to no one but himself:

'I had, some time before this, been asked many times to take a partner or partners, or to let some friends join in a limited company, but I always refused, not from a selfish feeling, but because I had always felt a pride in carrying on the business unaided; and even at this time (the autumn of 1874) I should have refused it had it been offered.'

Soon he was forced to borrow money in the City but he quickly found his shortcomings as a financier:

'I ought at this period to have called my creditors together and made some arrangement for time, and everything could have been accomplished easily; but I had an unaccountable aversion to anything like a suspension of payment, or paying less than twenty shillings in the pound, that I was determined to struggle on. Then I began financing to keep things going, and my credit being still first rate up to the end of the year, I was able to keep the ball rolling pretty well. I must admit that however well I succeeded as an engineer, at financing I was quite out of my element, as for any accommodation I received I had to pay the most ruinous terms in a good many instances, though not in all, and at the end of the year I began to hear ominous whispers as to my position and my credit, and people began to look upon my bills very suspiciously. All this meant paying higher still for assistance.'

Henley's difficulties were increased by the loss of one of his cable ships, the 1,600-ton *La Plata*, which sank in a gale in the Bay of Biscay with sixty men on board. In 1875 he went bankrupt. He wrote, 'From January of this year until the end of March, when I was compelled to suspend payment, I was so incessantly occupied in the City in endeavouring to raise the wind and scraping every pound together that was owing, that I could bestow very little attention to North Woolwich, and although I went down every night after the day's work in the City, and stayed until 9 o'clock, I could do very little good, and at last I was brought to a dead stand, and was unable to recover myself. The only consolation I had was that I had not given up until I was absolutely compelled to do so.'

In the same year the firm was converted into a limited company under the name of W. T. Henley and Co. Ltd., and it looked as though it might recover.

However, this attempt to re-establish the firm did not succeed. Probably the debt incurred by Henley earlier on was too great. In any case the economy was still in the doldrums and trade was still slack. The company was wound up after two years, the works were closed down, and all but a few skilled men were sacked. There was no alternative but to sell off the plant and machinery. The cover of the auction catalogue is shown in plate 5.

Henley was not finished yet, although it seemed that he was ruined. Some of his creditors realized that it would be worth investing money in what remained of the firm and so in 1880 a second company was formed, W. T. Henley's Telegraph Works Company Limited. Henley sold to the company his remaining three acres of land and all the remaining plant, good-will, trade marks, etc., for £50,000. Most of this money was used to pay off his debts. He was left with little wealth and his main satisfaction was that he could settle with his creditors. He was now the managing director and no longer the owner.

Two years later Henley caught a chill and died of pneumonia. The company, however, continued to flourish for another eighty years until it was absorbed by A.E.I.

THE CABLE WORKERS

What kind of work was done at Henley's works, who were the men who did it, and what kind of working lives did they lead?

As we have seen, the works produced many more things besides cables. On the site the cable shops with the rows of big circular cable tanks stood facing the wharves on the river front. Alongside them were the rubber shop and boiler house on one side, and the scrap iron yard and store shed on the other. Farther back from the river were ranged more than twenty different workshops for the whole range of processes of manufacture carried out: shops for corrugating, galvanizing, boiler making, turning, tinning, battery making, instrument making, joinery and pattern making, welding, coppering, as well as the rolling mill, the steel smelting house and the annealing house. Most of the men who worked in the shops were, of course, skilled artisans who had served a long apprenticeship. One of the boilermakers' jobs was to make iron-plate guards for the cable machinery; the carpenters made the drums for the cables and racks and spindles to hold the rubber used in the cables.

In the actual cable making most of the work was operating machines – unskilled work. But there was some skilled work closely connected with it, for instance wire drawing, for which a man had to serve a seven-year apprenticeship. There was also the jointer who made cable joints and who sometimes sailed with the cable ship to help lay the cable in a foreign ocean and splice the cable when necessary.

The cables were wound by a number of expensive and complicated machines and it was the job of the men operating them to keep them running. The cables passed along a series of these machines, each of which carried out a different operation at each stage on the cable core and its covering. Each machine wound on an additional layer of material: winding wire, winding cotton, winding silk, winding rubber, braiding, etc. The men operating them were not at all specialized. They often went from one machine to another and followed the job from shop to shop.

When the men were in work their wages were fairly good for those times. Many of them were paid for piecework; it was called 'mile money' and the wages were so much per mile of cable made. This came to an average of about 5½d. per hour so that a machine operator could expect to have, with some overtime, about thirty shillings for a week's work. This can be compared with the 'Docker's Tanner', the sixpence per hour which the dock labourers struck for and won in 1889. (In fact when there was no work at Henley's the men went to get work in the docks.) For this wage they worked long hours, under hard conditions, and were liable to be laid off at any time. The men, in gangs, worked twelve-hour shifts, from 6.0 a.m. to 6 p.m. and from 6.0 p.m. to 6.0 a.m. Some in each gang operated the cable-winding machines, others shipped the cable on to barges at the wharf and then on to the cable ship. On Saturdays knocking off time was 4.0 p.m. A typical factory record in 1871 is shown in plate 5.

When the particular cable was finished many men were sacked until the next job came along. They took what work they could get in the near-by docks or with the other cable manufacturers on the river. Many liked to return to Henley's for he had a good name as an employer.

These men were described as a rough lot, and no wonder.

There was no security of work, no welfare, no provision for sickness, old age and unemployment except the poor law. They ate their meals at work, as and when they could. There were no regular breakfast or dinner times. A man would eat his food off an upturned drum, sitting on a bundle of wire, and have to leave off and start work at any time the machines were started. Beer, however, was always available twice a day, at 11.0 a.m. and 3.30 p.m. It was brought into the works by five potmen each carrying two large cans swinging from yokes across their shoulders. Smoking was forbidden, except in the galvanizing shop, but it went on everywhere any time of the day or night.

Life for these men was hard and they worked long hours for their money, when they had work. But there were some compensations. The discipline in the works was not at all strict. Henley was easy-going with his foremen and this attitude was passed on to the workers. There were regular outings from the works. They went to Yarmouth or Clacton in brakes hired by the firm, or by train, or on the river in the firm's tug. Henley encouraged sports and clubs. He paid for the vans which took the cricket club to away matches and when the cricketers returned there was free beer for them in the public house opposite Henley's house. When the brass band, which was formed in the blacksmiths' shop, needed instruments and uniforms he paid for them too. There were also the Rifle Volunteers, one of many volunteer corps which were formed throughout the country in the 1860's during the national alarm about the ambitions of Napoleon III of France. Henley strongly encouraged the Volunteers and many of the men joined them. They drilled in the galvanizing shop and Henley gave prizes for shooting.

Every opportunity was taken to celebrate any special event. Whenever a cable ship left the works for a foreign ocean the factory was decorated with flags, guns were fired on the jetty, and crowds lined the river banks. Little work was done on such days.

Additional Reading

James Dugan, *The Great Iron Ship*, Hamish Hamilton, 1953.

Science Museum, London, *One Hundred Years of Submarine Cables*, H.M.S.O., 1950.
The Telcon Story, The Telegraph Construction Maintenance Co. Ltd., 1950.

CHAPTER FOUR

The Telephone

Originally the word telephone meant any instrument for sending sound over a distance, such as warning sounds in foggy weather. In the *Illustrated London News* in 1849 there was a description of a 'Telephone or Marine Alarm and Signal Trumpet' invented by a naval captain. The telephone as we know it was first called 'The Electrical Speaking Telephone'.

Once the telegraph had shown that signals could be sent anywhere by electricity it was inevitable that the next step of sending sounds, and especially human speech, would be taken soon. The scientists began to look into the problems. As a matter of fact, Wheatstone was a link between the telegraph and the telephone because he did try to transmit the human voice.

It was the desire to solve scientific and technical problems which led to the telephone, rather than a pressing demand from industry or business. It was only after it became a practical instrument that people felt they needed it and before very long industrial firms were as dependent on it as they are today.

Everyone knows the name of Alexander Graham Bell as the inventor of the telephone, but as usually happens there were men before him. One man got very close to making a practical telephone but he died when he was only forty before he could finish it. This was J. P. Reis, a teacher of physics in a school near Frankfurt-on-Main. Reis wrote in 1860 (when Bell was a boy of thirteen):

'I succeeded in inventing an apparatus that enables me to convert audible sounds into visible signs, and with which, moreover, sounds of every sort may be reproduced by the galvanic current at any distance. I called it the "Telephone".'

Notice that he still uses the old words, galvanic current, for electricity. What Reis did was to stretch an animal bladder over a hole in a cask and this vibrating membrane was his transmitter. His receiver was a knitting needle wound with insulated wire, in the body of a violin. After trying this out on his pupils he gave a demonstration of 'Telephoning by means of the Galvanic Current' to a conference of scientists. 'You will now hear music,' he said, 'which is being played and sung in a home a hundred yards away, with the doors and windows closed. I should like to add that we are, of course, still a long way from the practical use of the telephone, as I have called my instrument.'

Reis died before he could make a practical telephone but he had a dozen sets of his instrument made and one of them found its way to the natural science department of Edinburgh University. There Bell was a student in 1863.

ALEXANDER GRAHAM BELL (1847–1922)

Alexander Graham Bell was born in Edinburgh on 3rd May, 1847, the second of three boys in a comfortably off middle-class family. His father, Alexander Melville Bell, was an expert in the physiology of speech and a teacher of speech and elocution, and his grandfather was also a well-known teacher of speech. Bell's father had a great reputation in his day as the inventor of what was called visible speech. This was a kind of alphabet, a system of symbols which indicated the position of the vocal organs when a person uttered a sound, a vowel, consonant, or word. It was a visual guide to any sounds made by the human voice. His alphabet became widely used for the training of teachers of the deaf, and for recording unwritten languages and dialects. He also lectured on elocution in University College, London. There was a wide interest in elocution. In those Victorian days reading aloud to the family at home was frequently a way of spending the evening in the middle-class family. Many working-class men, women and children could not read and had to be read to. In 1870 less than half the children in the country attended any school at all.

Bell's mother was the daughter of a surgeon in the Royal

Navy. She taught him at home until he was ten. Bell was sent to a private school in Edinburgh and then to the Royal High School in that city. He was a tall thin boy, his pale face crowned with a mass of black hair. The most important part of his education took place at home. Bell and his brothers followed their father's ideas on visible speech and took part in his experiments.

The parents encouraged the boys to think for themselves and to experiment with apparatus for analysing sounds of the voice. Bell tried to make his dog make human sounds by holding his jaws in the right positions. Then the boys were taken to see the famous Charles Wheatstone, inventor of the electric telegraph and professor at London University, who was a friend of their father. Wheatstone had played with making a 'speaking machine' which would reproduce human sounds. He showed it to the boys and lent them a book which explained it. When they returned home they made a better device, a human head with mouth, tongue, and windpipe from rubber, wire and tin which, if blown into, could say Mamma.

Bell did not make good progress at the Royal High School. He worked at the subjects he liked, botany, natural history, science, music but neglected those he did not, mathematics, Latin and Greek, subjects which were then regarded as the most important ones. His father therefore took him away from school when he was thirteen and sent him to stay in London with his grandfather. The old gentleman, Alexander Bell had high ideas of the education and behaviour which a young gentleman ought to have. Bell soon changed from a gawky Scottish boy clad in rough tweed into a young man dressed according to the fashion in tight trousers, Eton jacket and top hat, and instead of roaming the hills he now walked, with a cane in his hand, in the gardens reserved for the residents. His grandfather taught him literature thoroughly and had him given a training in music, which sharpened his ear for sound and tone. Bell wrote later: 'He made me ashamed of my ignorance. This year with my grandfather converted me from an ignorant and careless boy into a rather studious youth anxious to fit himself for college.'

When Bell was sixteen he applied successfully for a post as

student/teacher at a private school at Elgin in Morayshire. He taught music and elocution; the work was unpaid and he was still dependent on his parents. This was followed by a year's study at Edinburgh University and then he went back to Elgin as a full-time paid teacher.

When Bell had seen how successful his father's system was in teaching the deaf to speak, he determined to make this his work. No doubt his mother's increasing deafness also led him in this direction. In those days many people said that deafness like all other defects and handicaps was imposed on men by God and as such should not be questioned but simply endured as part of God's will. Others, such as the Bells, said that men should help themselves and work out God's will by curing deafness. Even among these people, however, there were different methods of cure. Some of them put deaf people away in houses where they learned only sign language and so could not communicate with other people. Others taught the deaf to speak by lip-reading; and others, like the Bells, used the visible speech method. In those days there were more causes of deafness; scarlet fever, which often caused damage to the ear, was much more common.

Bell also became interested in electricity. While he was at Elgin he carried out experiments on the resonance pitches of the cavities of the mouth when vowel sounds were made. He sent the results to a friend of his father who was a specialist in phonetics, and this man told him about the research into vowel sounds by a famous German scientist, Helmholtz. Bell read Helmholtz's book in German but he did not know the language well, with the result that he quite misunderstood the book. What Helmholtz had done was to make tuning forks of the right kind produce vowel sounds by vibrating them with electromagnets. Bell thought he had sent these sounds by speaking over a wire, that he had, in the language of those days, telegraphed speech. It was a lucky misunderstanding because it gave Bell the idea of sending speech by electricity, like sending signals by telegraph in the Morse code. For the time being, however, Bell just stored up the idea in his mind, after having repeated Helmholtz's experiments for his own satisfaction.

His father moved to London and Bell became his professional

assistant. At the same time Bell was studying hard. He matriculated in London University and took courses in anatomy and physiology at University College. He overworked; he was attacked by tuberculosis of the lungs, more often than not a fatal disease in those days. Both his brothers had already died from the disease. His father realized that something drastic had to be done if he were not to lose his only remaining son and decided to emigrate to Canada immediately. The family settled at Tuleto Heights, four miles from Brantford in the province of Ontario. There Bell recovered slowly. Later on he described these first days in the new world:

'My father's house is built upon the Tuleto Heights on the banks of the Grand River. On the edge of the sand cliff in his orchard is a quarry depression shaped so like a couch that we call it the "sofa seat". There is my dreaming place. Miles and miles of country lie extended below me like a huge map. The Grand River comes from the extreme left, flows to my very feet and winds off into distance on the right.

'When I lived here I used to spend hours and hours at the "sofa seat". It was my custom in the summer time to take a rug, a pillow and an interesting book to this cozy little nook – and dream away the afternoon in luxurious idleness.'

In April 1871, twenty months after landing at Quebec, Bell started teaching at a school for the deaf in Boston. He was happy there. He liked the pleasant old New England town and his teaching was immediately successful. He would write a symbol of speech on the blackboard, put his mouth in the position required to make the sound and get the pupils to imitate him. The result was far better than by other methods; after a few weeks children could use hundreds of syllables. His methods became the basis for teaching the deaf. During that year he also taught at other schools for deaf children in Massachusetts and Connecticut.

In 1872 he opened his own school for teaching deaf people. It was in only two rooms, a reception-room, and a consulting-room which also served as a bedroom, but it had the grand name of 'School of Vocal Physiology and Mechanics of Speech'. Pupils soon came. He wrote home: 'Georgie Sanders made a good beginning yesterday. He lives in the same house. I propose to divide his education into two branches – speech and mental development. I hear Mabel Hubbard will be a pupil soon.' Georgie Sanders was the son of a wealthy leather merchant and Mabel Hubbard the daughter of a prominent lawyer. The girl was to become his wife. Both the men became his friends. They were so grateful for the progress made by their children that they became his partners and supplied the money for Bell's experiments and development of the telephone. Bell's name became known and six months later he was appointed to the new University of Boston as professor of vocal physiology and the mechanics of speech in the school of oratory. His lectures there attracted a great deal of of attention.

At this point, his old interest in telegraphy came back. The industrial boom after the Civil War increased the pressure on the telegraph system. It was not uncommon to see people queuing to send telegrams, and Bell was struck by the slowness of the American system compared with the British one. One of the American telegraph companies, the Western Union, was looking for a way to send a number of messages at the same time over a single pair of wires. Bell decided to try to find an answer. He meant to make what was called a multiple telegraph. He called it a harmonic telegraph because it was based on his earlier experiments with tuning forks and electromagnets. It was while he was working on this telegraph that, by accident, sound was sent over the wire. But before that accident he had worked out in his mind how a telephone could work. Therefore when the accidental discovery happened he recognized that it was important.

Let us see first how Bell worked out the theory of the telephone during his experiments with his harmonic telegraph.

He set up his first telegraph instruments so that pressure on a telegraph key would send current from a battery through an electromagnet. The electromagnet caused a tuning fork mounted over it to vibrate like the clapper of a bell. Each vibration of the fork caused one of its prongs to make a connection that would send a pulse of current from another battery along a wire. As long as the telegraph key was held down, this intermittent current caused another electromagnet to vibrate another tuning fork at the receiving end, in resonance with the sending fork. Therefore he could send a Morse message with the key and, according to his theory, only a receiving fork of the same pitch as the sender could receive the sender's message.

The problem, however, was to get each of *several* pairs of transmitting and receiving forks of different pitch to vibrate in resonance with each other – and *only* with each other – at the same time. Bell found the tuning forks unsatisfactory and decided to try steel organ reeds instead. Next he decided that the reeds would give better results if they were magnetized. He remembered that when a magnet is moved towards the pole of an electromagnet, a current is generated in the latter's coil, and when the magnet is moved away from the electromagnet a current of opposite kind is induced.

Then he saw that his rapidly moving magnetic reed would generate a current that would be alternately stronger and weaker, from instant to instant, as the vibrations of the reed varied. Next he asked himself this: If many reeds of different pitches were vibrating simultaneously over the electromagnet, would they not generate one complex varying current – the resultant of the combined motion of all the reeds?

Bell reasoned correctly that they would. He recalled that when someone sang into the sound box of a piano when the strings are not damped, several strings responded. If, then, a 'harp' transmitter were built with enough strings or reeds, properly tuned, it would pick up every sound of the voice. Therefore, the combined vibrations of the reeds, mounted over an electromagnet, would generate an electrical current which would vary in intensity just as the reeds were vibrated by the varying sound of the voice. And this current would vibrate a receiver harp at the distant end so that the sounds would be repeated.

Bell was on the track. But he thought that there were two things wrong with his idea. First, his 'harp' transmitter would be too complicated to be practical. Second, he thought the current induced in the coil of the magnet would not be strong enough to work.

Meanwhile his teaching of deaf people led him to study a

device used in the physics laboratory at Massachusetts Institute of Technology. It had a mouthpiece that guided sounds against a membrane. When words were spoken the membrane vibrated and moved a lever which made a wave pattern on a piece of smoked glass. He obtained from a Boston ear specialist a specimen of a human ear. This was mounted so that the eardrum functioned as it does in life, by moving the bones of the inner ear, except that Bell substituted for one bone a wisp of hay that would make patterns on smoked glass. This gave him the idea for the telephone. He marvelled that a tiny diaphragm like the eardrum could move the comparatively big bones of the ear. If that could gather and transmit complex sounds, could not a single diaphragm take the place of all the reeds in his 'harp' transmitter? The end of one magnetized reed could be attached to the centre of the diaphragm; as it vibrated to voice waves or music, *it would generate a current that would vary in intensity just as the air varies in density when a sound is passing through it.*

He had worked out the principle of the telephone and he had done it while he was trying to make his harmonic telegraph successful. It was another year before the mishap with the telegraph showed him how the idea could be put into practice. Fortunately for Bell he soon had the help of a clever and intelligent young electrician, Thomas Watson. Bell was not able to make his equipment himself and so he went to an electrical workshop in Boston where Watson was employed. The owner was well known as a maker of telegraphic and electrical apparatus and inventors frequently went to him to have equipment made up.

Watson had made something for Bell which was not satisfactory. He described his first meeting with Bell:

'A tall, slender, quick-motioned man with pale face, black side whiskers, and drooping moustache, big nose and high sloping forehead crowned with bushy jet-black hair, came rushing out of the office and over to my work-bench. It was Alexander Graham Bell, whom I saw then for the first time. He was bringing to me a piece of mechanism which I had made for him under instructions from the office. It had not been made as he directed . . .'

Watson was used to angry and rude inventors but he particularly noticed how polite and reasonable Bell was in contrast. After that the two became friends. After his working day Watson worked with Bell late into the night on his harmonic telegraph in an attic over the electrical shop. Bell told Watson about his theories. One day he startled Watson, saying, 'If I could make a current of electricity vary in intensity, precisely as the air varies in density during the production of sound, I should be able to transmit speech telegraphically.' This was when he discovered the principle of the telephone. Bell was aiming at what he called an undulatory continuous current. Though Watson was very doubtful he accepted the idea because he admired Bell so much.

Although Bell now knew how the telephone would work he could not see how his theory could be put into practice. He still doubted whether the induced currents would be strong enough to work. He therefore decided to get advice from one of the most famous scientists in the United States. Joseph Henry, whose name was later given to the henry, the unit of inductance, had discovered induced current at the same time as Michael Faraday. Although he was now nearly eighty years old he welcomed Bell warmly at the famous Smithsonian Institution in Washington, of which he had been secretary for many years. Bell wrote to his parents describing what happened after he had told Henry about his experiments and shown him his apparatus.

'He said he thought it was the germ of a great invention and advised me to work at it myself instead of publishing. I said that I recognized the fact that there were mechanical difficulties . . . I added that I felt that I had not the electrical knowledge necessary to overcome the difficulties. His laconic answer was "Get it". I cannot tell you how much these two words have encouraged me.'

Back in Boston he studied electricity and experimented with the transmission of sound until the early hours of the morning. 'You can't make an owl sleep at night,' he wrote. 'The more I explore this wonderful subject of electricity the more boundless seems the prospect before me.' He was very hard up. He had many debts for equipment and his income, fees from the University, was quite small. The head of his school at the University paid him the fees for the next year's lectures in advance. Without this his work could not have continued.

Bell and Watson went on experimenting with the harmonic telegraph until in June 1875 they made the accidental discovery which gave the clue to the telephone. Watson described later what actually happened.

'Bell and I had spent the day in the "attic" trying to make the harmonic telegraph behave itself. He had found that one reason why its messages got mixed up in transmission was inaccuracy in tuning the receiver reeds to match those of the transmitters. When tuning the receiver reed Bell had the fortunate habit of pressing it against his ear which enabled him to hear in the magnet the whine of the intermittent current coming from the distant transmitter. On that hot June day we were in the attic hard at work experimenting with renewed enthusiasm over some improved piece of the apparatus. About the middle of the afternoon we were retuning the receiver reeds, Bell in one room pressing the reeds against his ear one by one as I sent him the intermittent current of the transmitters from the other room. One of my transmitter reeds stopped vibrating. I plucked it with my fingers to start it going. The contact point was evidently screwed down too hard against the reed and I began to readjust the screw. While I continued to pluck the reed I was startled by a loud shout from Bell – out he rushed in great excitement to see what I was doing. What had happened was obvious. The too closely adjusted contact screw had prevented the battery current from being interrupted as the reed vibrated, and, for that reason, the noisy whine of the intermittent current was not sent over the wire into the next room, but that little strip of magnetized steel I was plucking was generating, by its vibrations over the electromagnet, that splendid conception of Bell's – *a sound-shaped electric current.* That delicate undulatory current, which at other times had been drowned out by the heavy intermittent current passing through the receiver Graham Bell had at his ear had been converted by it into a very faint echo of the sound of the transmitter reed I had plucked. Probably nothing would have come from the circumstances if any other man than Bell had been listening; but he knew he was hearing, for the first time in human history, the tones and overtones of a sound transmitted by electricity: the twang of that reed I plucked was the birth of one of the greatest of modern inventions.'

In other words what happened was this.

In the attic, Bell at one end of the line, and Watson at the other, in a different room, were tuning the reeds of the harmonic telegraph. One of Watson's reeds was screwed down so tightly that it 'froze' to the pole of its electromagnet. Watson plucked it to free it. *Twang-g!* Bell at the other end of the line heard in his receiver a sound quite different from the usual whine sent out by the vibrating transmitter. He heard the distinctive twang of a plucked reed, a sound with tones and overtones, coming to him over the wire. Quickly he ran to Watson, shouting, 'Watson, what did you do then? Don't change anything. Let me see.'

It soon became apparent that the reed, too tight to send an intermittent current, had acted as a diaphragm and sent an induced, undulating current over the line – a current that varied in intensity precisely as the air was varying in density within hearing distance of that spring. The receiving reed, pressed against Bell's ear, had also acted as a diaphragm. And, most important of all, the induced current had proved strong enough to be of real use.

Bell could now tell Watson how to make the first telephone. The next morning they tried it out. Bell was disappointed that he could not hear Watson's voice but Watson could hear Bell's because he spoke so clearly. Even so he could not distinguish words, only voice sounds, and much more remained to be done. He had to find a means of making the undulatory current stronger. Eventually he decided to use a battery current, the resistance to which could be made to fluctuate, stronger or weaker as the diaphragm of the transmitter vibrated. This was done by attaching a short wire to the diaphragm and as the diaphragm vibrated the wire moved up and down in a cup of sulphuric acid. When it moved down the resistance decreased and when it rose the resistance increased. In this way the current through the wire and the acid had to undulate in the same way as the sound waves. He included this method in the patent specification which he filed in Washington in February 1876. The first telephone made by Watson was a very simple instrument. Later on he described it:

'That first telephone was a very simple mechanism consisting of a wooden frame on which was mounted one of Bell's harmonic receivers, a tightly stretched parchment drumhead, to the centre of which the free end of the receiver reed was fastened and a mouthpiece arranged to direct the voice against the other side of the drumhead. It was designed to force the reed to follow the vibrations of the voice and so generate voice-shaped electric undulations.'

In the meantime Bell moved because he was afraid that people would find out what he was doing. He rented a two-room attic on the top floor of a boarding house as a workshop and living accommodation. Then the second accident in the discovery of the telephone happened. Bell and Watson were about to try out the new transmitter. Bell was in the workshop, Watson in the bedroom at the end of the passage with the receiver to his ear. Bell upset some acid on his clothes and shouted out, 'Mr. Watson, come here, I want you.' Watson, astonished to hear this on the other end of the line rushed along to Bell shouting, 'Mr. Bell, I heard every word you said, distinctly.' This was the first sentence to be heard on the telephone.

The year 1876 was the centenary of the American Declaration of Independence: 'We hold these truths to be self-evident, that all men are created equal, that they are endowed by their Creator with certain unalienable rights, that among these are life, liberty and the pursuit of happiness . . .' A great Centennial Exposition was organized in Philadelphia to be opened in May 1876. This was a wonderful opportunity to exhibit the telephone.

The Emperor of Brazil, Dom Pedro, had been invited to open the exhibition, and it so happened that Dom Pedro had met Bell and knew all about his methods of teaching deaf children. Day followed day in the humid heat of the great glass-walled hall and no one noticed Bell's telephone. Bell almost gave up in despair. He wrote to his young fiancée expressing his concern about his teaching in Boston:

'Oh! my poor classes! What shall I do about them. You don't know what a horrid mean thing it is for me to leave them at this time. The university building too closes on the 21st so that some other room will have to be found in order to close the session. I can't bear to think of it all, or I shall go right back. There is the expense which I cannot afford.'

At last, one day six weeks after the Exposition opened, the group of judges was just about to give up for the day when Dom Pedro recognized Bell and insisted that his exhibit should be inspected. The judges included no less than Sir William Thomson, later Lord Kelvin, and Joseph Henry. Dom Pedro went over to the telephone receiver in the organ loft of the hall while Bell remained with the judges and recited into the transmitter. 'To be or not to be, that is the question.' Dom Pedro, astonished, exclaimed: 'Look, it speaks!' The judges tested the telephone for three hours to make sure that it was not a trick but they were convinced. A friend of Sir William Thomson wrote to Bell on the same day:

'I returned to my hotel with Sir William Thomson and dined with him. He speaks with much enthusiasm of your achievement. What yesterday he would have declared impossible he has today seen realized, and he declares it the most wonderful thing he has seen in America. You speak of it as an embryo invention, but to him it seems already complete, and he declares that, before long, friends will whisper their secrets over the electric wire. Your undulatory current he declares a great and happy conception.'

Before Thomson sailed for England he spent some hours at Bell's workshop, watching tests being made. He took a telephone set back with him and described it as 'the greatest by far of all the marvels of the electric telegraph'.

Bell's aim now was, to test his telephone over long distances. Spending his holiday as usual at his parents' home in Canada, he made a successful test over eight miles of wire. At first, to provide for a continuous signal, he arranged for a friend to recite Shakespeare at the transmitter. When, eight miles away, he recognized, to his amazement, his father's voice intoning, 'To be or not to be, that is the question', he sent a telegram to confirm it. The next test was, however, a two-way talk over sixteen miles. An important technical improvement early in 1877 was an iron or steel diaphragm in the transmitter, instead of the membrane and armature, and Bell obtained a patent to cover this.

The next step for Bell and his friends, the leather merchant and the lawyer who were backing him, was to develop the telephone commercially and market it. To gain publicity Bell gave lectures and demonstrations; he was a natural actor and he made them entertaining. Large audiences were attracted; they brought Bell cash which he badly needed. The first lecture brought in eighty-five dollars and he was able to pay the rent he owed and to buy some clothes. He gave his fiancée a silver model of the telephone. But these lecture/demonstrations did have the effect of suggesting that the telephone was only a toy, without practical importance. This was the view of the newspapers at that time.

In 1877 Bell married the deaf girl who had been a pupil of his when he first went to Boston. He was thirty and she eighteen. They decided to take their honeymoon in Europe. It seemed an opportunity to introduce the telephone to England, particularly because an official of the English General Post Office had just taken a set to London with him.

The trip to England turned out to be longer than Bell expected. After he had shown his wife his native Scotland there were so many people to see about his invention that he took a house in London and decided to stay for a year. He showed the telephone to the meeting of the British Association at Plymouth, and gave lectures to the Society of Telegraph Engineers and the Society of Arts. Bell did not forget the cause of the deaf; he gave lectures on the education of deaf children and opened a school for them. The news of the telephone had reached the royal court in London and the great occasion came when Bell was invited to show it to Queen Victoria at her residence at Osborne House in the Isle of Wight. For the demonstration the queen with some of her family was in Osborne House and her secretary in the cottage in the grounds. It so happened that that year, 1878, was an important one for the English monarchy. The queen had just taken the title of

Empress of India and, with the beginning of imperialist feelings in England, the popularity of her early years was now returning, after her retirement from public affairs in mourning for the death of her husband, Prince Albert. She noted Bell's visit in her diary:

'After dinner we went to the council room and saw the telephone. A Professor Bell explained the whole process which is most extraordinary. I had been put in communication with Osborne Cottage, and we talked . . . also heard some singing quite plainly. But it is rather faint and one must hold the tube close to one's ear.'

But Bell found it difficult to get a company formed to market the telephone. In the following letter he tried to persuade investors to put their money in it, looking into the future. He referred to the network of gas and water pipes which then existed in the main cities and went on:

'In a similar way, it is conceivable that cables of telephone wires could be laid underground, or suspended overhead, communicating by branch wires with private dwellings, counting houses, shops, manufacturers, etc. etc., uniting them through a main cable with a central office where the wires could be connected as desired, establishing direct communication between any two places in the city. Such a plan as this, though impractical at the present moment, will, I firmly believe, be the outcome of the introduction of the telephone to the public.'

When Bell returned to the United States with a daughter as well as a wife, he found that his friends had started the Bell Telephone Company. However, at first progress was slow. There were two difficulties in the way. Before telephones could be widely used switchboards were necessary and they had to be designed and made. That difficulty was soon overcome in America by using the experience of working telegraphs. The first switchboard, in New Haven, Connecticut, had eight lines and twenty-one subscribers. The second problem was more serious, competition. The great Western Union Telegraph Company, a very big firm which had control of eighty per cent of all the telegraph business in the United

States, saw possibilities in the telephone and decided to enter the business. It bought an important improvement in the telephone, made by the famous inventor Edison. This was Edison's carbon transmitter, patented in 1877, only a year later than Bell. Western Union used its influence in Congress to prevent the Bell Company getting permission to set up telephones and to shut it out from the railroads. The little Bell Company fought back against this goliath and won. It grew rapidly after that. Only five years after Bell patented his invention there were 70,000 telephones in the United States and another seven years later there were 200,000. Before long Bell became a rich man but he played no part in the growth of his company. He realized he was no businessman and he kept out of business. He did, however, help his company to success in another way. For many years other inventors tried to break into the telephone business but they always came up against infringement of the Bell patents. The company fought hundreds of cases and in the years of legal proceedings it never lost one. This success was largely due to the evidence Bell gave which was so powerful because of his excellent memory and the letters he had written to his family giving accounts of his progress.

In England the telephone industry developed in a different way. There was more than thirty years of joint control by private companies and the State before the General Post Office finally took full responsibility. English businessmen did not take to the telephone as quickly as the Americans did. Bell's agents did what they could do encourage people to use it. Here is an example of the publicity they issued:

A CIRCULAR ISSUED BY COLONEL REYNOLDS ON BEHALF OF PROFESSOR BELL IN THE LATTER PART OF 1877

'The Articulating or Speaking Telephone of Professor Alexander Graham Bell has now reached a point of simplicity, perfection, and reliability such as give it undoubted pre-eminence over all other means for telegraphic communication. Its employment necessitates no skilled labour, no technical education, and no special attention on the part of any one individual. Persons using it can converse miles apart, in precisely the same manner as though they were in the same room. It needs but a wire between the two points of communication, though ten or twenty miles apart, with a Telephone or a pair of Telephones – one to receive, the other to transmit, the sound of the voice – to hold communication in any language. It conveys the quality of the voice so that the person speaking can be recognized at the other end of the line. It can be used for any purpose and in any position – for mines, marine exploration, military evolutions, and numerous other purposes other than the hitherto recognized field for Telegraphy; between the manufacturer's office and his factory; between all large commercial houses and their branches; between central and branch banks; in shipbuilding yards, and factories of every description; in fact wherever conversation is required between the principal and his agents or employés, or between the superintendent and his leading men, there the Telephone will find place and employment. Ordinarily it may be regarded as a speaking tube attended with all the advantages of telegraphic communication.'

Bell did not invent anything more to do with the telephone. But he made a number of other useful inventions. The French government awarded him the Volta prize of 50,000 francs for his invention of the telephone. With this money he set up the Volta Laboratory in Washington, staffed by a small team of scientists. The first notable invention to come out of it was an improvement on Edison's phonograph, the forerunner of the gramophone. The patent was sold and Bell's share of the proceeds was 200,000 dollars. Bell no longer needed the money for himself and his family and he decided to use it for the benefit of the deaf. He told his wife that he wanted always to be known as a teacher of the deaf. He therefore started a research unit, which he called the Volta Bureau, to study the needs of deaf people and to increase and spread knowledge of what could be done to help them.

His name was again given much publicity in 1881. On 2nd July the President of the United States, James A. Garfield, was shot. It was a great shock to the nation. Garfield was a popular hero, who had come up the hard way. An orphan as a young boy on an Ohio farm, he had experienced the hardship of the frontier, won a college education by sheer hard work, became a major general in the federal army during the civil war, then a member of congress, and had only just been elected as president. He was an example to all Americans, the boy who rose from log cabin to White House. The bullet which hit him could not be located. Bell offered his help and worked day and night to make an electric probe. The probe was tried on the wounded president but it failed. In spite of the order that all metal was to be removed from the room the doctors did not take away the metal bedspring. Bell came in for some criticism in the press; the president died. However later on the probe was used successfully and because of it Bell received a degree in medicine from Heidelberg University and was made an officer of the Legion of Honour by the French government.

A year later Bell applied for and was granted American nationality and became a citizen of the country which had taken up his invention so rapidly, and made him a wealthy man. He was not yet free from legal problems. There were still people who were eager to challenge the Bell Company and get the profits from the telephone. One company claimed that Bell had stolen his invention. A United States District Attorney filed charges against him for 'perpetrating the infamy of the most gigantic fraud of the century', which threatened to cancel his patents. The charges were dropped but only after proceedings which lasted several years, so much was at stake.

After these events Bell spent most of his life on his large estate in Nova Scotia. It was a place he had chosen on the shore of the Bras d'Or lake in Cape Breton Island. During his last twenty-five years his chief interest was the new science and art of flight. All but a very few thought it was a waste of time. His old friend Sir William Thomson, now Lord Kelvin, wrote to Mrs. Bell asking her to dissuade him 'from giving his valuable time and resources to attempts which I . . . still believe could only lead to disappointment if carried on with any expectation of leading to a useful flying machine'. Bell's opinion was: 'I have not the shadow of a doubt that the problem of aerial navigation will be solved within ten years.' In fact the Wright brothers did fly ten years later, in 1903. Not long after he gave this advice at a graduation ceremony:

'Don't keep forever on the public road, going only where others have gone. Leave the beaten track occasionally and dive into the woods. You will be certain to find something that you have never seen before. Of course it will be a little thing, but do not ignore it. Follow it up and explore all around it; one discovery will lead to another and before you know it you will have something worth thinking about . . .'

Bell received many honours, including degrees from the Universities of Oxford and Harvard. Two years before his death his native Edinburgh conferred on him the freedom of the city. He died of diabetes from which he had suffered for some years; there was then no insulin cure for it. He was buried on the top of the mountain at his estate and during the ceremony there was two minutes' silence on the telephones of North America. 'An inventor,' he said, 'is a man who looks around upon the world, and is not content with things as they are; he wants to improve whatever he sees; he wants to benefit the world; he is haunted by an idea. . . .'

THE TELEGRAPH AND TELEPHONE WORKERS (1870–1890)

The men working on the telegraphs were employed by the railway companies and the private telegraph companies, such as the Electric Telegraph Company, from the eighteen-forties until 1870 when the Post Office took over the telegraph system. Nothing is known about them during that period, not even how many there were. From 1870 onwards, however, we can learn something about their work and the conditions in which they worked, from the records of the Post Office Engineering Department and of the trade union which they struggled to form, the Post Office Engineering Union.

The great majority of the men permanently employed in the Post Office telegraphs were called linemen. There were also many more men in the construction gangs but they were paid off as the job finished. The other large group of men permanently employed were the telegraphists or telegraph clerks, who operated the instruments in the offices. By the eighteen-eighties there were about five hundred linemen. Their job was to keep the telegraph lines and the batteries in order. They were recruited mainly from the workmen in the construction gangs, those 'who have knowledge of over-house work, are not afraid to enter upon roofs and who have acquired by practice the necessary general handiness'. Some of them came from the railways and others were ex-soldiers from the Royal Engineers. After a time they became known as skilled linemen and battery men. They had to pass an educational test when they were appointed. The subjects of examination in 1879 were: 1. Writing Tolerably, a few lines. 2. Reading Manuscript. 3. Additions (simple and compound). 4. The requisite technical knowledge. Each man was responsible for a section of line, often working on his own and without much supervision. It was laid down that 'every lineman must be efficient for his own work as they are so greatly scattered.' Therefore apprentices were out of the question. 'It was essential that they should be steady and reliable men.'

No doubt it was for these reasons that they had to obey a strict discipline. Here is an example. In 1873 J. Smith, a lineman of High Wycombe, was reported because he did not attend to a fault, a 'partial earth' on the line, and change the cable wire after he had been instructed to by his superintendent. As he could give no good explanation and had been reported before he was to be either dismissed or fined one day's pay. Smith's explanation was: 'Sir, I had Not tools With Me or the galvanometer on friday Night and on Monday the line Was Reported Clear or i should have Been thair By First Train instead of Walking through Line.' However he was expected to clear the fault on Saturday or Sunday and because he did not do so the superintendent had to do it himself. He could have done the repair without a galvanometer, by using the coils on another working instrument for a short time. The official head office dictum was: 'This is a case of neglect quite unrelieved by explanation. The reason given on the first day imperfect as it is, cannot apply to the second. Please note a fine of one day's pay and return that the papers may be forwarded to the Engineer in Chief.' Four shillings was duly collected from J. Smith. But the Post Office preferred to call the fine a suspension from pay.

The average wage of the linemen in the seventies was 27

shillings a week and it varied from 23 shillings to 33 shillings for senior linesmen. Their work was heavy and dangerous. This is how one of them described it to a civil service committee:

'The charge of a section includes the care of instruments and batteries at a number of post offices, private offices, and, of course, a section of the line. The lineman may have to walk 20 miles after a fault, and his route may be along roads, or across fields and mountains, and all the time his eye is upon one particular wire, perhaps, amongst many; and if the season be summer, with brilliant sunshine, the strain upon the eyesight, mind, and muscle is very trying; while in the winter, with the snow and ice on the ground and poles, he is very fortunate if he arrives at his destination with dry clothes. Having had to wait perhaps hours for a train at some small railway station, he arrives home late at night completely done up, and fit only for bed, too exhausted from prolonged fasting and exertion to eat anything, and should he have been unfortunate enough to have passed the fault without seeing and clearing it, although he may have had a bright sky as a background to a number of thin wires and the latter may in places have been overhanging with trees, rendering a proper sight of the wires very difficult, no excuse is allowed, and he will have to repeat his journey next day, often climbing poles unnecessarily in his anxiety not to pass the fault again.'

It was difficult for these men to form a trade union. They were scattered, they had no special skill to bargain with; in the official words of the Post Office, 'the men have only a limited market value'. Earlier on the Post Office had forbidden its officers to hold meetings because they 'tended to create a spirit of discontent and restlessness among the whole of the lower body of Post Office Servants'. The first stirring came with a meeting of linemen at Liverpool in 1886, called to express grievances which had been felt for a long time. The meeting decided to form a national linemen's movement which was to place its grievances before the Royal Commission on the Civil Service. The next year there was a national conference at the Shepherd and Flock Hotel, Moorgate Street, London. It was attended by more than a hundred members from London alone and delegates from far afield, Belfast, Cambridge, Cardiff, Leeds, Liverpool, Manchester, Newcastle and other places. The linemen's movement now claimed 509 members. It sent its demands to the Royal Commission. They were:

> Promotion by merit 'to be decided by competitive examination open to all ranks, due allowance being made for engineering experience'. Pay increases for Senior Linemen from 36/- to 50/- and for Linemen from 32/- to 42/-.
> Hours to be reduced from 60 to 48 – because the work was 'both hazardous and laborious'.
> Full pay for sickness 'due to exposure' and two-thirds, instead of half pay, for the rest.
> Establishment for all after three years' service. (Permanent staff.)
> Three weeks' annual leave.
> Optional superannuation after thirty years' service.
> Improvements in travelling and overtime payments.
> Weekly not fortnightly wages.

The linemen debated whether to form a permanent association or trade union but they decided it would not be wise. Perhaps this was a mistake. The Royal Commission, on which they pinned their hopes, did not discuss anything to do with the Post Office. The linemen's leader and secretary, Bob Wallace of Bridgend, Glamorgan, fell from a fifty-foot pole and was killed. The national movement died in its infancy and only isolated groups of men survived for several years. Then in 1896 they came together again and formed the Amalgamated Association of the Postal Telegraphs Engineering Department. It was 'to embrace all continuously employed men, and all men entitled to holidays . . . and the object shall be the promotion of their interests as civil servants'. Soon after, the construction workmen and the storemen, the unskilled men, were allowed to join. The men were now in a stronger position to press their grievances with the Post Office.

When we turn to the telephone workers we find a rather different story. As soon as telephone switchboards began to be installed in 1879 new kinds of work arose and new skills were required. Again most of the men were telephone linemen, wiremen and construction workers. The work of the linemen and construction men was similar to that of the telegraph men. They were employed by the telephone companies throughout this time. Very little is known about them until 1889, when some four hundred men in Manchester, Liverpool, Sheffield, Hanley and Dewsbury had formed an Amalgamated Society of Telegraph and Telephone Construction Men. It had funds of about £200. With the help of the Manchester and Salford Trades Council this Society held a conference in the same year at the Crown Hotel, Manchester, where it was joined by a small London Union called 'The Union of Electrical Operatives' which had about 170 members and £75 in funds. These two unions agreed to form the Electrical Trades Union, now the Electrical Electronic Telecommunications Union.

The Electrical Trades Union was at the beginning a craft union for skilled men. The electricians of London had in fact applied for membership to the big union of skilled engineering workers, the Amalgamated Society of Engineers. They were told that they did not have the necessary qualifications and they were given advice on how to form their own union. They were rejected by the main body of engineers because the electrical industry was so new. The craft basis is shown by the first aim of this new union which was to resist 'any attempt to curtail or take away any of those privileges which are or may become the custom of the trade'. After this came the other aims: to help members in disputes, to help them get employment, to keep them when unemployed, to give help in circumstances of accident or death, and to get satisfactory relations with the employers.

However, it is clear that the telephone workers alone were not strong enough to form this trade union. It was possible only when the electric light industry had arrived. This is the subject of the next chapter. When that happened there were soon enough workers in that industry to join forces with the telephone men and form the E.T.U. This is clear from the following list of branches of work existing at that time; men had to be competent in one of these in order to qualify for membership of the new union: armature magnet and transformer winders, erectors and tenders, installation linesmen and wiremen (indoors and out), battery accumulator makers, fitters and inspectors, telegraph and telephone wiremen and linesmen, fault finders, instrument makers, installation attendants (land or sea), electrical traction employees.

All these jobs required skill, some more, some less. In this union, however, unskilled men were not excluded. Membership was open to labourers who had been employed for not less than six months as telegraph, telephone or electric light labourers. In fact, however, most of the first members were electric light wiremen (later known as contracting electricians) and telegraph and telephone wiremen and linesmen.

Additional Reading

R. Burlinghame, *Out of Silence into Sound*, Collier-Macmillan, 1964.
Bell Telephone System, *Alexander Graham Bell*, 1952.
John Golding, *75 Years: A Short History of the Post Office Engineering Union*, P.O.E.U., 1963.
The Story of the E.T.U., Electrical Trades Union, 1952.

CHAPTER FIVE

Light and Generation

'When all candles bee out, all cats bee gray,' said John Heywood the dramatist in the sixteenth century. Since the earliest times in history men have waged a battle with the dark. They have always wanted to see and be active during the long winter darkness. Through thousands of years they have tried continually to improve their own lighting. From the time of the Greeks to the eighteenth century the shape of lamps changed very much but the fuel remained much the same: fat or oil from animals, fish and vegetables. Since then the two great discoveries in fuel have been gas and electricity.

Coal gas was first widely used during the Napoleonic war because the war interrupted the import of tallow and so made candles expensive. At the same time the coking of coal for smelting iron, especially for guns, became a big industry and so gas was available. During those years of the early nineteenth century gas was used to light factories, streets, and even Westminster Bridge. But, although gas light was a wonderful step forward at that time, it was inefficient and unreliable. The burners were simply iron tubes with holes pierced in them; the pipes became corroded and the holes choked. It was only after fifty years, in 1858, that the invention of an orifice made of steatite made gas light more reliable. The incandescent mantle, which meant that gas could give a really good light, did not come for another thirty years. But by that time electricity had overtaken gas.

The three main kinds of electric light – in the order in which they came into use – are the arc lamp, the filament lamp, and the electric discharge lamp. Before the lamps could be widely used there had to be a good system of generation.

The arc light was discovered when gas lighting was still quite a novelty. Sir Humphrey Davy demonstrated it at the Royal Institution in 1809. Davy was Michael Faraday's teacher and, as we have seen in Chapter One, it was Faraday who discovered the principle of the a.c. transformer and invented the first generator. Davy had noticed the spark made between the terminals of the voltaic pile and that 'when instead of metal, pieces of well-calcined carbon are employed, the spark is still larger and of a clear white'. In his demonstration with carbon electrodes he used 2,000 voltaic batteries to give enough power to maintain the arc for a few minutes.

Arc lighting could not be used widely while the battery was the only known source of electricity. It had to wait for electrical machines to be invented. Faraday had not been interested in developing his discovery but a number of inventors followed it up. The generators were gradually improved. There was an urgent need for continuous arc lighting in lighthouses. In December 1858 a new era started when the South Foreland Lighthouse blazed out with more than 1,000 candle-power, a far greater light than ever before seen by mariners.

The dynamo became a practical success and very soon it was being widely used for arc lighting in France and Germany. Britain lagged behind but particularly in France a number of large railway stations and factories were lighted in this way. The first English installation was at the Gaiety Theatre, London, in 1878. Football was floodlit in the same year. A contemporary magazine reported the event: 'The intense interest aroused by the application of the electric light to novel uses was strikingly apparent on Monday night in Sheffield, when nearly 30,000 people gathered at Bramall-lane Grounds to witness a football match played under that light. The match, which was played by two teams belonging to the Sheffield Football Association, commenced at half past seven o'clock. The electric light was thrown from four lamps 30 ft from the ground, and the rays, which were of great brilliancy, lighted the whole of the ground, the players being seen almost as clearly as at noonday. The brilliancy of the lights, however, dazzled the players, and sometimes caused strange blunders. The illuminating power was equal to 8,000 standard candles.'

ROOKES EVELYN CROMPTON (1845–1940)

The man who did most to bring about the use of arc lighting in England, as well as pioneering electric supply in London, was Colonel R. E. B. Crompton. He was born near Thirsk in 1845, the son of a Yorkshire squire. He was taken up to London to see the Great Exhibition of 1851 when he was six. In his old age he remembered clearly the machinery hall in Hyde Park. He also remembered 'the extraordinary thunderous noise of the streets of London. The steel-wheeled and horse-driven vehicles which then crowded the streets rumbled over the granite paving blocks with a noise so deafening that I, as a child walking by my mother's side, could not make myself heard until we got away into the side streets'. Forty-five years later he was one of the founders of the Royal Automobile Club.

After eleven years in the army, Crompton resigned his commission and bought a partnership in an engineering firm in Chelmsford which specialized in steam and water valves. He increased his income by designing pumping plants and water wheels for private houses. After three years of this he turned to electrical engineering. Through a family connection he was asked to improve the lighting at an ironworks, and this he did with arc lamps. From then on he developed a business of contracting to supply arc lighting and established his own firm of Crompton and Company, Electrical Engineers, to manufacture plant and equipment. He improved the existing arc lamps to reduce the glare, and made improvements to the dynamo.

Crompton became the leader in light installations with arc lamps, and raised England to the level of France and Germany. In 1880 he supplied arc lamps, dynamos and switchboards for King's Cross Station, the Glasgow railway terminus and the General Post Office. In the same year he published his book on 'Industrial Uses of Electric Light: a practical treatise in construction and maintenance of the Crompton arc lamp and dynamo'. In the following year he was awarded a gold medal at the International Exhibition of Electric Lighting in Paris. In that year, 1881, an international conference agreed that the words ampere, volt, watt and ohm should be the standard terms used. Before that there were no names for units of current, pressure and resistance that were generally accepted. This fact illustrates the difficulties which pioneers like Crompton had in carrying out their work.

After this Crompton's work in lighting was linked with the filament lamp which had already been invented by Swan and Edison. He installed incandescent lamps in the Law Courts and in the famous Vienna Opera House. Crompton met Swan and manufactured generating plant for his lamps. He also built in 1886 one of the very first power stations, in Kensington. We will see how important this was later in this chapter when Ferranti is discussed.

The arc lamp was a great step forward for lighting large areas, but people wanted to use electricity to light their houses. The arc lamp was far too big. The problem was how to make small, light and cheap units. At the time it was called the problem of 'subdividing the electric light'. The solution came from Swan and Edison with their invention of an incandescent filament in an evacuated glass container.

THOMAS ALVA EDISON (1847–1931)

Edison's family had a background of rebellion and independence. During the American War of Independence his great grandfather was one of those who was loyal to the English king. He joined the English army but he was captured by the American forces. He was tried and sentenced to be hanged but his wife, through her family who were in the American army, got him released. The Edisons were forced to leave the new United States and they settled first in Nova Scotia and then in Ontario Province. In the war of 1812 between the United States and England Edison's grandfather became Capt. Samuel Edison in the British–Canadian forces and then returned to the task of clearing the frontier forests in Ontario.

Edison's father tried several trades – carpenter, tailor, innkeeper – and then married the daughter of a Baptist minister, a schoolteacher. In 1837 he joined Mackenzie's revolt against the Canadian government and when it was suppressed he was forced to flee across the border to the United States. He settled at the village of Milan, Ohio, and after setting up in business as a timber merchant and shingle manufacturer he was able to bring his family across from the Canadian side of Lake Erie. There on 11th February, 1847, Thomas Alva Edison was born, the last of seven children, three of whom had already died as infants.

Edison spent the first six years of his life at Milan, a busy and flourishing little centre of trade with a navigable river and a canal giving access to Lake Erie. When a railway was built it by-passed the village, trade dwindled and the Edisons migrated again, to Port Huron, Michigan, on the lake of that name; a small town of four thousand people. They lived in a large house in ten acres of ground, but they were no longer prosperous and the father found it difficult to make a living as a timber and grain merchant.

As a child he did not get on with his father but he was always close to his mother. At the age of eight he was sent to the little one-room school in the town. It was a harsh unpleasant place. Edison said later: 'I remember I used never to be able to get along at school. I was always at the foot of the class. I used to feel that the teachers did not sympathize with me, and that my father thought I was stupid.' He stayed there only three months, either because his father could not pay the fees or because his mother decided to teach him herself. He was happy being taught by his mother. She read the classics to him and he soon became a good reader but he never learnt to spell correctly. Here is a letter he wrote when he was nineteen:

'Dear Mother, Started the Store several weeks I have growed considerably I dont look much like a Boy now – Hows all the folks did you receive a Box of Books from Memphis that he promised to send them – languages.

Yours son.

Al

But from the age of nine he was very interested in science. He bought chemicals and books he could afford and experimented in the cellar of the house. His mother always encouraged him in this against the disapproval of his father who was afraid he would blow them all up. Later on he said, 'My mother was the making of me. She understood me; she let me follow my bent.' While other boys were out playing in the fields young Edison was happy to spend all his time in his cellar laboratory.

At this time the telegraph was still new enough to be exciting. In the United States the pioneers were building new lines as the frontier was pushed ever westward across the prairies, and the Atlantic cable was still in the future; so was the first trans-America cable. Edison like many boys of his age was fascinated by the telegraph, and by electricity. He made his own telegraph set: 'I build a telegraph wire between our houses . . . separated by woods. The wire was that used for suspending stone pipes, the insulators were small bottles pegged on ten-penny nails driven into the trees. It worked fine.' It is not surprising that later he became an expert telegrapher.

At the age of twelve his schooling finished. There was a job available, he needed the money, and his family were poor. When the railway was built to Port Huron a boy was wanted to sell newspapers, sweets and food on the trains. So Edison, with his big basket, travelled daily on the train between Port Huron and Detroit, leaving home before seven and returning after nine-thirty. He gave his mother a dollar a day from his profits. It was while doing this job that he became deaf. Scarlet fever some years earlier probably damaged his ears but the following incident brought on the deafness:

'I was trying to climb into the freight car with both arms full of heavy bundles of papers . . . I ran after it and caught the near step, hardly able to lift myself. A trainman reached over and grabbed me by the ears and lifted me . . . I felt something snap inside my head, and the deafness started from that time and has progressed ever since.' His deafness made him more lonely and led him to study on his own. He fitted up a little laboratory in the baggage car of the train, and he spent hours in the Detroit Free Library, reading widely all kinds of literature.

By the age of fifteen he had become a shrewd businessman. During the years of the Civil War he learned that when there was a big battle there was a heavy demand for his newspapers and he could raise the price accordingly. One day he saved the child of a stationmaster from being run down by a train. The grateful stationmaster offered to give him a training as a telegraph operator, and Edison jumped at the chance. His deafness did not prevent his hearing the instruments but in fact made it easier to concentrate on them.

In 1863, at the age of sixteen, Edison began several years as a telegraphist wandering from one job to another. After six months in his home town he became a railway dispatcher forty miles away on the night shift. He soon lost the job and in 1864, he had no less than three other jobs as telegraphist, at Adrian, Michigan, Fort Wayne in Indiana, and at Indianapolis. The following year he was working in Cincinnati in Ohio, then went south to Nashville and to Memphis, Tennessee, and finally he settled at Louisville, Kentucky, for a whole year. It was a hard, rough life and the work was sheer drudgery. Edison spent his money on apparatus and was all the time trying to invent improved instruments. Often he got into trouble and was sacked:

'I went one night into the battery room to obtain some sulphuric acid for experimenting. The carboy tipped over, the acid ran out, went through the ceiling to the manager's room below, and ate up his desk and all the carpet. The next morning I was summoned before him and told that the company wanted operators not experimenters.'

When he was twenty-one Edison decided to try his fortune in the east. He knew that he wanted to be an inventor and that in Boston he could find electrical engineers and manufacturers. He went to that famous centre of science and learning and immediately got a job as telegraphist with the Western Union. He bought and read Michael Faraday's *Experimental Researches in Electricity*. It made a deep impression. Faraday had been poor and uneducated, why could he not do as well?

A year later Edison started as a full-time inventor. He set up a little workshop in a corner of the famous workshop of Charles Williams where a few years later Alexander Graham Bell was to be found. In October 1868 he had applied for his first patent. It was for an electric vote-recording machine. He had noticed, when working for the Western Union, what a long time voting took in Congress and he was convinced that he could make a fortune with the invention. But the politicians did not want it.

Edison, bitterly disappointed, decided that his inventions in future must be based on a definite commercial demand. His next venture was a stock ticker. In the economic boom after the Civil War there was a railway mania and a wave of speculation in metals and land. The stock-brokers relied on the telegraph for news until a stock ticker, invented in Boston, printed stock-market quotations for them. Edison patented an improvement on it and his machine sold quite well. He then turned back to his old interest in the telegraph and produced a duplex instrument. If this had been successful it would have made a great deal of money. However, it failed to work; he was now heavily in debt and he decided to try his luck in New York. He had only a few dollars in his pocket when he arrived there in 1869.

New York was a turning point. A friend admitted him to a stock-broking indicator office and one day in the midst of a great rush to buy gold the telegraphic transmitter broke down and there was chaos in Wall Street. When Edison put it right the grateful owner gave him a job immediately. The gold crisis continued, the price rising all the time. Later on Edison gave a picture of it:

'On Black Friday we had a very exciting time with the indicators . . . New Street as well as Broad Street was jammed with people. I sat on top of the Western Union Telegraph Booth to watch the surging, crazy crowd . . . Amid great excitement Speyer, the banker, went crazy and it took five men to hold him; and everybody lost their head. The Western Union operator came to me and said, "Shake, Edison, we are O.K. We haven't a cent." I felt happy because we were poor. These occasions are very enjoyable to a poor man; but they occur rarely.' This crisis was a part of the swelling boom and inflation which lasted until 1873 when the crash came.

Before that, however, Edison started a firm of electrical engineers and soon began to make money. He brought out a telegraph printer to distribute the prices of gold and the rates of exchange with sterling, which brought him in five thousand dollars, and another improvement on a stock exchange ticker, for which with other inventions he received forty thousand dollars. He did not know what to do with the cash until friends told him to open a bank account. Now he could send money home:

I sent you another express purchase Saturday, enclosed you will find the receipt for same.

I. C. Edison writes me that mother is not very well and that you have to work very hard. I guess you had better take it easy after this. Don't do any hard work and get mother anything she desires. You can draw on me for money. Write me and say how much money you will need till June and I will send the amount on the first of that month. Give love to all folks, and write me the town news.

Your affec. son
Thomas A.

While the boom still lasted Edison became a manufacturer, on the basis of orders for his stock tickers worth nearly half a million dollars. In 1871 he found time to get married. The girl, only sixteen, worked in his factory, punching holes in telegraph tape. There were soon three children; the first two Edison nicknamed Dot and Dash. He continued to invent and produced a major improvement in the duplex telegraph – a quadruplex instrument. He said later:

'This problem was of the most difficult and complicated kind, and I bent all my energies to its solution. It required a peculiar effort of the mind, such as the imagining of eight different things moving simultaneously on a mental plane, without anything to demonstrate their efficiency.'

When he was thirty-one he became tired of business and decided to spend all his time on invention. With twenty thousand dollars he had left he started an industrial research laboratory, the first of its kind. In a field near the hamlet of Menlo Park, New Jersey, twenty-five miles south-west of New York he built a large wooden two-storey barn which he filled with expensive equipment, chemicals and metals. On the first floor was the main laboratory and workshop where thirteen skilled craftsmen worked; on the ground floor was Edison's office, library and drawing office. This was to be an 'invention factory'. Edison told a visitor that here he intended to produce 'a minor invention every ten days and a big thing

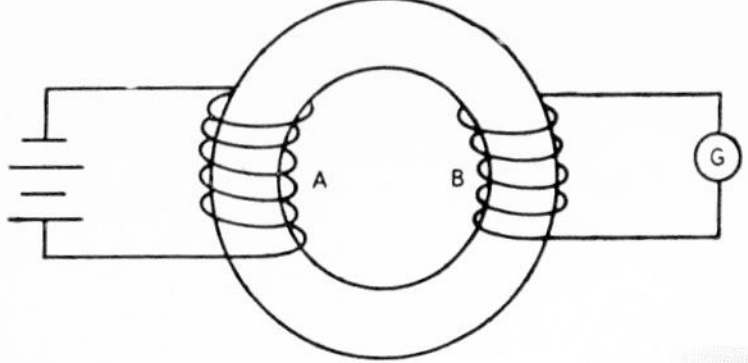

Plate 1. Wiring diagram of Faraday's induction ring. Movement of the galvanometer G when a current was set up in primary coil A indicated that a current had passed in secondary coil B.

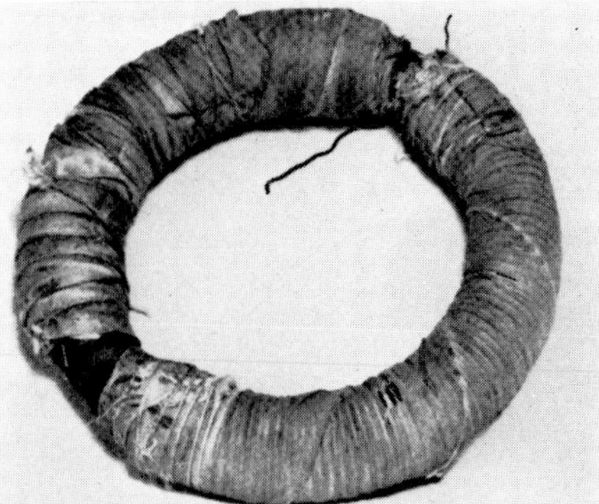

Plate 2. Faraday's induction ring.

Plate 3. Two-needle telegraph used on the London to Slough railway between 1843 and 1849. The plate on the base commemorates its part in the arrest of John Tawell.

Plate 4. Cable laying from the *Great Eastern* in 1866.

W. T. Henleys Telegraph Works North Woolwich
Cable Department

Tuesday 25th April 1871

A.M. No. 5 Cable Machine making a length of Cable (14x12) Hoopers core, for Gt. Nthn Tel compy.
No. 1. 5 & 7 core Machines at work. At 3 a small Nail was detected in the core of No. 5 whilst it was being served, cut it out and forwarded it with a report to Mr. Henley.
At 6. 54 hands employed, No. 5 at work as before, the same core Machines running, commenced to thread onto No. 7 Machine 7.012 Knots of Shore End of British Indian type so as to commence another section. Making preparations for starting No. 1 Machine on same type of cable as No. 7.

P.M. Same employment as this Morning at 3 No. 5 core Machine finished what core was ready for serving at 6 changed gangs for the Night.
34 hands employed. No. 5 Cable and Nos. 1 & 7 core Machines at work as before. Cable made at No. 5 from 6 to 6. 1.206 Knots.

Wednesday 26th April 1871

A.M. No. 5 waited from midnight untill 1 for a joint Length of core for No. 1. finished at 3.30
At 6 started No. 7 Machine on British Indian type and commenced loading up No. 1 Machine.
No. 5 as before. Nos. 1, 5 & 7 core Machines running. Noon started No. 1 Machine on same type as No. 7.

P.M. Same employment as this morning.
At 6 changed gangs for the Night 64 hands employed.

Plate 5.

Re W. T. HENLEY & Co., Limited, in Liquidation.

TELEGRAPH WORKS, NORTH WOOLWICH.

A CATALOGUE
OF
PLANT & MACHINERY,
INCLUDING
A 6-IN. BACK-GEAR SCREW-CUTTING LATHE,
By Shepherd, Hill & Spink,
YARN WINDING MACHINE
with Fourteen Spindles, Friction Wheels, Guide Rollers and Gear, a Jigger Bench and Blocks,
HEAVY BAND-SAWING MACHINE,
By Powis, James & Co.,
A 12-ft. PLATE PLANING MACHINE,
AN OVERHEAD TRAVELLER, 35-FT. 6-IN. SPAN,
WITH FIVE-TON DOUBLE-PURCHASE CRAB,
A POWERFUL ECCENTRIC SHEARING MACHINE,
with 2-ft. Knives, 18-in. Gap, driven by an 11-in. Inverted Cylinder Engine, a pair of extra strong Fir Shear Legs, about 60-ft. high, a Double Cylinder Steam Winch by Appleby Brothers, a pair of 10-in. Gun Metal Well [illegible]
TWO MULTITUBULAR BOILERS, 17-ft. long, 4-ft. 6-in. diameter,
PLATE-HEATE FURNACE.
A HIGH-PRESSURE TABLE ENGINE WITH 12-IN., CYLINDER,
A SCHEILE'S PATENT FAN,
A SCOTT'S PATENT WHEEL MOULDING MACHINE WITH GEAR COMPLETE,
CAST-IRON LOAM MILL with 28-in. RUNNERS,
THREE CUPOLAS with FEEDING STAGES,
Brick and Iron Erection of Core Drying Stove,
REVOLVING CRANE WITH RACKING IN AND OUT GEAR,
Floor Plates &c.;
Which will be Sold by Auction, by
MESSRS.
FRANK LEWIS & KEMP,
ON THE PREMISES AT NORTH WOOLWICH,
On MONDAY, DECEMBER 9th, 1878,
AND FOLLOWING DAY.
AT ELEVEN FOR TWELVE O'CLOCK EACH DAY

May be Viewed the Saturday before Sale, and Catalogues had on the Premises; of Messrs. Robert Fletcher & Co., Public Accountants, No. 3, Lothbury; of T. W. Sharkey, Esq., Solicitor, 8, Angel Court, Throgmorton Street; and of Messrs. Frank Lewis & Kemp, Auctioneers, &c.,
95, GRESHAM STREET, LONDON, E.C.

H. Kemshead's Steam Printing Works, Kennington Lane, S.E.

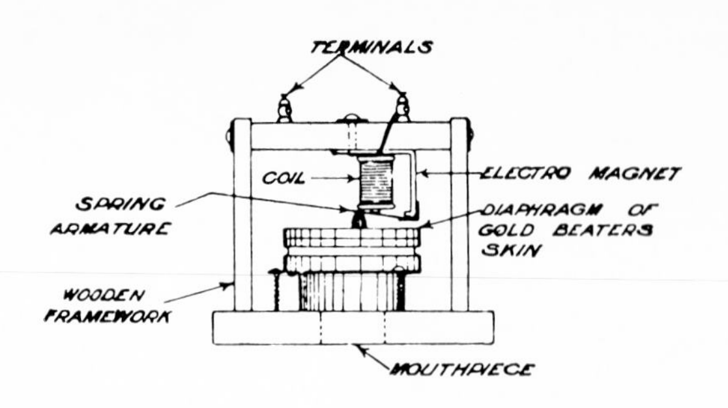

Plate 6. Diagram of Bell's first telephone.

Plate 7. Advertisement of 1879 showing practical uses of the telephone.

Plate 8. Replica of Bell's 'Harmonica' telegraph transmitter and receiver 1873–1874.

Plate 9. Greetings cards from Post Office linemen.

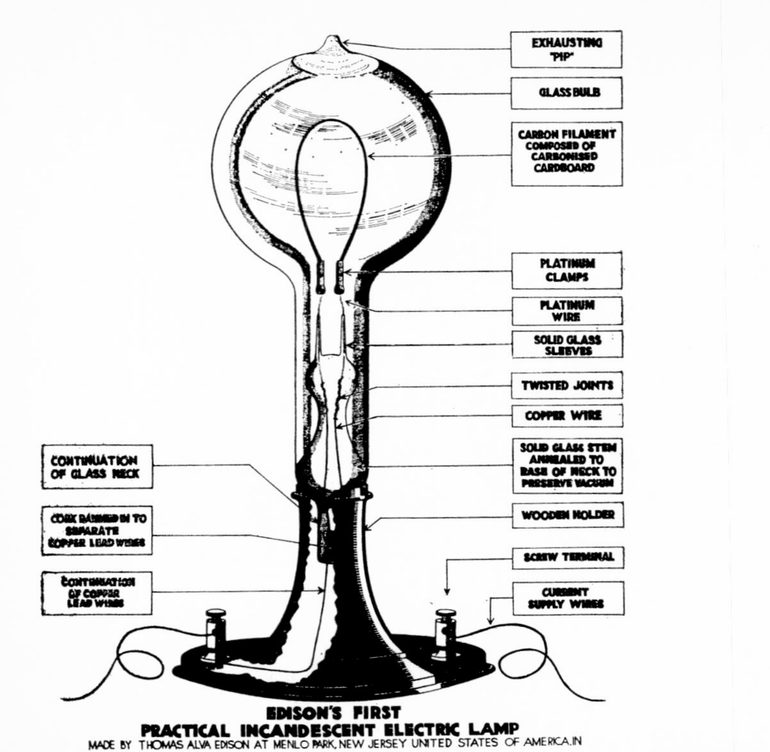

EDISON'S FIRST
PRACTICAL INCANDESCENT ELECTRIC LAMP
MADE BY THOMAS ALVA EDISON AT MENLO PARK, NEW JERSEY UNITED STATES OF AMERICA. IN
1879
PREPARED BY THE EDISON SWAN ELECTRIC CO. LTD. 155, CHARING CROSS ROAD, LONDON, W.C.2. AND BRANCHES
MAKERS OF THE FAMOUS **ROYAL "EDISWAN" LAMPS**

Plate 10.

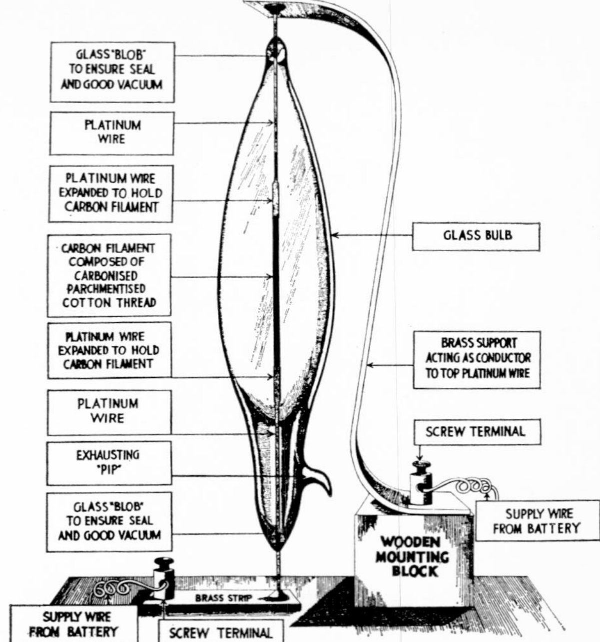

THE FIRST
PRACTICAL INCANDESCENT ELECTRIC LAMP
MADE BY SIR JOSEPH WILSON SWAN F.R.S. AND EXHIBITED AT NEWCASTLE ENGLAND, IN
1878
PREPARED BY THE EDISON SWAN ELECTRIC CO. LTD. 155, CHARING CROSS ROAD, LONDON, W.C.2 AND BRANCHES
MAKERS OF THE FAMOUS **ROYAL "EDISWAN" LAMPS**

Plate 11. Post Office heavy-construction gang, Edinburgh, 1899.

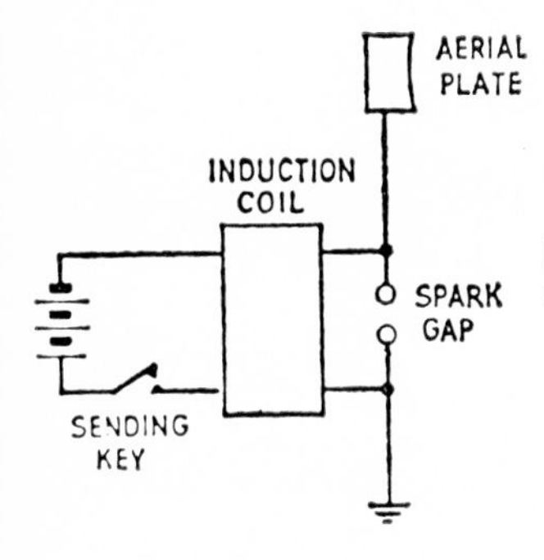

Plate 12. Marconi's first transmitting circuit.

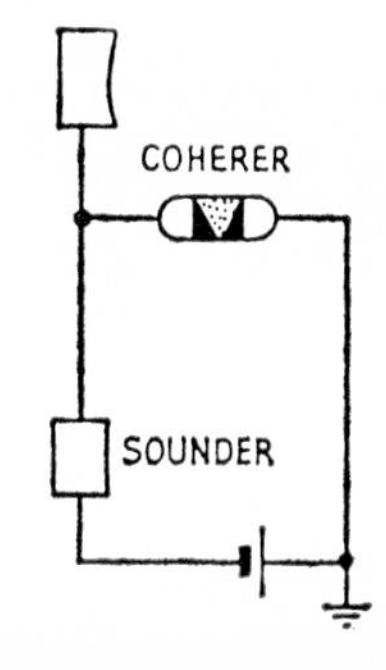

Plate 13. Marconi's first receiving circuit.

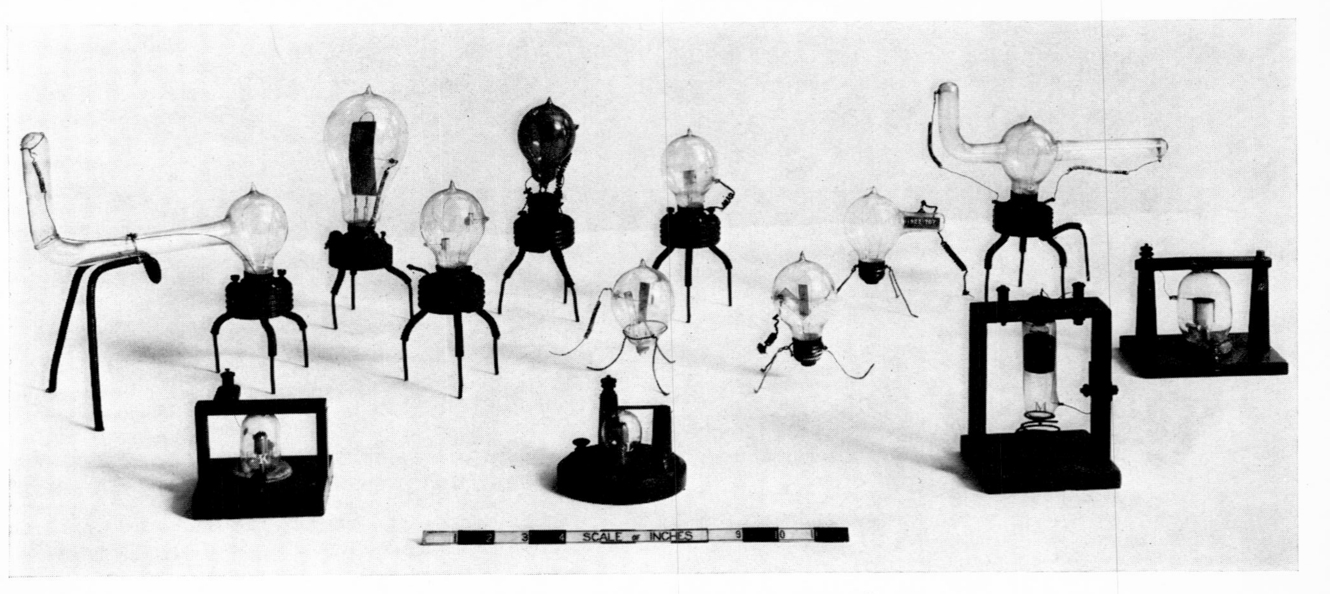

Plate 14. Original Fleming experimental valves.

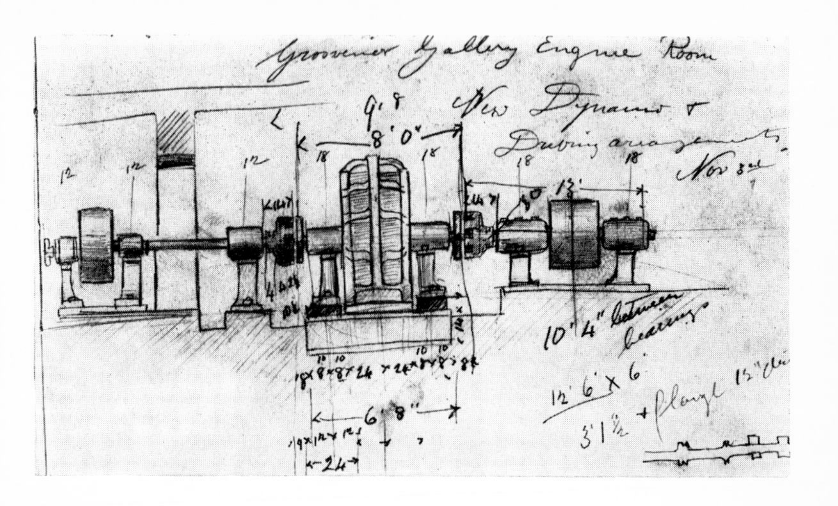

Plate 15. Examples of Ferranti's work. (a) Rough design of alternators for Grosvenor Gallery Station, from his sketch book of 1886. (b) Deptford Power Station, 1889, conceived and designed entirely by him at age 23–27.

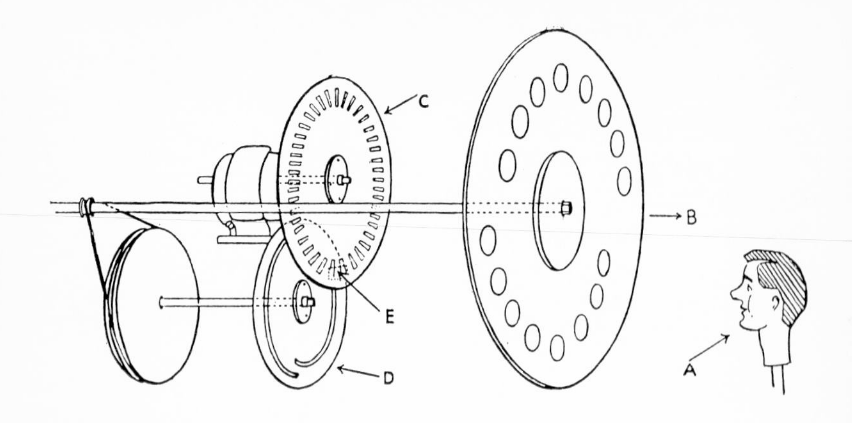

Plate 16. Diagram of first television transmitter, now in Science Museum, London. (A) dummy's head, (B) lensed disc, (C) and (D) slotted and spiral discs for scanning, (E) aperture through which image projected on photoelectric cell.

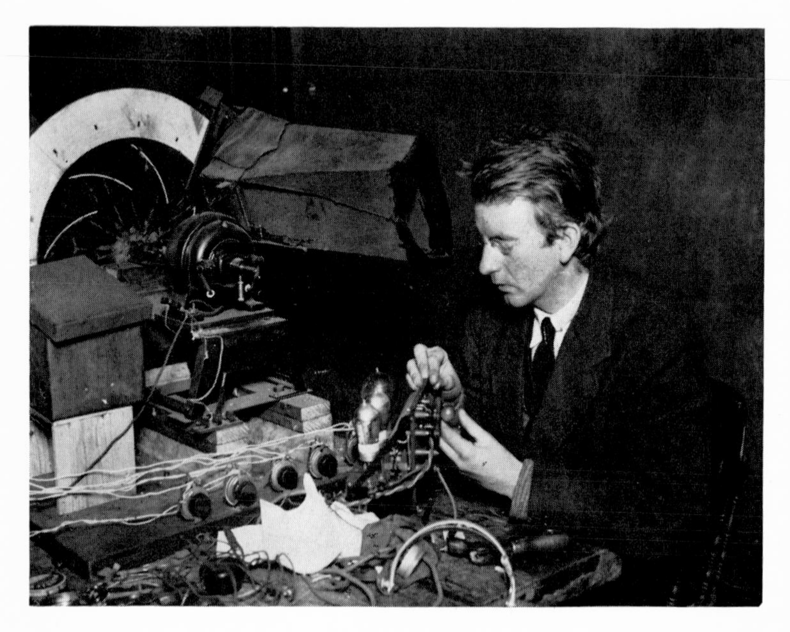

Plate 17. Baird at work in 1925.

Plate 18. Steel lattice masts 350 feet high. Combined with ultra-short-wave radiation, these allowed the outer edge of the radar 'fence' to be set far enough from the coast to give warning in time for raiding bombers at great height to be intercepted by planes starting from the ground.

Plate 19. Radar transmitter made at Bawdsey 1936–1937.

Plate 20. Electrical Trades Union banner.

every six months or so'. Many people said the enterprise would fail because Edison was not a scientist and did not have the training necessary for it. But he was confident that the big firms would seek him out and ask his help, in improving their instruments. He invited friends to see his 'brand new laboratory . . . at Menlo Park, Western Div., Globe, Planet Earth, Middlesex County, four miles from Railway, the prettiest spot in New Jersey, on the Penna. Railway, on a High Hill. Will show you around, go strawberrying'.

By then the great Western Union Telegraph Company was paying him to investigate Alexander Graham Bell's 'speaking telegraph', the telephone. Bell exhibited his telephone at the Centennial Exhibition at Philadelphia that summer (see Chapter Four). Edison soon invented his carbon microphone which made Bell's telephone a commercial proposition. He wrote:

'Besides I am so deaf that I am debarred from hearing all the finer articulations and have to depend on the judgment of others. I had scarcely gotten the principle working before was pressure in New York to introduce it immediately. I made 2 or 3 pair but found they were unhandy . . . That delayed. I have finished a new pair and they have been working two days without no change or adjustment . . . I have my man making a model for the Patent Office, which is essential I should get in . . . so you can see I have my hands full – Even working 22 hours per day.'

Then he produced the invention for which he is probably best known, the phonograph, the forerunner of the gramophone. This was not, as usually happened the result of a demand or an order from a firm, but it arose from his curiosity about sound and his work on the telephone. He worked out the 'talking machine' by trial and error, first using paper coated with paraffin, then tin foil covering a cylinder with grooves round the surface.

The phonograph made Edison famous throughout America and Europe. He was already an American hero, the poor boy who had made good. He was known as the Wizard of Menlo Park. The problems of lighting began to interest him.

The chief problem was to 'subdivide the electric light', to

make small, light and cheap units of mild light instead of the big blinding arc lights. From the first Edison planned a complete electric system including power station and distribution, even though the lamp had yet to be invented. When Edison's plan became known the value of gas shares tumbled down. He wrote down the following notes:

'Electricity versus Gas as General Illuminant.

Object: E. to effect exact imitation of all done by gas, to replace lighting by gas by lighting by electricity. To improve the illumination to such an extent as to meet all requirements of natural, artificial and commercial conditions. Previous inventions failed – necessities for commercial success and accomplishment by Edison. Edison's great effort – not to make a large light or a blinding light, but a small light having the mildness of gas.'

A group of financiers supplied fifty thousand dollars for the research, Edison added buildings and equipment to his laboratory, including an engine house and a glass blower's shed, and set to work by his usual method of trying anything he could think of or had heard about. His own maxim was that genius was ninety-nine per cent perspiration and one per cent inspiration. The lamp was the first nut to crack and it was the most difficult he had ever had. What he was looking for was some kind of filament which, in an evacuated glass chamber, could be heated to incandescence by an electric current. First he tried carbon but it would not do; in any case he could not get a good enough vacuum. He realized the job was going to be a long hard one and a number of trained mathematicians and scientists were enrolled at Menlo Park to help him. The problem of vacuum was easily solved. An English physicist, Sir William Crookes, had just obtained a high vacuum with the use of the new Sprengel pump, so called after the name of its German inventor. When Edison read about it he got hold of one immediately from Princeton College. This, and the skill of an immigrant glass blower from Germany, produced the necessary glass bulb. But the filament was far more difficult. The whole laboratory worked for six months on a platinum filament lamp but it was not good enough. It seemed that Edison had failed for the first time, gas shares recovered, and he was back where he started.

Nearly a year after he had started he decided that carbon must be the illuminant. Later on this is how he described the problem:

'Just consider this: we have an almost infinitesimal vacuum heated to a degree which it is difficult to comprehend, and it is in a vacuum under conditions of which we are wholly ignorant. You cannot use your eyes to help you, and you really know nothing of what is going on in that tiny bulb. I speak without exaggeration when I say that I have constructed 3,000 different theories in connection with the electric light, each of them reasonable and apparently likely to be true. Yet in only two cases did my experiments prove the truth of my theory.'

He concentrated on the use of lamp-black from kerosene lamps, mixed with tar, having it kneaded into thinner and thinner pieces, as fine as seven thousandths of an inch. Then one day having carbonized a piece of cotton thread in a furnace (ordinary thread Coats and Co. cord No. 29) he put it in a lamp, and it burned for forty hours. The problem was solved. On 1st November, 1879, he applied for a patent; the specification included the following:

'I have discovered that even a cotton thread, properly carbonized and placed in sealed glass bulbs, exhausted to one-millionth of an atmosphere, offers from one hundred to five hundred hours' resistance to the passage of the current and that it is absolutely stable at a very high temperature.'

The news of Edison's success after a struggle lasting fourteen months made a great sensation on both sides of the Atlantic. It had cost his financiers a large sum, but it was cheap at the price.

Edison now returned to his original plan for the 'Edison system, a comprehensive system of electric light distribution, analagous to gas'. He was again financed by a syndicate headed by two of the richest men in America – Cornelius Vanderbilt and J. Pierpont Morgan. He intended to build for the first time a central power station, and in New York itself. It was a bigger task than he had ever tackled, but as usual he was full of confidence.

First he installed a system on a small scale with 425 lamps at Menlo Park. A test showed that it worked and that it was economical; it would not cost more than gas light. When he had obtained permission from New York City to lay underground mains he set up his headquarters on Fifth Avenue. For the generating station he bought a site 100 feet by 50 feet and put up a building of structural ironwork. It was to serve an area of about half a mile square. The four boilers were on the ground floor, and the dynamos, directly connected to steam engines, on the second. There were to be six dynamos. They were a model which he had designed and nicknamed Jumbo; the armature alone weighed six tons. Each unit had 200 hp and could light 1,200 lamps. Edison himself supervised the gangs digging trenches and laying the cable in iron tubes into which hot tar was pumped.

By July 1882 Edison was ready for a trial run. He started with one dynamo, then everything went wrong:

'At first everything worked all right . . . Then we started another engine and threw them in parallel. Of all the circuses since Adam was born, we had the worst then! One engine would stop and the other would run up to a thousand revolutions; and then they would see-saw. . . . When the circus commenced the gang that was standing around ran out precipitately, and I guess some of them kept running for a block or two.'

Three months later, however, all went well as the lights went on in the district. But it was a small station and it lost money in the first few years. Only eighty-five customers were connected with a total load of four hundred lamps.

Later on the central generating stations multiplied rapidly and Edison made a great deal of money. He wrote:

'The Pearl Street station was the biggest and most responsible thing I had ever undertaken . . . There was no parallel in the world . . . all our apparatus, devices and parts were home-devised and home-made. What might happen on turning a big current into the conductors under the streets of New York no one could say. . . . All I can remember of the events of that day is that I had been up most of the night rehearsing my men and going over every part of the system. . . . If I ever did any thinking in my life it was on that day.'

Edison was still under forty and he lived to the age of eighty-six. He filled his life with a continual flow of inventions of many kinds. The most famous of these was the motion picture. Many people had worked on it before but Edison made it practical. As time went on he became very wealthy, especially from his phonograph and motion picture business. But several times during his life he was on the verge of ruin, and only recovered with another invention. 'I always invent to obtain money to go on inventing,' he said.

Edison's attitude to labour was typical of the industrialists of his time. He had no time for trade unions. He thought his employees should be willing to work as hard and long as he did. In this period, however, there was an upsurge of labour. The Knights of Labour, founded in 1869 by a tailor, grew rapidly by including all trades and all grades of skill, and became a national union. In 1885 the nation was swept by strikes, lock-outs, violence and waves of destruction. In the Haymarket Riot in Chicago in that year eight people were killed and four were executed for murder. Although the Knights of Labour faded away soon after, the American Federation of Labour, of the present day, had already started. Edison's policy may be shown by two incidents. Once when the men who did the skilled job of sealing the filament into the electric bulb formed a union, he invented a machine to do it; the need for the men disappeared, and the union with it. Another time when men in his New York machine works went on strike for higher wages he kept them in the dark about his intention to remove the whole works to Schenectady. Edison tells what happened:

'So when the men went out they appointed a committee to see us; but for two weeks they could not find us. Finally they said they would like to go back. We said all right. . . . When they went back to the shops they found them empty of machinery. It was quite a novelty to the men not to be able to find us when they wanted to, and they didn't relish it at all.'

In science, as distinct from invention, he made, in 1883, one important discovery. This was the Edison effect. He had noticed that the inside of his carbon filament bulb became blackened, and discovered that it was caused by carbon particles which must have been carried in some way on to the glass. He inserted another electrode in the bulb to see if it would collect the carbon particles, first a platinum wire and then a metal plate. To his surprise he found that a steady current flowed from the heated filament across the vacuum to the cold plate. This Edison effect was a complete mystery to scientists until J. J. Thomson six years later showed that it was caused by the passage of electrons. Ambrose Fleming followed this up and invented the diode. Thus Edison's discovery was the foundation of the electronics industry. He lost interest in it because he could not see any practical use to which it could be put. 'The point in which I am different,' he said later, 'is that I have, besides the inventor's usual make-up, a bump of practicality . . . the sense of the business-money value of an invention. Oh, no, I didn't have it naturally. It was pounded into me by some pretty hard knocks.'

SIR JOSEPH SWAN (1828–1914)

Joseph Wilson Swan was born near Sunderland, at Pallion Hall, a large house on the Wear, about two miles up-river from the town. His father, the son of a merchant captain, manufactured ships' anchors, chains and similar hardware, and at this time had a prosperous business. His mother was the daughter of a well-known stonemason and master builder of Sunderland. The family of eight children had its ups and downs. Before moving to Pallion Hall they had lived over the business premises in the town; after a few years' prosperity they had to move back to a street in the town and Swan's mother had to start a girls' school to increase the family income. His father was too generous and easy-going to succeed in business.

'The days of my youth,' Swan wrote as an old man, 'extend backward to the dark ages, for I was born when the rush-light, the tallow dip, or the solitary blaze of the hearth were common means of indoor lighting, and an infrequent glass bowl, raised 8 to 10 feet on a wooden post, and containing a cupful of evil-smelling train-oil with a crude cotton wick stuck in it, served to make darkness visible out of doors.'

With his three brothers and four sisters, he had a happy childhood. He was allowed to roam freely through the town, the busy port and the countryside. He could satisfy his curiosity about the local crafts and industries and by watching the wooden ships being built, the glass bottle making and the work in the lime kilns he learnt something about industry.

Young Swan went to a little day-school kept by three sisters. One day their father came into the schoolroom.

'He had come to show the children a very wonderful thing, a glass prism, and how, when the sunbeam was caught upon it, a rainbow was made on the wall behind. That was my first intentional lesson in physics, and I shall never forget it nor the strange pleasure it gave me.' Then he went to a boys' school for a few years. He left school when he was only thirteen, but he already had an interest in chemistry, in which he made his career, and in literature, which he enjoyed all his life. He also had the luck to be introduced to electricity. While Faraday was making his discoveries in London, young Swan was able to experiment with an electrical friction machine, Leyden jars, and other apparatus which belonged to a friend of the family.

When he was fourteen Swan was articled as an apprentice to a firm of chemists and druggists in Sunderland. The apprenticeship was for six years but when both the partners in the firm died he became free from his articles and he left after four years. He learned a great deal during these years, mostly in his spare time. There was a good library containing scientific books and journals. He read about one of the earliest attempts by an American inventor, J. W. Starr, to make an incandescent electric lamp. He met another inventor, W. E. Staite, a Sunderland man. Staite had made great improvements in the arc lamp, particularly his automatic feed, a clockwork mechanism which moved the carbons forward as they were used up. Swan went to several of his lectures and remembered them all his life:

'I remember that in addition to showing his lamp, which it was the principal object of his lecture to exhibit and which he proposed should be utilized immediately for lighthouse purposes, he also on one occasion, in the Athenaeum at Sunderland, illustrated the principles of electric lighting by means of a piece of iridio-platinum wire. . . . This arrested my attention and led me to ponder the question, even at this early period, how to produce electric light on this principle, but so as to avoid the use of a fusible wire. It was something like a seed sown in my mind, which germinated.'

Sunderland was a lively place. Swan learnt about electrotyping from craftsmen there and did some himself. This led him to learn about different types of battery. In the shop window of an engraver he saw a photographic portrait for the first time, it was one of the early daguerreotypes, a photograph on a silvered copper plate. This began Swan's interest and work in photography. Later on in life he was to make two important discoveries: an electrical storage battery, and bromide printing paper. 'During these three years,' he wrote, 'all my spare time was spent in chemical and electrical experiments, carried out for the most part by means of home-made apparatus and appliances.'

When he was eighteen Swan joined the chemists' business of his friend John Mawson in Newcastle. A few years later he became a partner. The firm of Mawson and Swan flourished for twenty years until Mawson was killed in an accident. Both partners were efficient and hard-working. Mawson freed Swan from much of the routine work so that he could develop his scientific ideas and experiments. This was profitable, as Swan became an expert who could advise the increasing number of photographers. He also made the firm famous for its manufacture of collodion, used in the wet-plate process.

He had two particular friends, one was an analytical chemist at a chemical works, the other a pharmaceutical chemist who became professor of pharmacy at the Newcastle College of Science. They had weekly meetings at each other's houses and spent their holidays together.

'The subjects discussed at our meetings were chiefly connected with the chemical work we had been doing incidentally to our employment. I frequently had something to say of what I was doing in connection with the construction of electrical apparatus, for I had added a new branch of chemical and other scientific apparatus to Mr. Mawson's business, and in leisure time was doing experimental work both in connection with electricity and photography.'

He and his friends were also interested in politics. They were left-wing Liberals, supporting the liberation movements in Europe in the eighteen-forties. When Garibaldi, the hero of Italian liberation from Austria, visited the north of England, they joined in presenting him with a sword of honour. Swan could never spare much time for politics but he did play a part in local affairs. Education was always one of his main interests. He describes a meeting at the time of the campaign for the first Education Act in 1870. Jesse Collings, the speaker, was leader of the campaign:

'I have just come in from a meeting held in the Mechanics' Institute to form a branch of the Birmingham Educational League. It was a most interesting meeting. I was greatly pleased with Mr. Collings of Birmingham. He has a very large business, employs twenty-six clerks and six travellers, and yet has time to come here to stir up the dull spirits of our townspeople on this important question of national education, and he does it with great ability and an enthusiasm that is quite refreshing, an energy that drags one along with it. I greatly admire and envy the possession of this rare quality.'

After sixteen busy and successful years at Newcastle Swan married the daughter of a Liverpool merchant, a teacher. Three children were born but his wife died after only five years of marriage. Four years later he married his wife's sister. From the second marriage there were five children. Swan spent a great deal of time helping to make toys and reading to them.

Swan's invention of the incandescent electric lamp was a result of work done from time to time throughout these years. It was only one of his interests. In fact most of his time was spent on photography. The first patent he took out was for his carbon or autotype process in 1864 and fifteen years later he patented bromide paper. His work on the lamp started as early as 1848, was laid aside and kept in the back of his mind for long periods, and was not finally successful until 1878. Swan himself remarked that 'every invention has a pedigree'. He started from the patent of the American, J. W. Starr, mentioned earlier. Starr had used a thin sheet of platinum foil or carbon for his lamp, and said that when carbon was used, 'it should be enclosed in a Torricellian vacuum'. Swan began experimenting with carbon. He realized that the carbon conductor must be as thin as possible. 'It appeared to me evident,' he said, 'that an advantage would be gained by making the incandescent carbon filament as thin as possible, and my first experiments were directed to the attainment of this object by means of carbonized paper and carbonized cardboard.'

After many experiments he got some very fine but strong and flexible strips of carbonized paper which were to be filaments. His method was to pack the strips in powdered charcoal in a fireclay crucible and bake them at a high temperature in a pottery kiln. The paper was saturated with various liquids such as treacle and tar. He mounted these filaments in glass bottles or jars from which he exhausted the air by a simple air pump with piston and barrel. These lamps he tried out with a battery in 1860. He succeeded in making incandescent a strip of carbon about $\frac{1}{4}$ inch wide by $1\frac{1}{4}$ inches long in the form of an arch, but the light lasted only a very short time. The lamp was not a practical proposition but the principle behind it was correct. The vacuum was not good enough to prevent oxidation of the filament, and no better vacuum could be obtained at that time. The battery power was not strong enough. In fact Swan was ahead of the times; arc lighting was still in its early days and the dynamo had barely come into use. So he stopped his experiments for many years.

Fifteen years later the dynamo had been greatly improved by William Siemens – it was now possible to obtain a nearly perfect vacuum. This had come about by the invention of a vacuum pump by the German Hermann Sprengel and its improvement by Sir William Crookes. Crookes announced his discovery in 1875 and two years later Swan decided to start his experiments with the lamp again.

He met with difficulties. The main one was to maintain the

vacuum after the current was switched on and this was overcome by continuing exhaustion of the lamp after the filament was heated. At last on 18th December, 1878, at a meeting of the Newcastle Chemical Society, Swan showed his incandescent lamp. It was a tube-shaped glass bulb, pierced with two platinum wires which supported between them a straight thin carbon conductor one twenty-fifth of an inch in diameter. The news soon spread and in February 1879 he demonstrated the lamp before an audience of seven hundred. He then pushed on with improvements in order to go ahead with production on a large scale. He altered the straight conductor to a hairpin bend. Instead of paper as the basis for the carbon conductor he used cotton yarn treated with sulphuric acid and patented this in 1880. He called this parchmentized thread.

In the meantime in the United States Edison had been busy on the same task at his Menlo Park laboratory, and in October 1878 he announced: 'I have solved the problem of the subdivisions of the electric light indefinitely.' Repeated announcements of Edison's achievement appeared, so that Swan wrote the following letter to *Nature*, the scientific journal, in January 1880.

'I observe in *Nature*, vol. XXI, p. 187, a statement to the effect that Mr. Edison has adopted the use of carbon in his new electric lamp, and that the carbon he uses is charred paper or card in the shape of a horse-shoe.

'Fifteen years ago I used charred paper and card in the construction of an electric lamp on the incandescent principle. I used it, too, of the shape of a horse-shoe, precisely as, you say, Mr. Edison is now using it. I did not then succeed in obtaining the durability which I was in search of, but I have since made many experiments on the subject, and within the last six months I have, I believe, completely conquered the difficulty which led to previous failure, and I am now able to produce a perfectly durable electric lamp by means of incandescent carbon.'

Swan did not take out a patent for his lamp because he thought that its basic features, a carbon filament in an evacuated glass bulb, had been thought of before. He patented only his own method of producing a vacuum. Edison, however, the professional inventor, patented his lamp immediately not only in the United States but also in England. Swan concentrated on production. By the summer of 1880 he was satisfied that the cotton carbon filaments were reliable enough for the lamps to be manufactured.

In forming a company and starting a factory Swan received help from R. E. B. Crompton whose work has been described earlier in this chapter. When the first Swan Electric Lamp Company was formed Crompton was its chief engineer. He described his first meeting with Swan in 1880:

'A gentleman (Mr. Morgan I think his name was) whom I believed to be one of the travellers of Messrs. Mawson and Swan, sent in his card to my office, 4 Queen Victoria Street, and said he had come with a request of such an urgent nature that I must take it as a mandate that I would accompany him that very evening to Newcastle to see Mr. Swan. I was not allowed to go home to get my clothes or sleeping things, but was carried off to Newcastle, and was there and then taken to Mr. Swan's laboratory, introduced to him, and shown a row of sealed glass bulbs containing carbon filaments which he informed me had been pumped by a form of Sprengel pump invented by Mr. C. H. Stern, to a higher degree of vacuum than had hitherto been considered practically obtainable. The filaments, he explained, were mounted on platinum terminals and were formed of cotton which had been made into cellulose before carbonizing.

'After explaining this, he had a gas-engine driving a Gramme machine started up, and lamps were switched on and glowed in a most satisfactory manner. He asked my opinion as to what could be done with it, and told me he was shortly afterwards to lecture to the Philosophical Society at Newcastle, and begged that I would be present to take part in the discussion, as he considered that I, as an apostle of the arc lamp, was to some extent in rivalry with him. He wished me to understand that there was a distinct place for the two kinds of illumination.

'This was the first time I came in contact with him, and I was then struck with the extreme fairness and openness of his mind, and with his extraordinary modesty.'

'The Swan lamp' was soon installed at many places; private houses first, Swan's own home, then the houses of the president of the Royal Society and of Sir William Thomson (Lord Kelvin). The light spread to ships and public places. The first ship, the *City of Richmond* of the Inman line, was fitted with electric light in 1887, and in the same year the Mansion House, the British Museum, the Royal Academy and the Savoy Theatre. Each installation had to have its own generating plant. In that same year Swan lighting was shown at the Paris Exhibition. Swan wrote:

Swan Eclairage Electronique Incandescent,
September 23rd, 1881

'I am taking the opportunity of a spare and quiet moment to tell you of our continued success.

Last night in the Salle du Congres there was a meeting of the Society of Telegraph Engineers. (This was the forerunner of the Institution of Electrical Engineers.) We, of course, lighted the hall with our lamps. There was only one opinion as to the manner in which it was done. We turned the lights in and out to accommodate the lecturer, who had magic-lantern demonstrations, and this was done just as promptly as if gas, instead of electricity, had been the lighting agent. . . . Did I tell you that it was settled that we were to light the interior of the Grand Opera House? Edison, Lane-Fox and others are to light parts of the building also. . . .'

In the following year a serious problem arose. The Edison Company in London which owned Edison's patents in England began legal proceedings against the Swan Company for infringement of those patents. Fortunately 'this bothering legal business', as Swan called it, was settled peacefully. The two rival companies amalgamated as 'The Edison and Swan United Electric Light Company Ltd.'

Swan then made a very important improvement to the lamp. This was his filament based on nitro-cellulose. He discovered this new filament at his new home in Bromley, then a little Kentish town. He had bought a house with ample room for his large family, together with a smaller house as a laboratory. The family enjoyed the clean warm air of the south. Swan wrote:

'We have been for a long drive this afternoon. . . . The white and red of the apple and pear trees is the only colour to be seen. It is a wonderful season, I never remember one so hot at this season, nor so beautiful in every way. The cuckoo is here and the nightingale. It is full summer in fact, so far as the temperature goes; and delicious late spring so far as the trees are suggestive of the season. "The brushwood sheaf round the elm tree bole is in tiny leaf", and has been for a fortnight. As we drove across the commons covered with gorse in flower, the ground dry and the air warm, it seemed it would be the very ideal of physical enjoyment to lie down on the dry grass among the gorse and contemplate "the blue liberality of heaven", or fall asleep there.'

Swan had not been satisfied with the filament of carbonized cotton thread and so he looked for a non-fibrous thread. His training as a chemist led him to a plastic material. Nitro-cellulose dissolved in acetic acid was squirted or extruded through a metal die. When it coagulated it formed long strips which were cut up and carbonized. This process which Swan patented in 1883, revolutionized the lamp industry; the filaments were now fine and much more uniform. It also started a chain of events which led to the manufacture of artificial silk twenty years later.

After these achievements Swan did not make any more major discoveries although he continued his research. He was a director of several companies but most of his time was spent in working in scientific bodies. There was a long roll of them: the Royal Society of which he was a fellow, the Royal Institution, the National Physical Laboratory; the Institution of Electrical Engineers, the Faraday Society, the Pharmaceutical Society, the Society of Chemical Industry, of all four of which he was president at different times, the Senate of University College, London, of which he was vice-president. At the age of seventy-eight, he enjoyed the excitement of motoring in its early days; this was in 1907:

'Motoring is a delightful mode of travel, but at 35 miles an hour it is to me a "fearful joy"; but that pace was an exception, and I did thoroughly enjoy 18 to 20 miles an hour on the smooth straight, and for the most part empty, roads of the Welsh hills. The *exhilaration* of it is beyond words.'

The last of many honours was the freedom of the city offered by his fellow townsmen of Newcastle a few months before the outbreak of war in 1914. But he died before he could go to receive it.

SEBASTIAN ZIANI DE FERRANTI (1864–1930)

Sebastian Pietro Innocenzo Adhemar Ziani de Ferranti was descended from an ancient Venetian family. The founder of the family, Sebastian Ziani, was Doge of Venice in 1173 and during the following centuries members of the family were leaders in the Italian states. Later some of the Zianis in Bologna added 'de Ferranti' to their name. Ferranti's father, César Ziani de Ferranti, emigrated to England in 1859 and had a photographic studio in Liverpool. In his studio César de Ferranti met William Scott, a well-known portrait painter, and married his daughter who had lost her first husband, a Polish count and musician by whom she had had three children. She herself had given piano recitals in many European cities. Sebastian, her second son by her second marriage, was born in Liverpool on 9th April, 1864.

He was a clever boy, even a precocious one. His interests were not in music or art but, to the surprise of his parents, in engineering and science. At the age of ten he was asking his father for a model drawing of a railway locomotive and a working model of a steam engine. A year later he wrote home:

'Please ask Vincent if he can get me a book on "Compound steam illustrated so that I can see about the condenser because I want to see about it for a particular reason I have thought of", and "I have seen some very cheap engines to put together so I am going to get one and get a safety valve and an indicator of water and get them put on and then I can put them together at school".'

First he went to a private boarding school in Hampstead, kept by a Frenchwoman, and then when he was thirteen to a Roman Catholic boarding school, St. Augustine's Abbey, Ramsgate, where he stayed for four years.

At school Ferranti's enthusiasm for engineering and science grew fast. He was no good at the ordinary subjects taught, even mathematics did not interest him much. His father was afraid that he would become a hare-brained inventor. He urged him to pass the London Matriculation so as to get entry into a profession but Ferranti was so busy with his own ideas that he did not reach the standard required.

Sometimes his ideas and those of his father were in sympathy. When his father was considering having his house lit by electricity he wrote (age thirteen):

'What a capital idea. . . . About what sized engine would it take to do it? I hope very much that you will have it; not only for the engine, but for the beautifully pure white light it gives; and it seems to me it must be a good deal cheaper, as the engine would not cost much to work, especially if it were made to go by coke and charcoal mixed, or it might have a self-feeding boiler and lamp, which, with a very little calculation, is very easy to be made and worked with safety with comparatively no looking after, except to oil the different parts.'

Ferranti was lucky to have a headmaster who recognized that he was an unusual boy who spent all his leisure on electrical experiments. He was given a room to himself where he could be free from the rigid routine of a boarding school. He was able to visit a monastery school in Canterbury which had a well-fitted workshop:

'Father Augustine also gave me some lessons in turning and I can get on pretty well with it now as I have made several tops for the boys . . . I wonder when the happy day will come when Papa will get me a good lathe. My head is always full of ideas and I can never carry them out on account of this most useful of tools. I often despair of getting one as Papa does not seem to take interest in my things and says I am over doing it when it is just the want of a Lathe that stops me from doing things which would make me seem much more moderate and would relieve my mind.' The price of a lathe was, however, more than Papa could afford. In Ramsgate he found an electric apparatus shop and spent many hours in the workshop at the back where he could use the equipment and exchange ideas with the electrician.

From the age of fourteen he worked at making a dynamo. At that time he wrote to his mother:

'As you have asked me to give you an explanation of my machine I will tell you a few things about it, as I want some tracing paper to do the separate plans on.

'The first thing which is well known and has often been proved, is that the North pole of one magnet attracts the South pole of another, but drives away the other's North pole. Another thing is that glass, when put between two magnets, nullifies their power altogether. Upon these two principles I have made my machine. It is circular and is ten inches in diameter; it is also three inches deep, so will work in a glass cylinder of the above dimensions, in which there will be a complete vacuum. The reason of working it in a vacuum is that the air, which has great resistance to bodies going at a high speed, would here have no force against it. There is one thing I will tell you about the machine, that is that it has always the power of 32 horse-shoe magnets, at a 4-inch leverage, being worked by 16 other magnets, which are not on the wheel but fixed. This machine would, I have calculated, drive a boat 5 feet long with the greatest ease . . .

'The sub-prefect, who teaches me Physics, says that he thinks it will work very well. It would have to be cast in about 50 pieces of steel and bars, and about 40 of glass. I think it would cost me about £2.

'Machines worked by magnets have always been given up by learned men, as they did not (in my estimation) know how to make them, and when they did come to anything they had to use a "galvanic battery", which was very costly. So magnetic machines are pretty well useless, but if Papa will let me go to London for the holidays, and be generous when he does, the world will soon see something which will surprise them much more than either the steam engine or the Electric Light.'

Ferranti left school when he was seventeen. By that time he had already partly made the alternator which was to bring him fame. He had also made a small dynamo which he sold for £5 10s. 0d. As his father could not afford the fees for an apprenticeship or further training he looked around for a job in engineering. Eventually be was taken on in the experimental department of the Siemens works at Charlton, Woolwich, at £1 a week. 'There,' he said, 'I really got what I wanted. I was surrounded by dynamos and everything electrical. I felt entirely happy.'

Siemens Brothers and Co. Ltd., was already a large, prosperous, and progressive firm. It had built its name on cable making but had been making dynamos for some years and was going into 'the electric light' business on a large scale. In the year that Ferranti joined them Siemens installed the first public power station, to light the town of Godalming in Surrey. It was just then that it formed an experimental or research department to develop new equipment for 'the electric light'.

Ferranti wrote to his mother about his new life:

'. . . the room which I now inhabit is a top one, and is exactly opposite the works, at some little distance; on each side of them I can see the river. In the evening the left side has the sun on it and looks like a sheet of gold. . . . There is a very nice eating house a few doors lower down, at the corner, where I get everything that I require. I go to the works in the morning at 8.30 and leave for dinner at 1; return at 2 and leave finally at 6, so that I do not have a bit more than I care for and am rather sorry when the time comes to leave. The only thing which I should like would be to be a bit better paid; which I hope will be the case later on.

'But I must say that I have got a most fortunate place, that is I am alone with a very nice gentleman in the Experimental Department which is as good for me as if I was spending piles of money weekly on experiments. Our work is to try all the experiments for the Electric Light Department; also all the new machines and different combinations of different lamps; to measure the strengths of currents given out and horsepower absorbed by the same, etc. etc. Three workmen do all that we require or tell them to do, so that there is no hard work and we can keep fairly clean and are supposed to look and act as gentlemen only. . . . The principal thing that a thorough electrician wants, besides a good knowledge of electricity, is mathematics and algebra so that I will be very glad if you can send me all my books on these subjects as I will set to studying them.

'. . . In the evening I go for a walk in the beautiful country which lies at our back or go and sit down on the Charlton landing stage until bedtime.'

In the evenings Ferranti also attended evening classes at University College, London, where he heard lectures by Sir Oliver Lodge.

At the Siemens works he made himself so useful that he helped Sir William Siemens in his experiments with electric furnaces for making steel and met many of the electrical pioneers of the day. Within little more than a year of joining Siemens he had left the firm, taken out his first patents and become known as an inventor. In 1882 he had just finished the alternator and arc light he had started while still at school. He was introduced to a lawyer, Francis Ince, a prosperous city solicitor who had a good knowledge of electricity and a keen interest in its future at a time when London lived by gas light. He persuaded Ferranti to leave the Siemens works and to form a company to manufacture and sell the alternator. Ferranti, aged eighteen, was engineer to the company and held one share. However, Sir William Thomson (later Lord Kelvin, see Chapter Three), had invented a similar machine. It was agreed that the two inventions should be combined, that Thomson should receive a royalty of at least £500 per annum and the machine should be made as the Ferranti–Thomson dynamo. The name linked together the fifty-eight year-old famous scientist and the eighteen-year-old unknown electrician.

The Ferranti–Thomson dynamo made a sensation when it was demonstrated because it gave five times more output than any machine of its size, and it was very compact, measuring 24 inches by 20 inches by 18 inches and weighing only 11¾ cwt. Output was then measured by the number of incandescent lamps which could be lit; in this case it was 500. The new feature was the zig-zag form of armature winding made from a single strip of copper.

The Times reported the new dynamo on 22nd September, 1882.

'Electrical scientists have been diligently at work trying to improve upon the bulky and expensive dynamo machines now in use, and we understand that Sir William Thomson patented a new invention for a simpler and more efficient dynamo machine only a short time before an electrician in Messrs. Siemens establishment hit upon much the same thing. The great feature in the new machine is the absence of iron in the revolving armature, very greatly decreasing its weight, and, by enabling the field magnets to be brought very close together, greatly increasing its efficiency. In fact it is stated that a Ferranti machine to produce 10,000 incandescent lights can be manufactured for less than one-fifth of the cost of the cheapest dynamo at present before the public. The increased efficiency of the new machine is aided by the abolition of the commutator. The announcement of the new machine has been, we are informed, greeted with incredulity, and naturally some perturbation has been caused among those interested in existing dynamo machines. . . .'

The new company started a small factory at Finsbury which made dynamos and an electrolytic meter which Ferranti had invented. It installed a thousand-light dynamo in a hotel in Holborn. However after a year Ferranti bought back his own patents and started his own business in a small workshop on the top floor of 57b Hatton Garden in the City. He soon moved to larger premises in Charterhouse Square. Two years later, however, he was chief engineer of a small power station in New Bond Street. This is how it happened.

Very soon after Edison and Swan invented the incandescent lamp certain towns and some businessmen put forward lighting schemes. Each scheme was a local one, covering only a small area; it was not technically possible to light a large area from a central station. All the promoters had to obtain permission from Parliament by means of private bills. In 1879 there were thirty-four private bills before Parliament asking for authority to supply electricity and to break up the streets. It became clear that a standard policy was necessary or else every little electrical undertaking would go its own way and there would be chaos. As a result the Electric Lighting Act of 1882 was passed. It said that a private company or local government authority could be licensed to provide electricity but that any company's undertaking could be compulsorily bought by the local authority after twenty-one years if it wished to. No body supplying electricity could combine with another. Parliament wanted to ensure that private monopolies did not control 'the electric light' and exploit the consumer. The compulsory purchase discouraged businessmen from starting companies, and in fact Parliament preferred local authorities to supply electricity. However, so great was the interest in the new lighting that quite a number of power stations did very soon appear, but they were small stations normally serving a local thickly populated area.

As generation and supply began to go ahead the great question was, should the current be continuous or alternating? The argument about this went on for many years. It developed into the 'battle of the systems'. Some experts were for direct current, others for alternating. The strongest argument for direct current was that batteries could be used if the machinery broke down, which often happened. Also at night the load could be transferred to batteries and the generators shut down, with a saving in cost. When the Ferranti–Thomson dynamo appeared it strengthened the argument for alternating current.

One of the new small generating stations was at the Grosvenor Gallery in New Bond Street. This fashionable art gallery was mentioned in the Gilbert and Sullivan opera, *Patience:* 'a Grosvenor Gallery, greenery yallery, foot in the grave young man'.

The owner wanted to improve the lighting and early in 1883 he installed a portable plant in the yard to supply arc lamps. It consisted of two steam engines with belt drives on two separately excited single-phase 2,000-volt alternators. From this small beginning there grew, under Ferranti's leadership, a large electric supply company with the biggest generating station in the world. The Grosvenor Gallery plant became overloaded because neighbours were also supplied, by lines across the roof-tops. Then a generating station, using alternating current at high voltage, was installed under the Gallery; series transformers were supplied to each customer and fed by two generators, each of 250 kW. However, the system did not work at all well and customers complained about the breakdowns.

Ferranti was asked to help, and he completely changed the system according to his own ideas. These ideas revolutionized electrical supply and became generally used throughout the industry later on. He converted the whole system from series to parallel, with transformers of his own design, stepping down 2,400 volts. He also replaced the machines by two 750-hp alternators, which he designed and built specially, each capable of supplying ten thousand lamps, probably about 400 kW. They were enormous for their time, each weighing 33½ tons, and running independently. 'The method adopted for bringing the separate machines in to service required both skill and courage. When an already loaded machine had reached the limit of its capacity a second set was run up to speed and, by means of dog clutches and a countershaft, was coupled up for use. When the speed was exactly right the operator brought the claws of the clutch into engagement, feeling his way in so as to effect a smooth transition . . .' From a tower on top of the Gallery five separate circuits radiated; the overhead network was remodelled for parallel working.

Ferranti carried all this out in a few months. The Grosvenor Gallery station became completely successful, and before long the system spread from the Thames to Regent's Park and from Kensington to the Law Courts. Ferranti had now started the practice of generating and transmitting electrical energy at high voltage although the battle between a.c. and d.c. had hardly begun.

The Grosvenor Gallery site was cramped and dirty and the increased demand could not be met. The directors therefore decided to build a very much larger generating station. They were influenced by Ferranti's ideas. He said that, if electricity supply was to grow, there must be large central stations outside the densely populated areas, where land was cheap, water was available, and coal could be brought in easily. These stations would serve large areas like London, and use high-pressure current. A new company was formed in August 1887, the London Electric Supply Corporation, of which Ferranti was chief engineer and electrician, and half a million pounds was invested. He chose a site at Deptford, about eight miles from London, on the south bank of the Thames where sea-borne coal could be brought in and the river water was available for condensing. This was quite against the usual practice of placing stations inside the load area. But Ferranti aimed to supply all London north of the Thames with sub-stations in London.

The Deptford power station was many times bigger than any before. Ferranti designed the whole station except the roof, and the machinery was built there under his supervision. He was one of the very few engineers of that day who said that transmission should be at high voltages. He decided to have the unheard of pressure of 10,000 volts at a time when no machinery or cable had been made for more than 2,500 volts. In view of the uncertainty, he gave a demonstration at the Grosvenor Gallery in which he stepped up the 2,400 volts there with an experimental transformer to 10,000 volts. Nothing like Deptford had ever been tried and it was no wonder that many critics said it was bound to fail. Ferranti was only twenty-four and he was in sole charge of the huge enterprise.

First of all quayside facilities, a concrete raft, 40,000 feet square and four feet thick to carry the heavy machinery, and a layout for handling coal and ash had to be built. During 1888 and 1889, the first part of the plant was installed. It included two 5,000-volt Ferranti alternators driven by two 1,250-hp engines, and 80 boilers working at the unprecedented pressure of 200 pounds per square inch. Ferranti planned to put in four more 10,000-volt alternators each coupled to a 10,000-hp engine. In October 1888 the Press was invited to see the progress made. The *Electrical Engineer* wrote:

'On Wednesday the designer of the great Deptford installation was laughingly dubbed the Michelangelo of that installation, because from first to last, from foundation to top of highest turret, architecture, materials, foundations and machines, all were specified and designed by one man, and the credit of the success of the really first central station in England, will have to be given, without detracting one iota in favour of any other person, to Ferranti. It required some courage to jump from supplying tens to supplying hundreds of thousands of lamps, to put electric lighting on the same footing as gas lighting, to supply an area as large as that supplied by the largest gas company. It required not only courage on the part of the engineer, but also a degree of confidence in himself that few men possess in the earlier days of industrial development.'

During these busy months of 1888 Ferranti, who was being paid a good salary, married the daughter of the lawyer who had encouraged him from the beginning. While the turmoil of construction continued he frequently slept in a cottage on the site.

By mid 1889 the power station was under steam. However as soon as everything was ready to send current to London the first of several setbacks occurred. The cables which had been made under contract and laid along the parapet walls of the railway tracks and bridges were not able to take the high-pressure current. In this emergency Ferranti made new mains himself, some 30 miles in length. Typically, he broke from previous practice and used wax-impregnated paper for insulation, thus starting a new type of high-voltage cable. Twenty years later he described it:

'The inner conductor consisted of a copper tube . . . insulated by means of ordinary brown paper soaked in ozokerite or black earth wax, which was a residue obtained in candle-making. The effectiveness of the insulation was the result of a very large number of layers of this wax-coated paper which were interposed between two conductors. The outer copper tube was slipped over the roll of paper and then the whole main was drawn through a die in a heavy tube draw bench and so squeezed very tightly down upon the paper. This made a solid structure from a mechanical point of view and thoroughly protected the paper. The outer conductor was then insulated in the same way and fitted tightly into the outside wrought iron pipe which was used as a means of protection. These mains were set to work on 10,000 volts pressure in 1889 and were the first extra high-tension mains which I believe were ever laid underground.' These mains were still being used in 1910.

The second setback was far more serious. Government

control placed a fatal handicap on Ferranti's plan to supply London. The Electric Lighting Act of 1882 (mentioned earlier) with its compulsory purchase at the end of twenty-one years was amended by an Act of 1888 which increased the period to forty-two years. This encouraged many new electricity companies to compete for supply areas. As a result, in 1889, the government allocated districts to various rival companies, where they could build small generating stations. The government merely continued what was happening everywhere except at Deptford. It was also still afraid of monopolies in lighting. As a result the area allocated to the London Electric Supply Corporation was much smaller than Ferranti had planned for, and nearly all the valuable City area was given to his main rival. It became clear that the Deptford station could not go ahead as planned. In the following year there was another blow when the Grosvenor Gallery was burned down and the sub-station was out of use for several months. Ferranti himself was still under attack for using alternating current. The famous Edison had visited Deptford and he advocated direct current.

Thus in 1891 the directors of the L.E.S.C., short of money, decided not to develop the Deptford Station further as Ferranti had planned. They abandoned the giant 10,000-volt 10,000-hp engines and alternators which he was already building. He left the Corporation in that year. The Scots chairman said, 'You are a very clever man, Mr. Ferranti, but I'm thinking Ye're sadly lacking in prevision . . .'. Ferranti, now twenty-seven, went back to his manufacturing firm in Charterhouse Square. The Deptford power station continued to work and after fourteen years it began to make a profit.

Ferranti had the last word in the controversy. He said:

'. . . in the future our railways will be worked, our lighting will be done, our power will be transmitted to a great distance; all this will be done entirely by the aid of High Pressure Electricity; it is high pressure in electricity like high pressure in steam, which is going to carry – which is carrying – everything before it, and this high pressure will be used, and will be doing the work of the world when the low pressure system . . . has passed away and been forgotten.'

For the next three years Ferranti had a hard struggle to make his firm successful. The electrical industry in Britain did not expand as fast as the pioneers had hoped ten years before, not nearly as fast as in America. He had to travel all over the country to get orders and raise loans to finance his business.

Soon the firm prospered. Ferranti's name was sufficient to bring orders for the alternators, transformers, switchgear and meters which his firm made. The business grew so much that in 1896 it was moved to a larger factory at Hollinwood, Lancashire. Before then, Ferranti had designed and supplied the whole plant for the power station of Portsmouth Corporation. At first the Corporation had meant to have low-tension direct current but changed its mind in favour of high-tension alternating current. The plant included the first slow-speed, direct-coupled alternators at 300 kW, 2,000 volts, 96 rev/min. At the opening ceremony the names of Franklin, Faraday and Ferranti were linked together. He had also equipped many generating stations abroad, notably in Paris, Nancy, and Le Havre.

Ferranti and his family moved to Oldham, and he tried to electrify cotton spinning, which then and for many years after used steam power, but the mechanical problems were never solved although he continued working on them for thirty years. In 1903 Ferranti's firm was again in financial difficulty. It was wound up and the new firm of Ferranti Ltd. was established, in which Ferranti remained a director but was no longer chairman as before. He returned to the chairmanship of the firm twenty-five years later; by that time the firm had grown several times bigger. In between, during the First World War, it made handsome profits from munitions. Ferranti used his skill and energy for the war effort and converted the factory to making shells. After the war, turning to radio, he invented improvements in audio-frequency transformers and Ferranti Ltd. entered that rapidly growing industry. He had always campaigned for electricity to be used to lighten domestic chores, three years before he died he patented a radiant fire.

Society gave Ferranti its highest scientific honours in recognition of his vision and achievement. The Institution of Electrical Engineers elected him president for two successive years and awarded him the Faraday medal; the University of Manchester gave him the honorary degree of Doctor of Science; and the Royal Society elected him a Fellow. In his Faraday lecture at the end of his life he said '. . . Today we are all trying to work less and to get more, to expand less energy or to take less trouble; to do things more easily. Well, the really attractive feature of electricity is that it makes these ideas possible.'

THE ELECTRICAL WORKERS (1890–1900)

The beginning of electric light in people's homes, even though it was only in the houses of the rich, and of central generation and supply meant that more electricians and new skills were required. The Electrical Trades Union, which had been started by electric light and telephone wiremen, was able to recruit some of the new men. The E.T.U. was formed in 1889, the year in which Ferranti's Deptford power station first got under steam. Although it made a good start with 1,123 members in 1890, it had a hard struggle to recruit members. Five years later the membership had fallen as low as 236, although it soon recovered.

The E.T.U.'s motto, which it took over from the Amalgamated Society of Engineers was 'Defence not Defiance'. This was its outlook, as expressed by its executive committee, in its first year or two of existence:

'We were told by many that a Union was not required; we ask, has the first year's work of a union justified us in forming a Society for electrical workers? Look at the benefits paid out; notably that of Unemployed Benefit. There is something much more important than the amount paid. It is the fact that this benefit creates an independence amongst men; it prevents men through unfortunate circumstances from selling his labour below its value to unscrupulous employers, who are ever willing to take advantage of a depressed market, even to buying men's labour to the detriment of their more fortunate brethren, who may be employed.

'Again, Accident Benefits, just think what have been done; prevented men and their families from becoming pauperized by appealing to their parish authorities, also by obviating the necessity of getting rid of household effects to raise the wherewithal to support body and soul . . . We have been called on to use influence in obtaining better wages and conditions. If not obtaining all we required in every case we have at least obtained improved concessions. Notably, in the case of London, where electrical operatives, union and non-union, have ample cause to be thankful, in Manchester substantial increases have been obtained, likewise in Liverpool, Leeds, Dewsbury, Sheffield, Belfast and many other districts.'

One of the most important arguments of the time had already been settled for the time being:

'In the formation of this union, differences of opinion occurred over the question of admitting all classes of labour, skilled and unskilled, into our ranks. It was decided to admit all who performed any part, however menial, in this great industry, and in looking back on our past record we see no cause to regret the action taken.'

The E.T.U. was soon involved in disputes with employers. They were usually about wages, hours of work and recognition of the union. Their first strike, in 1891, was against the Brighton district of the National Telephone Company. Fourteen men, mostly telephone wiremen, but including some armature winders and light wiremen, formed a branch and demanded better wages and shorter hours. The company was ready to reduce hours by one per week but the men handed in their notice. What happened then is told by the union general secretary:

'We encountered a great deal of trouble from the unskilled workers, army reserve men and others of which Brighton can provide a fair sample. The sending away of such men ran us into considerable expense. The second week of the strike saw a special gang of experienced men drawn from various towns on the Kent coast but owing to the energy of our pickets, who intercepted them 30 miles from Brighton, and gave them good advice, they only arrived there to refuse to become blacklegs. They left Brighton amongst cheers and hearty wishes of a number of strikers and several friends.

'We were gradually but surely defeating the District Authorities; when one or two of our members began to waver . . . like a great many men who have never travelled any distance they would sooner lick their chains at home, than become free men away . . . it is doubtful whether it is not as well to get rid of such persons before you gain the day, as it is notorious that such men as soon as they get their purposes served inevitably desert the means by which it was gained.'

After a month on strike the men failed to get what they wanted and went back to work. They had been given money from members all over the country, including those in the Ediswan factory at Ponders End, London.

The following year however the first victory was won when the union members in Belfast refused to work overtime without the overtime rate. The employers, again the National Telephone Company, locked them out and tried hard to import blacklegs but the only two they got were 'removed from the town'. After a short time the men got the overtime rate. They meant to 'make our Society the admiration of electrical operatives throughout the Kingdom'. But the Belfast men were told by the union leaders that 'it is absolutely necessary that we should act prudently and not be led away by impulsive action'.

It was a hard struggle to build the union against hostility and apathy. For instance in 1895, after the lamp makers and exhausters at the Edison and Swan works, Ponders End, had won a strike for better wages, the local union branch collapsed because the members were 'too busy working overtime to attend to branch affairs'. The next year the electrical wiremen employed by the Sheffield Electric Light and Power Company were told that they would be sacked if they joined the union and so it was impossible to form a branch there. In 1897 the union had to show great determination when it gained an agreement with Thos. Parker Ltd., a manufacturer in Wolverhampton. The union demand was for a minimum wage of 26s. for all men over twenty who had been in the trade for one year. The then general secretary and a six-man deputation gained an interview:

'Mr Parker at first refused to allow the secretary to speak on the main question, and tried to intimidate the deputation, but finding that they were not frightened and stuck to their demands, he allowed the secretary to state the case on behalf of the union and contented himself with a sharp cross examination of the members of the deputation. Finally he decided to give his answer to our request by the end of the week but emphatically refused to communicate his reply to the secretary who has much pleasure in testifying to the splendid spirit shown by the members of the deputation in refusing to allow Mr. Parker to bully or browbeat them.'

The minimum wage was agreed and the branch grew to sixty-three members. This success encouraged the Wolverhampton men to try recruiting the women workers. A considerable number of them were employed on winding, many doing the same work as the men but receiving only ten shillings a week. But in spite of help from the Women's Trade Union League there was no success with the women.

By the last year of the nineteenth century there were a number of power stations in the country; Ferranti had installed the Portsmouth alternators in 1894. More electrical workers were needed for them, new skills and new trades arose. Among the members of the E.T.U. there now appeared, as well as armature winders and builders, dynamo erectors, fitters, and attendants; instrument, switch and appliance makers, coil winders, commutator builders, cable jointers. One dispute was with the British Transformer Company, in Harrow Road, London. (The winders demanded a minimum rate of 9d an hour and abolition of the piecework and bonus system.) At the great Siemens works at Charlton, a meeting was held outside the factory gates, and watched by Alexander Siemens himself. The expansion of the industry caused the E.T.U. to change its objects: it found it desirable to gain recognition of the electrician as a craftsman and in 1899 it resolved:

'to prevent further encroachments on trade rights and privileges; to establish an apprentice system, and a higher standard of skill . . . to cultivate feelings of friendship among men of our craft, to settle all disputes between employers and employees by arbitration (where possible), to assist each other in sickness and distress, to secure employment, to reduce the hours of daily labour, to secure adequate pay for our work, and by legal and proper means to elevate the moral, intellectual and social conditions of all members . . .'

It then formed an apprentice section of the union. At the same time it refused to adopt socialism as its policy. There was trouble over boys and apprentices. A colliery company at Bradford was guilty of 'sending a lad to a firm of electrical engineers to learn the main points in winding and at the same time alluding to the possibilities of him supplementing a fully-priced man'. Employers were obliged to agree to a fixed number of apprentices to each man; at Salford it was one apprentice to every six winders and one to every four wiremen.

In its struggle to improve wages the E.T.U. brought pressure to bear on the county and town councils for which manufacturers were installing plant. The London County Council agreed to insist that a firm on contract to install electric light in the fire brigade headquarters should pay the union rates. Such agreements did not always work. When the union complained in 1899 to West Ham Council that Ferranti Ltd. was trying to evade the trade union clauses in its contract Ferranti had to withdraw its tender for a lighting installation. Although Ferranti still refused to pay the union rates the Council gave it the contract when it put in a second tender. When private firms undertook contracts for local government the union could have some control through Parliament. The Engineers' and Electrical Workers' Parliamentary and Industrial Affairs Committee was watching Ferranti and Johnson and Phillips in 1899, so that it could, if necessary, object to their being given contracts. The union used the same method against a firm when it inquired into the character of its employees; it decided:

'That the general secretary be instructed to wait upon the Anglo-American Brush Corporation in conjunction with the Amalgamated Society of Engineers if possible and inform the firm that if the "Character Note System" is not dispensed with we shall be compelled to oppose them when tendering for government and municipal contracts.' Applicants for employment were asked to give their age, where they were last employed, how long they were there, and the reasons for leaving.

During these first ten years of its existence, the E.T.U. was always anxious to have a reputation as a serious, respectable, trade union with professional standards of behaviour. It reprimanded its officers if they behaved incorrectly in disputes:

'That the executive committee having discussed the Bolton strike and the manner in which Brother Senior has conducted the business with the corporation representatives, consider his conduct deserving of severe censure and record their disapproval of his action and general negligence.' The union stressed that its members must behave properly at work if the union was to flourish. If a member did not obey the orders of his foreman (especially if the foreman was a union member) he would not have the union's support. The following appeal was addressed to all members in 1900:

'We have had before us on several occasions complaints from employers as to the bad time-keeping of some of our members, and we wish to point out to those members who are guilty of this offence that their conduct tends to bring discredit upon the Union. We hope for the Union's sake they will try to improve, and also when at work that they will take more interest in what they have to do and prove to the employers that it is to their advantage to employ Union men.'

By the beginning of the twentieth century the E.T.U. had succeeded in raising the agreed wage rates for electricians to 9½d. an hour in London and district rates were being built up to 8d. to 9d. an hour in the provinces. Fifty-three or fifty-four hours per week was the general rule.

This was a little more than the wage of an engineering fitter or turner and several shillings less than the average wage of a railway engine driver.

The telegraph workers were in quite a different position. As we saw in the previous chapter, they were employees of the Post Office and their struggle to build a useful trade union was more difficult. Ever since the Post Office had taken over the telegraphs it had lost money on them. It introduced a 6d. telegram without success and the deficit grew larger; the profit on letters covered the loss on telegrams. This made it difficult to get better wages for the telegraph workers. All the same the newly formed Engineering and Stores Association put forward to the Post Office in 1896 its claims on behalf of the men. Its members were employed in the Engineer in Chief's department of the Post Office. The work they did was mainly of two kinds – construction of telegraph lines, and maintenance. In outdoor construction the labourers were paid 26s. to 33s. a week, and their foremen 29s. to 40s. a week. A construction gang also included some skilled men. For instance a gang of ten who were renewing telegraph poles at Jedburgh in Scotland in 1899 was composed of the foreman, a leading wireman, three wiremen, a lineman and four labourers.

It was the linemen who expressed their grievances in 1896. What they wanted is shown by the following petition:

'*To his Lordship, the Chairman, and Committee appointed to enquire into the Grievances of the Post Office Servants*

We, the undersigned Linemen, employed on the Post Office Telegraphs, do hereby most respectfully ask that the following grievances which we complain of may be favourably considered and redressed:

1. That our hours of duty may be 8 hours per day, or 48 hours per week, instead of as at present, 9 per day or 50½ hours per week, or if the occasion requires it, 60 hours per week.
2. That when we are asked to be on duty more than 8 hours per day, that we may be paid overtime for it.
3. That our rate of travelling allowance be increased from 1½d. per hour to 2d. per hour.
4. That the time for claiming allowance counts from leaving the Post Office until returning back thereto.
5. That all Linemen, after their appointment, receive 2s. per week per year as increment until they reach the maximum of 40s. per week, then that they be placed on the Senior Linemen Roll until they reach 50s. per week.
6. That Senior Linemen, who possess a knowledge sufficient to warrant them being raised to the position of Inspector or Engineer, be so promoted.

7. We Linemen, looking back for a period of 25 years, think it a great hardship that not one of our class has been so promoted.
8. Linemen are a class of men who must, as a natural consequence, acquire both a technical and a practical knowledge of repairing Instruments, fixing Instruments, testing out faults of all kinds, building lines, and securing the same at every point and corner. We therefore fail to see what other capability or quality is required in a man to be promoted from Lineman to the rank of Engineer. It is from the Lineman that the Engineer derives the most of his information. We therefore think the Lineman has as much right to promotion as any test clerk or anybody else.
9. That our Annual Leave be three weeks instead of two, as at present.
10. That we be paid £1 1s. od. for Boots, the same as Postmen. We think this an important item and hope it may be conceded.
11. That with regard to our Uniform Cap we are of the same opinion as our fellow-linemen in other districts – that it makes men the laughing stock of others – and that an entire suit should be given or none.
12. In conclusion, we Linemen express a hope that the above claims may be favourably considered and receive due justice. We have just cause for expressing these concluding remarks. There is not another class of Government Servants but who do gradually rise to superior positions except us Linemen who, for the long period of 25 years cannot, to our knowledge, cite a case wherein a Lineman has been promoted to a superior rank.

Finally, we express a hope that the meaningless word "Lineman" may be changed to that of "Inspector".'

Three men gave evidence to the committee on behalf of their workmates – Edgar H. Morgan, Daniel Joseph Gorry and Robert W. Holliday. Morgan had started work at the age of ten; as the boy who carried the firepot and tools for the linemen he was paid 12s. a week. After twenty-six years his wage as a senior lineman was 35s. He described his responsibilities:

'The number of battery cells of various forms under a

lineman's care may be 500 or 600, scattered over an area of many miles, and to clean and to refresh these he has to convey to each office in his section from time to time the necessary tools, chemicals, and elements necessary for the work, often walking six or seven miles from one office to another with a heavy basket of stores. And in maintenance work he has to carry in the same way the insulators necessary to replace broken ones. Another very laborious and difficult part of his work being the trimming of trees overhanging the lines with a special apparatus supplied for the purpose. As regards indoor work, a lineman is expected to be able to fit up any kind of apparatus. He must also be able to send and receive on at least two systems, and to detect and rectify instrument faults quickly, very often performing the work of a skilled mechanic; and to emphasize the extremely varied nature of his work, it is no exaggeration to say that the same man may be seen repairing a delicate instrument in the morning and digging a hole for a telegraph pole in the afternoon, in the latter case getting his clothes covered with clay and dirt, or creosote from the poles.'

Gorry was a junior lineman who had started as a labourer on 23s. per week fifteen years before. He argued for a higher subsistence allowance as well as wages:

'If the sufferings of these men were known, I am sure the heads of the Department would do something to make their lot a little easier. Imagine men, after working on poles, digging, or drawing wire across fields all day in wet weather, going to a lodging with all his clothes wet, and no means of getting them dried, because the poor people with whom these men lodge cannot afford to burn coals late into the night to dry men's clothes who, perhaps, only pay them 6d. or 8d. per night for a bed; consequently they often have to put on the same wet clothes the following morning. I can safely say that this is true, because during the nine or ten years that I was working in the gangs I often underwent these painful, unpleasant, and dangerous experiences. More than a quarter of his wages is lost to him each week, viz., about 3s. for railway fares to and from his home at the week end, 3s. for his bed while away, and if he receives 23s. per week, which is a very common wage,

17s. is left for his wife and children's support; not only that, but he will take away with him on Monday mornings six or seven shillings' worth of groceries for his own consumption during the week. Is it right that these men should be paid so badly?'

The Post Office gave the linemen an increase in their subsistence allowance from 1½d. to 2d. per hour, and increased their wages slightly. These were now from 24s. per week with yearly increments of 1s. 6d. per week up to 42s. per week.

Additional Reading

M.E.S. and K.R.S., *Sir Joseph Wilson Swan, F.R.S.*, Benn, 1929.

The Electrical Trades Union, *The Story of the E.T.U.*, 1952.

John Golding, *75 Years: A Short History of the Post Office Engineering Union*, P.O.E.U., 1963.

Matthew Josephson, *Edison*, Eyre & Spottiswoode, 1961.

Arthur Ridding, *S. Z. de Ferranti, Pioneer of Electrical Development*, H.M.S.O., 1964.

Ferranti Ltd., *Centenary of Sebastian Ziani de Ferranti.*

P. Dunsheath, *A History of Electrical Engineering*, Faber & Faber, 1947.

CHAPTER SIX

Radio

RADIO is short for radio telegraphy, or telegraphy by radiation; telegraphy by electric current has been described in Chapter Two.

The three men who did most to produce radio, were Guglielmo Marconi, the Italian, Sir John Ambrose Fleming, the Englishman, and Lee de Forest, the American, who called himself the father of radio. Like all inventors and scientists they built on the ideas of other men before them. The most important of their forerunners were James Clerk Maxwell, the Scottish mathematician, and Heinrich Hertz, the German physicist. The whole story of the beginning of radio lasts over a period of forty-two years, from 1864 when Maxwell stated the existence of electromagnetic waves to 1906 when Lee de Forest invented the triode valve.

Let us first look at the forerunners. James Clerk Maxwell was born in Edinburgh in 1831, the son of John Clerk, brother of Sir George Clerk of Penicuik, Midlothian. John Clerk took the name of Maxwell when he inherited an estate in Kircudbrightshire from the Maxwell family. In 1871 the seventh duke of Devonshire, who was not only Chancellor of Cambridge University but also a mathematician, gave the money to pay for a professor of experimental physics there. Maxwell, then forty, became the first professor in the subject and organized the famous Cavendish Laboratory.

Before he went to the Cavendish Laboratory Maxwell made the great discovery which marks him as a forerunner of radio. In 1864 he showed that in theory electromagnetic waves could travel through space and at the speed of light. He worked out four differential equations as the basis for the electromagnetic theory. These are the famous Maxwell equations. Eight years after Maxwell died the German physicist, Hertz, proved by experiment that Maxwell's theory was correct.

Heinrich Hertz was born at Hamburg in 1857. At first he

trained as an engineer but then specialized in physics at Berlin University. He was a student of Helmholtz who, as we have seen in Chapter Four, influenced Alexander Graham Bell. Hertz was a university teacher and research worker all his life. In his experiments to test the existence of electromagnetic waves Hertz used a spark oscillator as transmitter and a coil with a tiny gap in it as receiver. Sparks across the gap showed that the receiver had picked up the waves from the transmitter. It was 1887 when he demonstrated that this radiation existed. The waves became known as Hertzian waves. Hertz himself never had any idea that they could be used for radio communication.

Before Marconi could carry out radio communication in practice improvements to Hertz's discovery were necessary. A more sensitive detector of the radio waves than Hertz's spark gap was required, and this need was met when a few years later Sir Oliver Lodge produced his 'coherer'. In Russia Alexander Popov, of St. Petersburg University, followed up Hertz's discovery before Marconi did. He was the first man to use an aerial on the transmitter and in 1897 he could send signals from ship to shore over a distance of three miles. In fact the U.S.S.R. has always claimed that it was Popov, not Marconi, who invented radio telegraphy.

GUGLIELMO MARCONI (1874–1937)

Marconi was born in Bologna, an ancient university town, the second son of an Italian father and an Irish mother. Marconi's father owned an estate of fields and vineyards with a fine large old house at Pontecchio, eleven miles from Bologna. Marconi's mother, Anne Jameson, from County Wexford, was the daughter of one of the founders of the famous firm of whisky distillers. The two met while she was studying singing in Italy. They married much against the wishes of her parents who did not want their daughter to marry a man seventeen years older than herself, a widower with a young child, and a foreigner. Guglielmo was born nine years after their first son.

He spent most of his childhood in the big stone house, Villa Grifoni, at Pontecchio, surrounded by its estate, approached by an avenue of chestnut trees from the road. Marconi was a solitary boy, without companions, except for his brother nine years older than he, and his mother with whom he was very close. He was happy playing by himself, fishing was a favourite hobby, and there were plenty of books to read. Electricity began to interest him as a boy, after he had read a life of Benjamin Franklin. He became absorbed in making experiments but this annoyed his father who resented his son wasting time and money in this way and broke up his apparatus. His father found him an unsatisfactory son, but his mother protected him and taught him herself, with the help of a tutor, until he was twelve.

His first school, at Florence, at the age of twelve, was an ordeal. Shy and reserved, he suffered mockery from the boys, but this did not last long. When the family spent the next winter at Leghorn Marconi went to the Technical Institute there. The physics he learnt fascinated him so much that his mother arranged for him to have private lessons from a professor at a local college. Years after Marconi remembered 'the clear and practical method with which Professor Rosas started me in the study of electro physics'. By a strange coincidence at about the same time he met an old telegraphist who taught him the Morse code.

From that time on Marconi had little time for anything but his experiments with electricity. (The exception was music, in which he followed his mother, and he became a competent pianist, often accompanying his mother as she sang.) He had no instruction in electrical techniques and learned on his own the principles of transmission of currents and electrical wiring. Help came from his mother when she introduced him to Professor Righi, a famous physicist at Bologna University, with whom he had many discussions. He could also use the University library.

The turning point in Marconi's life work came when he was twenty. In the spring of 1894, while he and his brother were on holiday in the Italian Alps, he read an article in an electrical journal in which Righi described his discoveries with Hertzian waves. Righi had shown, among other things, that the shorter waves, at least, could be reflected in the same way as light waves. Marconi read about the simple apparatus which

Hertz had used and the use of reflectors to strengthen weak sparks. The article fired his imagination.

On his return home Marconi hurried to see Professor Righi and ask his advice about the possible practical use of his discoveries for radio communication. However Righi was not encouraging. He told Marconi that it was necessary to know more about the theory first; the Hertzian waves were nothing new, they had been known about for eight years and there was a great deal more to learn. He pointed out that the short waves seemed to fade away in the upper air; long waves might be better for radio communication but no one knew how to create electrical impulses to send waves long enough to travel any considerable distance.

Marconi was not discouraged. His mother saw that he needed a laboratory and she allowed him to use the top floor of the villa where formerly silk worms had been kept. In December 1894 he began his first experiments. 'It seemed to me,' he wrote later, 'that if the radiation could be increased, developed and controlled, it would be possible to signal across space for a considerable distance. My chief trouble was that the idea was so elementary, so simple in logic, that it seemed difficult to believe no one had thought of putting it into practice. I argued there must be more mature scientists who had followed the same line of thought and arrived at almost similar conclusions. In fact, Oliver Lodge had, but he missed the correct answer by a fraction. From the first the idea was so real to me that I did not realize that to others, the theory might appear quite fantastic.'

In fact, unknown to Marconi, a number of scientists had been very close to the idea and had even suggested it. In the meantime, however, in spite of his doubts and his father's refusal to waste any money on his son's efforts, Marconi managed to collect pieces of apparatus and made progress. One day in the winter of 1894–95 he revealed his secret to a girl friend of his childhood; she remembered the incident:

'. . . we found our way upstairs to the top of the house where Guglielmo's workroom was. I looked round. In every direction there were white jars and curious-looking pots full of water, etc. "Well, Guglielmo, there is nothing much to see here.

What have you invented?" I asked. I have forgotten to mention two curious carved pieces of wood which I saw lying in the next room, covered with tin, and which Guglielmo called "reflectors". "Well, come and look here," said my cousin. "Do you see this needle?" On receiving my answer in the affirmative, he added: "Then look, I will put it on this table." He then took a small mariner's compass and put it at the opposite side of the room where the needle was lying, saying: "Now look, I will make that needle move without touching it." I looked well to see that there was no wire near the needle, or anything to connect it to the compass. Guglielmo then seated himself before an ordinary electric pear-shaped glass bulb (the ones we see daily) from which a blue light played. He touched the small globe, and in an instant both the needle and the compass began to move instantaneously. At first I could not believe my eyes. I walked from the needle to the compass, and tried in vain to find a very fine wire (even as fine as a hair) in communication, but there was simply nothing. I thought Guglielmo was joking and in a moment we would hear a burst of laughter and see him thoroughly enjoying my stupidity, but nothing of the kind happened. He was in fact more than ordinarily serious and quiet, and seemed to be pondering over something.'

From that time onward Marconi worked fast. The year 1895 was his wonderful year. He increased the range of reception to the whole length of the house and then to include the lower floors of the house. Then at last his father was persuaded that there were possibilities in his son's experiments and he gave encouragement and money. Now he could really go ahead. Here is his own picture of his early experiments:

'I reproduced with rather rudimentary means an oscillator similar to that used by Righi; I likewise reproduced a resonator using as a detector of the electrical waves a tube of glass with pulverized metal based on much that was already published by Hughes, Calzecchi-Omesti, Branly and Lodge. By means of slabs of curved zinc I formed two reflectors which I placed one in front of the other at the maximum height permitted by my laboratory. At the centre of the far room I put the detector of the electric waves and bound this to a battery.'

Marconi set about improving his apparatus. First he tackled the coherer or detector. After many experiments he found the best results came from a mixture of nickel and silver filings carefully sifted and mixed, of which the silver was five per cent. These were placed between two silver plugs sealed into a glass tube which was exhausted of air. But it was still a clumsy device. The filings clung together each time an electrical impulse was received and it was necessary to tap the tube in order to loosen them for the next impulse. Marconi saw a way round this:

'To shake the metal filings automatically I inserted a lodestone in the origin of the voltmeter circuit. This commanded a little clapper, placed where it could serve as a contact with the tube containing the filings. Every time I sent a train of electric waves, the clapper touched the tube and so restored the detector at once to its pristine state of sensibility.'

This device made it possible to send impulses rapidly and without pauses.

But in the meantime he wanted to see if he could send radio signals outdoors as well as in the house. In order to do this, he thought, he had to increase the wavelengths many times. Later on he described how he solved this problem:

'In my first experiments outdoors towards the end of September, 1895, I considered increasing the dimensions of the transmitter in order to get waves longer than any that had been used up to that time – waves thirty or forty metres long. With this in view, I replaced the two outside balls of the Righi oscillator (which had four) with two slabs of sheet iron I got by breaking up an old tank. I did the same thing to the resonator.

'I found out then how to obtain waves at distances of hundreds of metres. By chance I held one of the metal slabs at a considerable height above the ground and set the other on the earth.

'With this arrangement the signals became so strong that they permitted me to increase the sending distance to a kilometre.

'Next I thought of substituting copper wires for the slab

that I had suspended in the air. These I separated from one another by wooden spokes. The slab on the ground I replaced with a piece of copper, buried in the earth. Once more the effect was impressive.'

This was Marconi's great contribution to radio – the invention of a long-wave transmitter far more effective than anything before. It then occurred to him to do the same thing for the receiver as for the transmitter. He connected also the coherer, or detector, to an aerial and to the earth. His use of two sets of aerials and earths was the starting point of radio telegraphy.

During September 1895 Marconi carried out tests over greater and greater distances. His brother carried the receiver across the large garden with the help of one of the estate farmers, and while Marconi sent the signals his brother waved a white handkerchief on a pole to show that he had received them. The final test was whether it could work over a hill. 'I knew my invention would have no importance,' he wrote later, 'unless it could make communication possible over natural obstacles like hills and mountains.' His brother, armed with a rifle, carried the receiver out of sight over a hill behind the house, helped by the farmer and the carpenter, and set it down a kilometre away. Marconi remembered the event; he wrote:

'After some minutes I started to send, manipulating the Morse Key connected to the Ruhmkorff bobbin. In the distance a shot echoed down the valley.'

After much family discussion Marconi wrote to the Minister in the government responsible for posts and telegraphs, offering the use of his invention. But the Minister could find no use for it. Italy had just suffered the military disaster of Adowa when her army was massacred by an Abyssinian force, and she had to say goodbye for the time being to her dream of a colonial empire. No doubt the government had other things to think about. But the result was that England gained the new invention. Marconi decided to go to England as the chief seafaring nation where, if anywhere, there would be uses for radio.

Marconi and his mother set out from Bologna, with the

radio apparatus. A disaster occurred when they went through the English customs shed. The officials regarded with great suspicion Marconi's black box which contained his apparatus. Italian anarchists were known to be active; the French President had been murdered two years before; in fact the King of Italy was to suffer the same fate four years later. The customs men dismantled the radio apparatus and it could not be re-assembled.

After they had taken lodgings in the respectable middle-class neighbourhood of Bayswater Marconi set about preparing his patent specification. After several months' hard work he submitted the provisional specification, which began – 'According to this invention electrical actions or manifestations are transmitted through the air, earth or water by means of electric oscillations of high frequency.' It was followed by the complete specification for 'Improvements in Transmitting Electrical Impulses and Signals, and an Apparatus therefore', and the patent was granted in July 1897.

'Having established my priority in this new system of communication,' said Marconi, 'my next thought was how to launch my invention. After much consultation my parents and I were advised to obtain, before all else, a favourable opinion from a person of indisputable public authority.' Such a person was W. H. Preece, Engineer-in-Chief of the engineering department of the Post Office, who twenty years before had brought over Bell's telephone.

Fortunately for Marconi the Post Office had a keen interest in radio since it owned, wholly or in part, most of the short sea telegraph cables and it worked closely with the big companies which owned the ocean cables. A boy assistant in the Post Office left an eye-witness account of Marconi's all-important first visit to his chief:

'The Chief came along and as we entered the room I noticed that everything was just as left, with the exception of a piece of paper which had been placed under the contact of the telegraph key. This was removed and after one or two preliminary adjustments to the connections and brass balls by Mr. Marconi, the key was depressed and immediately the bell on the adjacent tube commenced and continued to ring.

Mr. Marconi then went over to the glass tube, gave this a few sharp taps and the bell ceased ringing. I knew by the Chief's quiet manner and smile that something unusual had been effected. The following day and the rest of the week experiments were run off.'

From that time Preece gave Marconi full support on behalf of the Post Office, if only because he saw the possibility of helping ships in distress. On Salisbury Plain, with similar equipment to that used in Italy, signals were transmitted over distances of several miles, in the presence of army and navy experts.

The next step was to see if the transmission would carry over sea as well as land. Accordingly in the spring of 1897 Marconi went down to the Bristol Channel. The points chosen were from Lavernock Point near Penarth to Flat Holm Island and from there to Brean Down in Somerset, over a distance of 8½ miles. First signals were successfully received at Brean Down from the island and then from Lavernock. For this test Marconi used kites to take up the aerials.

His fame had now spread to Italy and his native land which had rejected his invention now found an interest in it. This helped to solve the problem of military service for which Marconi was now liable. He could have avoided it by becoming a British subject but he preferred to remain Italian. The King of Italy gave him permission to stay and work in England; officially he was a naval cadet in training, attached to the Italian Embassy in London, without any duties. He sent his pay to an Italian hospital. Soon after the Italian government asked him to demonstrate the new wireless to the navy. Using the masts and rigging of a warship for the receiver, he succeeded over a distance of 16 kilometres. More important for Marconi, was the fact that over the longest distance the receiver had been out of sight, below the horizon. His one aim, from which he was never diverted, was to lengthen the distance step by step. However, there was a theoretical difficulty in doing this. At that time scientists believed that wireless waves travelled in straight lines so that they were at a tangent to the curve of the earth's surface and were gradually lost in the upper atmosphere. Marconi became convinced that this belief was wrong and continued to increase the distance of transmission.

In the meantime, while he was in Rome, relations and friends in London were forming a company to launch his invention and it was necessary to return there. His mother wrote:

'My dearest Guglielmo:

We were delighted to get your dear letter yesterday and to hear that your experiments are getting on so well, and that the King and Queen wish to see them and like you very much too, for everyone seems to like you. I hope you will keep well, dear, and at Spezia your experiments at sea will be equally successful.

Your Papa is anxious about the Company and hopes no bad terms for you will be made. I trust if Mr. Owen arranges anything with the Company that he will do it in a way to protect and guard you against them. Your Papa and everyone say that the Company should be called after your name "Marconi's Telegraphy Without Wires" that if it is not it takes the honour from you and might be called after some other person's name to make money. I hope you keep the money safely, and have not lost the Post Office order.

I trust you have got yourself some cool clothes.

Fondest love in which Alfonso joins.

Praying the Lord to bless you

Your very loving Mama'

Marconi was able to look after his interests better than his mother feared. When the company was formed in July 1897, the Wireless Telegraph and Signal Company, he received for his patent 60,000 £1 shares out of the total of 100,000 £1 shares of the authorized capital, plus £15,000 in cash. This money was essential for his further research and development. In addition, a year or two later, the name of the company was changed to Marconi's Wireless Telegraph Company, as he wished.

The period of demonstration tests was now over and the time had come to establish permanent stations. The first, a shed, with a mast tall enough to carry a 120-foot aerial was in the grounds of the Needles Hotel on the cliffs above Alum

Bay in the Isle of Wight. In November and December 1897 Marconi and his men went to sea in a hired tug with a receiving set and aerial on a sixty-foot mast. For weeks they tossed about round the coast; they found that bad weather made little difference to transmission and the results were so good that the next step was taken, to set up a permanent station on the mainland. First of all this was in the garden at Madeira House, where Marconi was staying in Bournemouth, 14 miles from Alum Bay. In April 1898 Ambrose Fleming, who later invented the diode valve, was astonished to receive at Bournemouth a message radioed from the Isle of Wight. The great and famous visited Alum Bay, among them Lord Kelvin and Tennyson, the poet laureate, who lived at Farringford House near by. Kelvin, who had been doubtful about wireless, now sent a message to his laboratory at Glasgow, via Bournemouth, and insisted on paying the shilling charge for a post office telegram, the first to do so.

Several events gave Marconi opportunities for useful publicity, which he was not the man to miss. Lloyd's, the London underwriters, asked Marconi to signal from Rathlin Island, off the north-east coast of Ireland to the mainland, a distance of seven miles, so that they could get reports of ships passing the headland. Anything connected with the safety of ships at sea was dear to Marconi's heart. His success was thought all the more marvellous because of the high cliffs on the coast, between transmitter and receiver. In the meantime in London the Speaker of the House of Commons sent a message across the Thames to St. Thomas's Hospital. This event led to a request from the *Dublin Daily Express* to report from sea on the Kingstown regatta. When Marconi did this among those whose interest was aroused was no less than the Queen herself. Victoria, living at Osborne House near Cowes, was still concerned about the well-being and behaviour of her fifty-seven-year old son, the future King Edward VII. The Prince of Wales, suffering from a sprained knee, preferred to recover on board the royal yacht in the Solent, rather than under his mother's eye on land. The Queen therefore asked Marconi to install wireless so that she could have the doctor's bulletins and the messages came to her thick and fast:

'H.R.H. the Prince of Wales has passed another excellent night, and is in very good spirits and health. The knee is most satisfactory.' Soon after this Marconi established wireless communication between the South Foreland lighthouse and the lightship, anchored twelve miles away at the east end of the Goodwin Sands.

He was determined to transmit across the Channel and on 27th March, 1899, he sent the first signal from Wimereux to the South Foreland lighthouse and received the reply V (the call signal) M (your message perfect).

While he was carrying out his intention of gradually extending the range of wireless Marconi was working at an important technical problem. This was what he called 'syntony' or tuning. Both scientists and laymen had pointed out that as wireless grew, unless many different stations could send and receive messages at the same time, the invention would be useless. In October 1899, while Marconi was in America to report the America Cup races, as he had the Kingstown Regatta, he was still working on the problem. During demonstrations for the American navy, messages sent simultaneously from a land station and from one ship to another were unintelligible.

On the way home on the S.S. *St. Paul* he made contact with the Needles and the ship's newspaper included the news he received, see opposite.

Six months later he had a solution to the problem of interference and obtained the famous patent of which the object was 'not only to increase the efficiency of the apparatus hitherto employed, but also to be able to control the action so as to cause intelligible communications to be established with one or more stations out of a group of several receiving stations.' To achieve this Marconi had changed his transmitting circuit and introduced tuning facilities in both transmitting and receiving aerials. Next year Marconi made the first commercial use of tuning when two simultaneous transmissions were made between St. Catherine's Point, the Isle of Wight, and Poole. Ambrose Fleming, by then consultant to the Marconi company, described the event in a letter to *The Times:*

'Two operators at St. Catherine's, Isle of Wight, were

THE TRANSATLANTIC TIMES

Volume 1 — Number 1

The Transatlantic Times

Published on board the 'St. Paul', at sea, *en route* for England, 15th November, 1899.

One Dollar per Copy in aid of the Seamen's Fund.

Mr. W. W. Bradfield, Editor-in-Chief. Mr. T. Bowden, Assistant Editor. Miss J. B. Holman, Treasurer. Mr. H. H. McClure, Managing Editor.

Through the courtesy of Mr. G. Marconi, the passengers on board the 'St. Paul', are accorded a rare privilege, that of receiving news several hours before landing. Mr. Marconi and his assistants have arranged for working the apparatus used in reporting the Yacht Race in New York, and are now receiving dispatches from their station at the Needles. War news from S. Africa and home messages from London & Paris are being received.

The most important dispatches are published on the opposite page. As all know, this is the first time that such a venture as this has been undertaken. A Newspaper published at Sea with Wireless Telegraph messages received and printed on a ship going twenty knots an hour!

This is the 52nd voyage eastward of the 'St. Paul'. There are 375 passengers on board, counting the distinguished and extinguished.

The days' runs have been as follows:

Nov.	9th	435
,,	10th	436
,,	11th	425
,,	12th	424
,,	13th	431
,,	14th	414
,,	15th	412

97 miles to Needles at 12 o'clock, 15th Nov.

BULLETINS

1.50 p.m. — First Signal received, 66 miles from Needles.

2.40 'Was that you "St. Paul"? 50 miles from Needles.'

2.50 Hurrah! Welcome Home! Where are you?

3.30 40 miles. Ladysmith, Kimberley and Mafeking holding out well. No big battle. 15,000 men recently landed.

3.40 'At Ladysmith no more killed. Bombardment at Kimberley effected the destruction of ONE TIN POT. It was auctioned for £200. It is felt that period of anxiety and strain is over, and that our turn has come.'

4.00 Sorry to say the U.S.A. Cruiser *Charleston* is lost. All hands saved.

The thanks of the Editors are given to Captain Jamison, who grants us the privilege of this issue.

instructed to send simultaneously two different wireless messages to Poole, Dorset, and without delay or mistake the two were correctly recorded and printed down at the same time in Morse signals on the tapes of the two corresponding receivers at Poole.

In this first demonstration each receiver was connected to its own independent aerial wire, hung from the same mast. But greater wonders followed. Mr. Marconi placed the receivers at Poole one on the top of the other, and connected them both to one and the same wire, about forty feet in length attached to the mast.

I then asked to have two messages sent at the same moment by the operator at St. Catherine's, one in English and one in French. Without failure, each receiver at Poole rolled out its paper tape, the message in English perfect on one and that in French on the other.

When it is realized that these visible dots and dashes are the result of trains of intermingled electric waves rushing with the speed of light across the intervening thirty miles, caught on one and the same short aerial wire and disentangled and sorted out automatically by the two machines into intelligible messages in different languages, the wonder of it all cannot but strike the mind.

. . . So perfect is the independence that nothing done on one circuit now affects the other, unless desired.'

By that time Marconi's mind was full of what he called 'the big thing', bridging the Atlantic. He decided on the best site for the English end, Poldhu high on the top of the cliffs at the fishing village of Mullion in Cornwall. Ambrose Fleming went down there to supervise the engineering arrangements; an alternator driven by a 25-hp oil engine worked through transformers to give 20,000 volts. In the meantime Marconi was planning the American end and decided on Cape Cod, the long, narrow, curving peninsula of Massachusetts, as the site. At Poldhu the new aerial was unlike anything ever made before. Twenty masts, 200 feet tall, stood in a ring 200 feet in diameter. This was to be the frame for an aerial of four hundred wires, in the shape of an inverted cone. When all was ready for the aerial a storm completely wrecked the whole structure. Marconi immediately designed a simpler aerial; it required only two poles, 150 feet tall, with a triangular stay between them, in which fifty-five copper wires were suspended in the shape of an enormous fan. Then a storm destroyed the Cape Cod station, which had been built on the same system as at Poldhu with masts of local pine. There was no time to rebuild, so Marconi decided to rely on kites or balloons for the aerial. He transferred the site to Newfoundland.

Marconi sailed from Liverpool with two assistants, two balloons and six kites for St. Johns, Newfoundland, and selected a site:

'After taking a look at various sites which might prove suitable I considered that the best one was to be found on Signal Hill, a lofty eminence overlooking the port and forming the natural bulwark which protects it from the fury of the Atlantic gales. On the top of the hill there is a small plateau of some two acres in area which I thought very suitable for the manipulation of either the balloons or the kites. On Monday, 9th December, barely three days after arrival, I began work on Signal Hill, together with my assistants.'

On Tuesday, 10th December, Marconi's team flew a kite with 600 feet of aerial as a preliminary test. On Wednesday, the 11th, the weather became worse but they decided to fly a balloon instead, but the wind broke the rope and the balloon disappeared out at sea. On Thursday, the 12th, the critical day, they managed to fly a kite up 400 feet, in spite of the gale. One of the assistants described the scene:

'It flew over the stormy Atlantic, surged up and down in the gale tugging at its six-hundred-foot aerial wire. The icy rain lashed my face as I watched it anxiously. The wind howled around the building where in a small dark room furnished with a table, one chair and some packing-cases, Mr. Kemp sat at the receiving set while Mr. Marconi drank a cup of cocoa before taking his turn at listening for the signals which were being transmitted from Poldhu, at least we hoped so.'

In the meantime Marconi had given detailed instructions to his men at Poldhu to transmit the Morse letter S, three dots, from 3.00 p.m. to 6.00 p.m. G.M.T., from 11.30 a.m. to 2.30 p.m. in St. Johns. He recorded what happened:

'It was shortly after midday on 12th December, 1901, that I placed a single earphone to my ear and started listening. The receiver on the table before me was very crude – a few coils and condensers and a coherer, no valves, no amplifier, not even a crystal.

'I was at last on the point of putting the correctness of all my beliefs to the test. The experiment had involved risking at least 50,000 pounds to achieve a result which had been declared impossible by some of the principal mathematicians of the time.

'Suddenly, about half past twelve there sounded the sharp click of the "tapper" as it struck the coherer, showing me that something was coming and I listened intently.

'Unmistakably, the three sharp clicks corresponding to three dots sounded in my ear; but I would not be satisfied without corroboration.

' "Can you hear anything, Mr. Kemp?" I said, handing the telephone to my assistant. Kemp heard the same thing as I. P. W. Paget, a little deaf, was unable to hear it, and I knew then that I had been absolutely right in my calculations. The electric waves which were being sent out from Poldhu had travelled the Atlantic, serenely ignoring the curvature of the earth which so many doubters considered would be a fatal obstacle, and they were now affecting my receiver in Newfoundland. I knew that the day on which I should be able to send full messages without wires or cables across the Atlantic was not far-distant.'

'After a short while the signals stopped, evidently owing to changes in the capacity of the aerial which in turn were due to the varying height of the kite. But again at 1.10 and 1.20 the three sharp little clicks were distinctly and unmistakably heard, about twenty-five times altogether.'

Marconi was quite sure that the experiment, as he called it, had been successful, and he gave the news to the world. Public opinion accepted it as true, although many scientists were doubtful because it challenged the accepted theory of radio waves. The doubts expressed by the scientists had to be answered, and the Press in England had not believed Marconi's statement as wholeheartedly as in America. Accordingly Marconi planned tests, with witnesses, to be carried out on a ship sailing westward across the Atlantic to prove his invention to the world. In February 1902 sailing on the *Philadelphia* from Cherbourg he had an aerial put on the 160-foot mast and a tuned receiver with Morse tape inker in a cabin. He invited the ship's captain, officers and passengers to witness messages being received from Poldhu. When the ship docked in New York he had a handful of Morse tapes to show the newspaper reporters giving such messages as 'Stiff south-west breeze. Fairly heavy swell' signed as genuine by the captain. The ship's log recorded:

'Messages received on board from Marconi station at Poldhu (Cornwall) as follows: No. 1 – 250·2 miles; No. 2 – 464·5 miles; No. 3 – 1032·5 miles; No. 4 – 1163·5 miles; No. 5 – 1551·5 miles. Signals 2,099 miles from Poldhu when we were in Latitude 42·01 N, and Longitude 47·23 . . .'

All doubts about Marconi's invention were now answered.

From that year until the First World War Marconi worked on technical improvements in wireless and to establish a practical commercial service. Both these aims meant that he had to bring about major changes. The first of these was his invention of a new type of detector in 1902, to replace the coherer, which had certain defects, reacting to the rolling and pitching of a ship and to the vibration of its engines. The new type was his magnetic detector. An essential part was a loop of fine iron wire which travelled through the centre of two concentric coils, and near to two horse-shoe permanent magnets. Marconi's daughter has told how he cycled from Poole to Bournemouth one morning in search of the thinnest possible wire and how after going from shop to shop he eventually got what he wanted in a flower shop where a girl was using wire as thin as thread to make bouquets.

During these years more and more powerful transmitting stations were built. In October, 1907, the first regular press and commercial wireless service started, with 10,000 words of press messages being transmitted on the opening day.

At sea the use of wireless by ships grew, but only slowly. In 1908 only seventy-two British ships had wireless installations. Then there were two famous sea disasters. In 1909 the S.S. *Republic*, a luxury liner, was rammed in fog twenty-six miles south of the Nantucket lightship. Because the *Republic* had wireless, rescue came in time and 1,700 lives were saved, only six being lost. By 1912 the number of British ships equipped with wireless had risen to 450. Then in April that year the *Titanic* disaster occurred. When the great liner, thought to be unsinkable, with 2,206 people on board, struck an iceberg in the middle of the night the two wireless operators stayed at their posts until their cabin was awash. Their signals – C.Q.D. (Come Quick Danger) and the new signal, S.O.S., were picked up but there was much confusion on the air because of the activities of land stations and wireless amateurs. One New York newspaper reported that all had been saved and that the *Titanic* was being towed into harbour. The price of Marconi shares rose rapidly on the stock exchange. But when the *Carpathia* came to the rescue it picked up only 703 people, and the *Titanic* had sunk to the bottom. Marconi was reported by the Press as saying:

'It is worthwhile to have lived to have made it possible for these people to have been saved . . . I know you will understand me if I say that all those who have been working with me entertain a true feeling of gratitude that wireless telegraphy has again helped to save human lives. I also want to express my thanks to the Press for the hearty approval it has given my invention.'

The number of British ships with wireless had increased to 879 in 1914 but there were 21,000 ships, including nearly 13,000 steamships, on the British register in that year. 'The wireless message itself,' wrote an economic historian, 'had so far done little towards the filling of anyone's belly, the raising or lowering of anyone's wage or salary or profit-rate or rent.' The First World War soon changed that.

The use of wireless by the armies and air forces grew enormously. Marconi and his family were in a difficult position until Italy joined the Allies in 1915 when he volunteered for the services and directed the use of radio. At the end of the war the Italian government sent him as a member of its delegation to the Versailles Peace Conference. Much disappointed by the Peace, and particularly by the way in which Italy was treated, he said:

'I can't help hoping that the League of Nations will save us. I am very much in favour of the League. I've met President Wilson and discussed his idea with him, but the rest of the world will have to help him if the League is really to exist.

'If this grand and noble idea fails, the next war will be infinitely much more complicated. Cities would be blotted clean out from the air – I hope men will soon turn their thoughts away from war.'

From 1919 Marconi turned in a new direction. Up till then his work had been with long waves but he now became interested in short waves. At that time the world radio services were based on high power spark transmitters using long waves, and a great deal of capital had been invested in them. It was thought that wavelengths of 200 metres and below were useless and they had therefore been allotted to the activities of radio amateurs. In 1922 Marconi reported on his research:

'Some years ago, during the war, I could not help feeling that we had perhaps got rather in a rut by confining practically all our research and tests to long waves. . . . Progress made with long waves was so rapid, so comparatively easy, and so spectacular, that it distracted practically all attention and research from the short waves. I have brought these results to your notice as I feel – and perhaps you will agree with me – that the study of short electric waves, although sadly neglected practically all through the history of wireless, is still likely to develop in many unexpected directions, and open up new fields of profitable research.'

Experiments with short waves on his yacht in the Atlantic and the Mediterranean were increasingly successful and in 1924 he signed a contract with the British government to provide short-wave communications with the far-flung empire. This was the end of the old long-wave transmissions.

As one of the most famous Italians of his age, Marconi often mixed with the rich and famous. He and his wife were friends of the King and Queen and the aristocracy of Italy and so it was likely, though not inevitable, that he would support Mussolini and Fascism. Another famous Italian, Toscanini, left his country rather than help the Fascist régime. Marconi joined the Fascist Party in 1923 and always wore its green, red and white badge. He said: 'I am a Fascista by conviction. Fascism is the régime of strength necessary for the salvation of Italy.' In 1926, at the celebrations in his honour in his native town of Bologna he recalled: 'In 1917 I used the first beam or "fascio" apparatus, using short waves of two or three metres in length, and perhaps I may be allowed to claim in this way I was the first fascist in Italy.' Here he was referring to the fact that the symbol of fascism was the old Roman 'fascio' or bundle of rods. He declared '. . . fascism is doing a fine work in Italy. Italy under Benito Mussolini has turned the corner. His bold, audacious political and financial policies have transformed the country.' By 1928 he was a member of the supreme council of the Fascist Party and President of the Royal Italian Academy.

The Italian invasion of Abyssinia in 1935 aroused strong opposition in Europe and the League of Nations decided to impose economic sanctions on Italy to stop her aggression. Marconi broadcast from Rome a plea for sympathy for Italy:

> 'You Americans, who luckily for yourselves are outside the League of Nations, breathe the free invigorating air of two oceans and of great spaces, somewhat different from the confined atmosphere of Lake Geneva, will be able to form your own unbiased opinions and you will not fail to recognize the justice of Italy's claim.'

Only ten years before he had addressed a meeting of the League of Nations union at the People's Palace in the east end of London and expressed his hopes for peace and that wireless would create a better understanding between nations. Now he was so anxious to justify Italy's attack on Abyssinia that he asked the B.B.C. to allow him to broadcast, only to be refused by Sir John Reith. Feeling was high in England.

Marconi was married twice. In 1905, when he was thirty-one and already a famous man, he married the daughter of Edward Donough O'Brien, the thirteenth Baron Inchiquin of

Dromoland in County Clare. This noble family lived on its ancient estate surrounded by servants. The wedding was a fashionable event at St. George's Church, Hanover Square. There were a boy and two girls of this marriage. After eighteen years Marconi divorced his wife and married the daughter of one of the Roman aristocracy. A few months later he had a heart attack. By the second marriage there was a daughter.

The heart attacks continued at intervals until they caused his death in 1937 shortly after he was due for a routine meeting with Mussolini. He had insisted on continuing to work against his doctor's orders. Marconi received a great many decorations, honorary degrees of universities, and awards, including those of hereditary marquis of Italy and the Nobel prize for physics. At the funeral in Rome many thousands followed the coffin and in Britain the radio stations were silent for a few minutes.

SIR AMBROSE FLEMING (1849–1945)

John Ambrose Fleming, to give him his full name, had a very long life. He could remember the Indian Mutiny in 1856 and he died just before the end of the Second World War. Of all the many changes during his ninety-five years radio was one of the greatest. He was so famous in the scientific world that the name Fleming meant valve and vice versa.

Fleming was the son of the Reverend James Fleming, D.D., a Congregational minister in Lancaster. His mother was the daughter of a well-to-do manufacturer who pioneered the making of Portland cement. When he was five the family moved to London and lived at Tufnell Park, at a time when fields stretched all the way to Highgate and Holloway. After being taught to read by his mother, he went to a private school. When he was fourteen he was sent to University College School, a day-school, in Gower Street. The school was closely connected with University College, London, which had been started for dissenters and nonconformists whose religious beliefs barred them from going to Oxford or Cambridge which were open only to members of the Church of England. Mathematics he found easy but Latin and Greek, which he also had to learn, were a struggle. He had already shown a strong interest in mechanical engineering. However the only way to become a professional engineer was to be articled as an apprentice by paying a large premium and this his father could not afford. It was therefore decided that he should go on to University College for a degree in science.

As a small boy Fleming's interest in machinery had been aroused by the railway locomotives of the eighteen-fifties and by the steam engines in his grandfather's cement works. Visits to the Polytechnic in Regent Street and the lectures on chemistry and exhibitions there had made an impression too. His life-long study of electricity began, quite by chance, before he went to university. It happened that a friend of his father explained to him an electric battery and a frictional electrical machine. He decided to make them for himself.

'All available pocket money was therefore expended in the purchase of a dozen jam pots, some zinc and copper plate, and a supply of sulphuric acid for the manufacture of a voltaic battery . . . Each pot contained a plate of amalgamated zinc and a copper plate not touching it. Then the zinc in the pot was joined by a short wire to the copper of the next pot, and so on for the series. The copper in the pot at one end had a wire attached to it, and similarly for the zinc at the other end pot. When these two end wires were made to touch so as to complete the circuit, an electric current flowed through it. If these terminal wires were closely covered with cotton thread to insulate them, and then wound many times round an iron bar such as a poker, the current caused the bar to become a magnet as long as the circuit was complete.'

He made his frictional electric machine by using a revolving glass cylinder and a silk cushion. He also made a Leyden jar, which was charged from the machine, from a large pickle bottle lined inside and outside with tin foil. Another of his father's friends was a telegraph engineer and from him Fleming learnt how to make an induction coil. At home he gave demonstrations of his experiments, using a spare leaf of the mahogany dining-table, placed in a corner of the sitting-room, as his bench.

At University College he failed to pass the intermediate examination at the end of the first year and succeeded only after a second year. Because of shortage of money at home he then had to find a job. First he went to work for a small salary with a firm of shipbuilders in Dublin, as there seemed to be a chance to learn some engineering. But he found that all he had to do was copy plans of ships in the drawing office without getting any practical experience in the shops. And so after a few months his parents agreed to his returning home to continue studying for his degree. However, as he had to earn some money, he was found a job as clerk in the Stock Exchange.

For two years now he was a part-time student. Fortunately the hours of work at the Stock Exchange were short, ten or ten-thirty till four. Fleming learnt about buying and selling stocks and shares and the meaning of Bulls, Bears, and Stags. He always found later on that his experience in the City was very useful. At home, early in the morning and at night he worked so successfully that in 1870 he was one of the only two candidates to gain first-class honours in the B.Sc. examinations.

In January 1871, through the influence of a professor of chemistry in London whom his father had known at Lancaster, he began as science master at Rossall School. His salary was £140 a year plus free board and lodging. At this public school little time was given to chemistry (which Fleming was to teach) and there was little apparatus to teach it. After two years, because he felt he needed to learn more himself, he became a research assistant in the advanced chemical laboratory of the Royal School of Mines at South Kensington. During his time there the Physical Society was formed and he was asked to read the first paper to it; it was about his research into a new kind of battery.

By 1874, at the age of twenty-four, he needed to earn more money and he went back to teaching. This time it was a better paid post at Cheltenham College which was worth £400 a year. There was no properly equipped chemistry laboratory and Fleming spent much time in making apparatus. He always tried to combine theory and practice in teaching science; the only way was for boys to do or see the things about which they were learning. He quoted as an example the method of teaching used by Wackford Squeers, the master of Dotheboys Hall, in Dickens' novel *Nicholas Nickleby*.

'We go upon the practical mode of teaching, Nickleby,'

said Mr. Squeers, calling up a boy to whom he said, 'How do you spell window?' 'W I N D E R,' said the boy. 'Quite right, now go and clean it,' said Mr. Squeers. 'That's our system, Nickleby. When a boy has spelt "winder" he goes and cleans it.'

Fleming went on with his research. He had bought a second-hand copy of Faraday's famous book *Researches on Electricity*. One of Faraday's theories was that the flow of rivers across the earth's magnetic field produced electric currents in them. Fleming made some experiments to show that this was correct and gave the results in a paper he read at a meeting of the British Association. He was then twenty-six.

After three years at Cheltenham College it seemed to him that he was in a blind alley. He had the idea of studying at Cambridge University although he already had a degree of London University, with first-class honours. Clerk Maxwell had just published his treatise on Electricity and Magnetism in which he had expressed Faraday's ideas mathematically. Maxwell was a professor of physics at Cambridge and so Fleming decided to study under him. His problem was to have enough money to keep him at Cambridge for three years. He had saved about £400. He won a scholarship at St. John's College, Cambridge, worth £50 a year for three years, and he was appointed as an examiner in the Science and Art Department at South Kensington, which was worth another £50 a year. This was enough, and so at the age of twenty-eight, he became a Cambridge undergraduate.

At Cambridge Fleming lived in lodgings, not in College, as he thought it would be better for serious study. In the second year he became a scholar of his college, thus winning another £50 to £100 a year and he won several prizes. With £200 a year he was just able to pay his way. His main purpose was to go to Clerk Maxwell's lectures and to work in his Cavendish Laboratory. Maxwell's lectures on heat, electricity, and electromagnetism were difficult to follow. Often there were only two students present, Fleming and an American. Once the American said to Fleming: 'Sir, this man (Maxwell) is great! He does not come here and tell us what he has read out of books. He gives it to us hot out of his brain.' Occasionally Maxwell had only Fleming as his audience. In the laboratory Fleming worked on electrical measurements. As he found that Wheatstone's Bridge was not suitable for his research in comparing resistances he designed his own instrument, which, because of its shape, was called Fleming's Banjo, and was used in the Cavendish Laboratory for some years.

While he was still an undergraduate at Cambridge Fleming was awarded the degree of Doctor of Science by London University. When he came to take his final examination at Cambridge in 1880 he passed with first-class honours in physics and chemistry. A few months later he became demonstrator in the engineering laboratory and taught engineering drawing. He was glad to accept this post because it meant he could stay in the traditional surroundings of Cambridge but he left in the following year for a more modern world.

In the eighteen-seventies the government and the country were beginning to realize that England needed more scientific and engineering education. This had been brought home by the fact that countries such as Germany and the United States were beginning to overtake England in the chemical and metallurgical industries. For this reason a number of new colleges were started which after some years, became the well-known civic universities. At Nottingham the town council built a university college. In 1881 Fleming went there as its first professor of mathematics and physics. Interesting though this was he stayed only a few months; another opening appeared, which was even more attractive to him.

During Fleming's time at Cambridge Edison and Swan had each invented the incandescent lamp. The Edison Electric Light Company was formed in London to manufacture under Edison's patents in England, and it was to this firm that Fleming was appointed 'electrician' in 1882. With this company Fleming was responsible for some of the first electric lighting in ships. He came to know Edison, Swan who had just discovered how to use cellulose for lamp filaments, and Sir William Thomson (Lord Kelvin) and gained much useful industrial experience.

Three years later Fleming became the first professor of electrical engineering at University College, London where he remained for forty-one years. At first all he had was a blackboard, chalk and a small lecture-room. In a few years, however, the college built new laboratories, for which Fleming himself raised £800. Although he preferred teaching and scientific research he undertook at the same time a good deal of consultancy. Much of this work was to advise corporations and companies about their electrical power installations; these included the famous Deptford generating station after Ferranti had left it. He became consultant to the Marconi Wireless Telegraphy Company and this led to his most famous invention, the diode valve.

In April 1898 he was on holiday in Bournemouth when Marconi was sending messages between a station at Alum Bay in the Isle of Wight and one near the pier in Bournemouth. He watched the transmission; much later on he wrote:

> 'I do not even now forget my astonishment when I saw a telegraphic instrument begin to print down in the Morse code of dot and dash the message "Compliments to Professor Fleming" which had found its way across twelve miles of sea and had been picked up by an aerial wire 150 feet high attached to a mast in the garden of the house in which Mr. Marconi was then residing at Bournemouth.'

When Marconi decided to transmit across the Atlantic from Poldhu, Fleming drew the plans for the building and chose the electrical machines and the power unit. In December 1901 radio signals were sent from Poldhu to Newfoundland. Three years later Fleming invented the diode valve. He had worked with Edison and Marconi. He now combined the work of both these men in the following way.

While Fleming was with the Edison Electric Light Company, Edison had discovered the passage of electric current from a hot filament to a cold plate in an evacuated bulb, the Edison effect (see Chapter Five). This interested Fleming and he studied it carefully in his laboratory at University College. He had some bulbs made like Edison's and found, in his own words, 'that negative electricity from any battery could pass from the hot filament to the cold plate, but not in the opposite direction. The space between the filament and the metal plate sealed into the bulb is a one-way street for electricity'. A year or two later the great scientist, J. J. Thomson, the discoverer of the electron, explained this mystery. He found that electrons were emitted from the hot filament. No one as yet thought of any practical use for these discoveries.

The practical use came when Fleming was trying to make a better detector for the Marconi company. The Marconi detector was a coherer in the form of a glass tube containing metal filings and two electrodes. This was quite practical but it was unreliable. Fleming saw the need for a rectifier which would convert the high-frequency alternating current received on the radio to direct current. He wrote 'The problem before me then was to discover how to change this feeble electric oscillation into a feeble direct current which could work with the ordinary cable-recording instruments. There were known devices for "rectifying" as it is called, low-frequency alternating currents, but nothing then known which would do it for rapid electric oscillations.'

He puzzled over the problem and then suddenly he saw the connection between his present problem and previous discoveries:

'Thinking over the subject intensely, I had in October 1904 a sudden very happy thought. I recalled to mind my experiments on the "Edison Effect" and in particular my observation that the space between an incandescent carbon filament and a cold metal plate in a bulb exhausted of its air had a one-way conductivity for electricity. Then I said to myself, if that is the case, we have here the exact implement required to "rectify" high-frequency oscillations. I asked my assistant, Mr. G. B. Dyke, to put up the arrangements for creating feeble high-frequency currents in a circuit, and I took out of a cupboard one of my old experimental bulbs. The experiment was at once a great success, and I found I could use a mirror galvanometer which is one of the instruments Lord Kelvin invented for submarine cable signalling, to detect feeble electric oscillations . . .'

The next day he ordered from the Edison-Swan factory a dozen lamps in which the filament was surrounded by a metal cylinder carried by a wire sealed through the bulb.

'I then found that the space between the filament and cylinder would only allow negative electricity to pass from the filament to the cylinder, but not the other way. Hence the bulb acted like a valve in a pipe, which lets air or water only move in it one way. . . . Accordingly I called the instrument a "valve". At first I named it an oscillation valve, but before long it was usual to speak of the small particles of electricity sent out from a hot-surface as "thermions", and accordingly I called it a "Thermionic Valve". This name has been very widely adopted, although it is often called a "Fleming Valve". I regret to see that some authors prefer to denote it by the unmeaning name of "diode". There seems to be no advantage, quite the reverse, in coining a scientific gibberish to replace plain English short words for scientific apparatus.'

Fleming's valve was soon used as a detector by the Marconi Company, although he never received any money for his invention. The diode became valuable for rectifying weak radio signals so that they could be detected by a telephone receiver. However, before radio could be used for broadcasting an improvement on the valve was necessary; this was Lee de Forest's triode. The year after Fleming discovered the valve he gave an account of it to the Royal Society in a paper entitled 'On the Conversion of Electric Oscillation into Continuous Current by means of a Vacuum Valve'.

He retired eventually at the age of seventy-seven. By then about two thousand students had been under his supervision, some of whom became famous themselves. He was in much demand as a lecturer to the general public; a crisp voice and great skill and care with demonstrations made him successful with big audiences. No less than four times between 1894 and 1921 he gave the Christmas lectures for children at the Royal Institution, which Faraday had begun.

As a scientist Fleming had firm religious beliefs. He changed from the Congregational Church of his father to the evangelical wing of the Church of England. In his view the universe could never be fully explained by science but would always be 'the manifestation and outcome of a Supreme Intelligence'. He maintained this view as President of the Victorian Institute.

He was better qualified than most to speak about invention. He wrote:

'Scientific research and invention, however great the genius which guides it, is largely a matter of perseverance. We have to try systematically the ninety-nine things that do not succeed before we find the one that does.'

He was able to see the full result of his rectifier before he died at the age of ninety-five. He married twice but had no children.

LEE DE FOREST (1873–1961)

De Forest's name came from Huguenot ancestors who had fled to the American colonies in the seventeenth century. It was a family with a keen sense of history. On his father's side his great grandfather had served in the American cavalry in the War of Independence and had built the de Forest farmhouse. His mother was the daughter of the Congregational minister of the town of Muscatine in Iowa, on the Mississippi river. He also was descended from a long line of New Englanders, the first of whom had left England in the early seventeenth century.

De Forest's father saved enough from work on the family farm to enter Yale University. When he had taken his degree the civil war started and he became chaplain to the Eleventh Connecticut Volunteer Regiment serving throughout Grant's last victorious campaign in Virginia. After the war he obtained the degree of doctor of divinity and became minister of the Congregational church at Council Bluffs in Iowa, where de Forest was born. A few years later the family moved to Muscatine.

The first six years of de Forest's life were spent in this prosperous little town. One of his earliest memories was of hearing an early Edison phonograph in a local shop; this was a year after the Centennial Exposition where Bell had shown his telephone. The children spent hours on the banks of the Mississippi, watching the river, the steamers, and the great rafts of logs being carried down. This comfortable life changed when his father accepted a call from the American Missionary Society to go down south into Alabama and take on the headship of a school for Negro children. The stern upright man saw this as his duty and his wife, leaving her social life and comforts, followed him. To the children it was an adventure. In his autobiography de Forest described the scene:

'Thus it was that in the early fall of 1879 Henry Swift de Forest, D.D., his lovely young wife, and their three children alighted from a sooty day coach of the East Tennessee, Virginia, and Georgia Railroad on the dusty, hot platform of a dingy, rust-coloured frame depot in Talladega, Alabama. Waiting for them was a two-seated buckboard buggy and a plank wagon for the baggage. Up unpaved, red, dusty streets from the village square to the hill on which stood the college, the forlorn little caravan wended its way.'

The 'college' was then no more than a school which had been struggling for years to give some education to the Negroes. By great efforts de Forest's father raised it to a high level, the pupils trebled, the curriculum was extended from agriculture, handicrafts, domestic science and nursing to include the classics and theology. The de Forests and all the teachers were ostracized by the white people. In their fights the de Forest boys allied with the Negro boys against the southern white boys who despised them. De Forest recalled an event about 1880:

'I remember one occasion when my father, my sister Mary and I were walking along a country road near our house and passed a typical Southern gentleman of the name of Colonel Hardy and my father spoke a word of salutation. Thereupon the "genial" Southern gentleman moved hastily to the other side of the road and snarled "I don't wish to be spoken to by a damned Yankee".'

At school, however, although all the teachers were white, there was no racial segregation. Black and white children shared the same desk. He enjoyed school and usually kept ahead of the others. At home there was strict discipline. 'Firm rules and strict discipline, accompanied before and after with prayer, combined to rear us all in the paths of God's children.' De Forest was quickly taught to do the family chores and at an early age shown how to use the axe and saw to maintain the supply of fuel. When his father was away raising money he was sent away to earn his keep at a farm. Although the family was not well off the open air freedom to roam the woods and forests and swim in the creek meant a happy boyhood. In the hot Alabama summers the boys wore no shoes from June to September. They played marbles and baseball on the bare earth with the Negro children. De Forest read Fenimore Cooper's adventure stories and imagined himself as their heroes. One special interest was aroused when an iron ore blast furnace was built and, although it was soon closed because it lost money, he learnt all the details of a furnace, foundry and machine shop.

By the age of thirteen he had decided to be an inventor. He had found in the college library the *Patent Office Gazette*, and always, when rainy days kept him indoors, he was to be found carefully copying the drawings, lying flat on the library floor. He was convinced he could invent a perpetual motion machine, and he drew what he thought to be one, on paper and wrote under the drawing:

'I am actually amazed that I, a mere youth of thirteen years, by my inventive genius and concentrated thought and study, have succeeded where illustrious philosophers in times past have failed. I have at last furnished to humanity a machine which without cost can supply forever any and all demands of the human race for power.'

De Forest stayed at school in Talladega until he was nearly eighteen. He had a 'thorough high school training' in English and American literature. Bible study was the daily task and at the age of twelve he had read the Bible from cover to cover, and written his comment:

'The practical lesson I get from the last chapter of Genesis is that there is no merit without great labour and that diligence is always rewarded. By perseverance, merit and application, one may live to eminence and prosperity, as is so plainly shown in Joseph's life.'

He read *Paradise Lost* and *Paradise Regained*, Scott's novels and Longfellow's poems. His mother, who was a skilful pianist and singer wanted him to learn the piano but he revolted against it as a girlish occupation. Instead he was allowed to have lessons in the cornet. Music played a great part in the family life. His father wanted strongly that he should follow in his footsteps at Yale, where a wealthy cousin had founded a de Forest scholarship, and become a minister or a teacher.

But by now de Forest had decided that he would study engineering and go to the Sheffield School at Yale if he went at all.

When he was seventeen he began to keep a diary:

'January 25th: Be good, it will pay in this world and the next. I am resolved to do – not live and die and world be as bad as it was and not know I ever lived. They shall know and be glad, and sorry when I die – so help me God. After meeting I sang and played cornet, can't sing very good tenor. After supper we all went to prayer meeting and Papa led, and Mr. Burnell spoke another good Bible talk.

January 29th: At 2 p.m. we had Prayer Meeting in our room until 2.45. Then I came home and practiced, and then we took a plank over to the shop and ripped it up in ¼-inch strips . . . After supper I composed my letter to Edison asking his advice about the kind of education needed to become an inventor. May it get a favorable answer. The strips are for our tennis court. Now read and bed.

June 26th: Finished the job and typewriting and wrote a letter to the Yost Typewriter Company for a place in their factory for the summer. Hope it will be more successful than Edison's. Went to town and bought a box of loaded shells, Papa's gift for Fourth of July. Read *Conquest of Peru*, very interesting, no dime novels for me. The Fourth of July number of *Youth's Companion* came and I read it most of the evening. I don't believe my offspring will have better reading than I have.'

He pleaded with his father to be allowed to study science, and his father agreed he should do as he wished.

Before he could enter Yale it was necessary to study for entrance for two years at a preparatory school at Mount Hermon in Massachusetts. He found the school was, in his own words, 'founded on basic rock-ribbed fundamentalism and rock-studded dirt farming'. In the curriculum farm work was as important as the academic studies. As well as the study of Latin, mathematics, and physics, long hours were spent in digging, milking and clearing the land, and of course hours on Bible study and listening to long sermons. Money was always very scarce. He saved some by working overtime on the farm and earned more in the vacations by selling books from door to door and by chair pushing for visitors to the Chicago Exhibition and World Fair.

'The Fair,' he wrote in his diary, 'is immense and grand. I must stay as long as possible. Many chair-boys have struck and been discharged. I spent Friday in the United States Building studying models and gun manufacture, Saturday in the railroad department of the Transportation Building. I don't waste time or money in Woman's or State Buildings, or the Midway Plaisance, but study machines, engines, models almost entirely, and learn a great deal that will be of use to me. I want to stay longer and study all of this sort possible, as it is really money and a paying education for me, as well as the highest enjoyment.'

In 1893, now twenty, he entered Yale and was very happy to be there. In this environment of more freedom he began to free himself from his strict religious upbringing. A conflict developed between his religious training and his new education in science. He gradually relinquished his religion in favour of agnosticism.

Although his tuition was free, thanks to the de Forest scholarship, he was always hard up and so he made various small inventions and tried to sell them; a new typewriter movement, an improved compass joint, and a puzzle game, but without any reward. He worked as a waiter, did gardening for the professor of Greek in return for lodging, and helped postgraduate students in the psychology laboratory for a small fee. At the same time he wrote articles regularly for the College magazine and worked hard at the subjects for the final examination – mechanics, mathematics, drawing, heat engines, French, German and English. A lecture on the X-rays just discovered by Roentgen caused much excitement and made de Forest decide that after his degree he would continue at Yale with postgraduate study. He graduated in 1896 and, according to his diary, 'I am voted the Nerviest in the class, also the Homeliest.' Then it was hard work in the vacation to earn some money:

'I worked four days this week for the Gas Company for eight dollars, getting enormously tired and learning more about the sickly sores of this world's denizens. In what filth and inexpediencies most people live. I wonder that they live. Oh, who shall teach this sick and stupid world that subtle art of living, the most abstract of sciences? Few have learned it in these days. Large spaces and the weeding out of slums are imperative.'

He started postgraduate work at Yale, still meaning to be an inventor. Among his efforts at invention to make money at that time were a telephone relay and a hydraulic gear for the bicycle, replacing the chain. His studies were now mainly in electrical engineering although the equipment for it was very poor. He read the works of Oliver Lodge, Hertz and Clerk Maxwell and repeated Hertz's famous experiments in the laboratory. In mathematics he was fortunate in having as his professor one of the greatest mathematical physicists of the age. He knew the direction he wished to take and wrote:

'My mathematical training this year I find already of the greatest practical value. Without such, and every bit of it, I could not read these books leading up to Maxwell. I want another year, still higher. Then I can expect to deal intelligently with light wave phenomena, along which lines I see the great future of electronic advance.'

At this point there came the Cuba war and de Forest was eager to join it.

The American war with Spain in 1898 to free Cuba from Spanish rule was a very popular one in the United States. The savage Spanish suppression of the Cuban revolt and the accidental sinking of a U.S. battleship in Havana harbour stirred up widespread enthusiasm for war among the Americans. Along with other students de Forest joined the Yale Artillery Company, part of the Connecticut Volunteer Militia Battery and was made a bugler in view of his skill on the cornet. Aften ten weeks' fighting, both Spanish fleets had been sunk, the Spanish army in Cuba had been defeated and, at the cost of 289 men killed and some 3,500 dead of disease, the United States had destroyed the remnant of the old Spanish empire. De Forest was not even called on to leave the depot, where he spent four months on drill and guard duty. He was glad to get out with 60 dollars pay. Back at Yale he finished his thesis after seven months' laboratory work and was awarded the degree of Doctor of Philosophy. The title of his thesis was 'The Reflection of Hertzian waves from the Ends of Parallel Wires'.

Now twenty-six, de Forest got his first job with the Western Electric Company in Chicago. It was a humble job, for a Doctor of Philosophy, in the dynamo department:
'There I worked like a slave from seven in the morning to five-fifteen with three-quarters of an hour for lunch. I was learning a little but not very much of use. There was far too much chasing of parts and mopping of grease, and all for 8 dollars per week.'

Soon however he was promoted to laboratory work on telephone equipment and circuits.

'December 31st, 1899: The new century is starting out well, for yesterday I was notified of my first raise, ten dollars a week, $520 a year. Think of it! Ah, I shall begin to live indeed, buy a pair of new socks, a phonograph and an automobile at once, and move into a steam-heated flat before next winter. Never again shall I endure the discomfort of a stove, nor wear the same collar longer than three days. The prospect is wildly entrancing. I can have my shoes now shined twice a week, and take the streetcar oftener.'

De Forest had already started on the work which was to bring him fame and fortune from radio. He had used the type of coherer which Marconi was using but he was determined to invent a better detector. If he could do this it would mean faster operation and he could compete successfully with the Marconi system. He invented a device which he called a responder, an electrolytic detector, using a fluid instead of metal filings.

As soon as he could see that his responder was successful he left Western Electric and went to work in Milwaukee for a professor who was also president of a wireless telegraphy company. His pay rose to 15 dollars a week but the professor sacked him because he would not hand over his detector. He was determined to profit by it himself. 'I do not yet know what practical possibilities it possesses,' he said, 'but I believe in it; I will not let it go into the hands of any company until that company is my own.' A magazine called the *Western Electrician* wanted someone who could translate papers on electricity in French and he became assistant editor.

Concentrating all his efforts on making his responder more reliable, he tried everything for electrolyte, even face cream. To give more time to it he left the magazine and lived on five dollars a week from teaching evening classes and on loans from a friend. His position at the end of 1900 was not promising:

'December 23, 1900: And now what of myself and my state; what do I accomplish through these days; my performance what? Twice have I renounced good and fairly promising positions for my faith in an idea and in myself. Risks have they been, and serious, for I am ageing in years and will soon be twenty-eight. Money I have none, influence none, acquaintance none. In industry, diligence, I am not lacking, nor have lacked for many years . . . time is short and Marconi sails fine and weatherworthy boats, and these boats are already headed towards America. Yet I alone seem to realize that if our craft cannot meet him next spring, it might as well sink now. And if it sink, I sink deeply with it.'

The tide soon turned. De Forest interested financiers in forming the American de Forest Wireless Telegraphy Company with a nominal capital of three million dollars. Publicity came from the *New York World* in April 1902:

'A NEW YORK RIVAL OF MARCONI

Far up in the air, on the roof of the Chesebrough Building, at No. 17 State Street, is a wireless telegraph station, of the existence of which few persons have heard.

The system employed is the invention of an American, a Yale man not yet thirty years old, and is in no respect similar to that invented by Marconi.

The operator here has exchanged messages with the steamship Deutschland while that vessel was 100 miles at sea, and for simple demonstration, messages are constantly sent to another station located on the Hotel Castleton, on the heights at St. George, S.I., from which the replies made may be seen recorded as undeniable proof.

It is asserted that the newest system has many advantages, notably in speed and freedom from interruption, over that of Marconi; that it is no longer an experiment, but is so far advanced that when the next big Hamburg–American liner Deutschland crosses from the other side, commercial messages will be exchanged between it and the Manhattan station. Plans are under way for the erection of five new stations along the Atlantic Coast.

The speed of transmission by the Marconi system is at present limited, by mechanical barriers, to fewer than fifteen words a minute, less than one-third the speed of the fastest work on land wires.

It is said that a speed of forty words a minute has been reached by the new wireless system, which is good work on a land wire and beyond the skill of an average Morse operator...'

The army, having thoroughly tested his system and found it better than Marconi's gave him a contract to report manœuvres for the U.S. Signal Corps; the navy followed suit. Then *The Times* correspondent who was on his way to report the Russian–Japanese war of 1904 took a de Forest wireless set with him. With the set on board a tug at sea the correspondent was able to radio dispatches to the port of Wei hai Wei whence they were forwarded by telegraph. The result was a scoop for *The Times* and publicity for de Forest. Soon in the United States radio stations increased, with a commercial service, and the navy gave the de Forest company a contract for other more powerful stations in Puerto Rico, Florida, Cuba and Panama.

De Forest's work on detectors led naturally to his most important invention, the triode valve. He had been investigating a detector which used a gas flame between platinum electrodes in a battery circuit. How he made a triode is best explained in his own words:

'Although I now had proof that I was on the right track, I was still not satisfied. My diode detector permitted part of the high-frequency energy to pass to earth through the telephone and battery circuit instead of concentrating it upon the ions between the plate and the filament. To overcome this imperfection and to improve still further the sensitivity of the detector, I wrapped a piece of tin foil around the outside of the cylindrical-shaped glass tube and connected this third electrode to the antenna or to one terminal of the high-frequency tuner. I then realized that the efficiency could be still further enhanced if this third electrode were introduced within the tube. I therefore had McCandless construct another "Audion" – as I now for the first time began to call it. This new device contained two plates with a filament located midway between them. This detector showed distinct improvement over its predecessors.

'It now occurred to me that the third, or control, electrode could be located more efficiently between the plate and the filament. Obviously, this third electrode so located should not be a solid plate. Consequently, I supplied McCandless with a small plate of platinum, perforated much better than anything preceding it, but in order to simplify and cheapen the construction I decided that the interposed third electrode would be better in the form of a grid, a simple piece of wire bent back and forth, located as close to the filament as possible.

'I now possessed the first three-electrode vacuum tube – the Audion, granddaddy of all the vast progeny of electronic tubes that have come into existence since.'

That was in 1906 and de Forest was thirty-two.

This was the basic improvement on Fleming's diode valve, the difference being that it amplified signals. Now the valve could be used in radio communication and broadcasting. De Forest always said that he knew nothing about Fleming's invention in 1904 but there was a long and bitter controversy as to whether he had imitated Fleming's valve. Legal battles went on until 1943 when the United States Supreme Court ruled in de Forest's favour. Fleming did recognize that there was a big difference between the two inventions; he wrote:

'Sad to say, it did not occur to me to place the metal plate and the zig-zag wire in the same bulb and use an electron charge, positive or negative, on the wire to control the electron current to the plate. Lee de Forest, who had been following my work very closely, appreciated the advantage to be so gained, and made a valve in which a metal plate was fixed near a carbon filament in an exhausted bulb and placed a zig-zag wire, called a grid, between the plate and the filament.'

From that time until the First World War de Forest struggled continually to promote radio communication and the use of his valve in various ways. He became involved in many business deals and legal battles and he came to realize, as many had before, that however good an inventor he was he was no good as a businessman. He lost two fortunes and started making a third. At one point he was tricked by his financiers, found that his company had lost money and had to look for employment. He found it in the laboratories of the Federal Telegraph Company, on the other side of the continent, in San-Francisco. The directors of his own company, including himself, were prosecuted for fraud. He was under an order for arrest, was bailed out, and was able to raise a defence fund in loans from his former classmates at Yale. At the trial the counsel for the prosecution stated that he, with his co-directors, were charged with – 'The use of the mail to defraud, by selling stock to the public in a company incorporated for two million dollars whose only assets were the de Forest patents directed chiefly to a queer little bulb like an incandescent lamp which he called an audion and which device had been proven to be worthless and was not even a good lamp.' (This was the radio valve.) Three of the directors were sentenced to imprisonment, but de Forest himself was acquitted. Within a year he had organized a new company to manufacture valves, oscillators and transmitters and had repaid the loans for his defence with interest. This was the start of a third fortune.

In the meantime he made some progress with his ambition to broadcast music from a central station. The Press reported in 1909:

'De Forest's predictions regarding the developments of the wireless telephone are older than the dreams of fiction. He foresees the time when news and even advertising will be sent out to the public over wireless telephones and that opera will be brought into every house by the same means.'

The next year he did actually arrange for opera to be sent

out from the Metropolitan Opera House in New York. He also found time to be married. His wife (his first), a graduate in engineering of Cornell University working in the New York City Engineer's Office, became his business partner. Their honeymoon was also a business trip to Europe to sell the radio telephone. Before long they separated and de Forest married again – a musical comedy chorus girl.

The First World War made de Forest a rich man. In 1919, feeling he had exhausted the existing uses of the valve, he decided to branch out in a new direction and improve motion pictures by adding sound. He became a pioneer of sound and film motion pictures. He recorded in his diary 'Today I made my first "talking movie" picture – of myself, very hot and somewhat flurried; talked too loud and the photography very poor . . . But it was at last made, despite all jinxes and hoodoos – two months behind schedule, and after two years' hard work in preparation a definite promise of great things to come.' His 'phonofilm', as he called it, gave in New York the first public performance of talking pictures in a cinema and soon more and more cinemas were wired for sound.

In the nineteen-thirties he worked on the problems of television and even colour television. In the meantime his second marriage had ended in divorce and he had married again for the third and last time, a film actress. Much of his leisure in his sixties he spent in mountain climbing. By then he had three grandchildren by his first marriage and one by his second. He always regarded himself as the father of radio. The American Institution of Electrical Engineers recognized this when it awarded him its Edison medal 'for pioneering achievements in Radio and for the invention of the grid-controlled vacuum tube with its profound technical and social consequences'. Yet he felt his invention had been misused and expressed this strongly on the fortieth anniversary of his discovery to the National Association of Broadcasters:

'What have you gentlemen done with my child? He was conceived as a potent instrumentality for culture, fine music, the uplifting of America's mass intelligence. You have debased this child, you have sent him out in the streets in rags of ragtime, tatters of jive and boogie woogie, to collect money from all and sundry . . . You have made of him a laughing stock to the intelligence, surely a stench in the nostrils of the gods of the ionosphere; you have cut time into tiny parcels called spots (more rightly "stains'), wherewith the occasional fine program is periodically smeared with impudent insistence to buy or try.'

De Forest died in Hollywood in 1961. He often criticized himself: 'Perhaps a little more of good nature, of early affability, of social friendliness, generosity of spirit, a broader point of view would have found more friends worth while able and willing to aid over life's roughest obstacles.' He was a complex character; at the same time in harmony with his times, and in conflict with them.

THE ELECTRICAL WORKERS (1900–1918)

There was one unusual thing about the electrical workers. As we have seen in Chapter Five, they had two different kinds of employer. While most of them worked in private enterprise, for instance for contractors, many were employed in public enterprise by the Post Office. Because of this they had two trade unions, the Electrical Trades Union and the Post Office Engineering Union as it was called later. The division was not clear-cut; members of the E.T.U. also included men who worked in another kind of public enterprise, the town councils which had generating stations and lighting systems.

Two main changes were going on during these years. As the use of electricity grew in industry and for lighting, so more and more industries employed electricians and new kinds of work arose. The second change was in the economic situation. Prices rose considerably, and the values of wages fell. These changes meant that the unions had the opportunity to increase their membership, if they could take it, but also that they had continually to press for higher wages to compensate for the rise in the cost of living.

In 1914 the president of the E.T.U. declared: 'We embrace the ship, engineering, building, tramways, mines and maintenance work.' By then branches had been formed for electricians in shipbuilding, in various steel works, and cotton mills, and in Nobel's explosive works. Ships were now increasingly being equipped with electric light and generators. But this created problems for the workers: 'the conditions under which a large squad of men will be working practically night and day for a month or two to finish a ship and then nearly all of them stood off while the ship goes away, first for trials and then to wait for another ship when she goes for good.' There were struggles in the shipyards, sometimes successful, sometimes not, to get the recognized rates of pay. The contractors putting in electrical fittings on the battleships *Duncan* and *Cornwallis* refused to pay the union rate of 9½d. an hour; but Harland and Wolff at Belfast accepted it. A great contrast with this activity was the start of the first branch for cinema operators, in Glasgow.

The increase in generating and supplying electricity also brought problems. An attempt to form a branch of the men employed by B.T.H. at Rugby failed: 'Until we get B.T.H. into line with our other winding centres they will always constitute a menace,' said the E.T.U. organizer, 'I trust that any members going to work there will try to plant our flag. Get a move on inside and I will try to do the rest.' There were reports, too, that the power station engineers had begun to get together on their own and formed a separate Association of Station Engineers, and they had to be brought into the fold.

It was often the pressure on wages from the rising cost of living which caused the strikes in the years before the 1914–18 war. One of these was at an Earls Court exhibition in 1912. Twenty-seven union members were paid off when they refused to work on Bank Holiday for single-time pay. Immediately all five hundred men on the job stopped work. The contractor called in blacklegs but within two days he was obliged to agree that the job should be a closed shop, and that the blacklegs should be fired as well as the 'American Electrical boss', the American foreman whose ignorance of the customs had caused the dispute. The men refused to start work until he had gone.

It was clear to the unions that they would never be able to improve their members' wages unless their right to organize men anywhere was recognized by the employers. Two years later just before the First World War began the electricians were involved with the building trade workers of London in a long strike. The two trades had often worked closely together on sites. The building trade workers had been locked out by the London master builders because they refused to accept the 'document'. This was an agreement which men were required to sign that they would work peacefully for the employer, whether all of them were in the union or not. The E.T.U. had asked the electrical masters for a rise in wages from 9½d. to 11d. an hour. They were offered a ½d. immediately and another ½d. after three months if they would agree to work peacefully with non-unionists. This the E.T.U. refused and the five hundred members in London stopped work on 1st April, 1914. Their attitude was firm; next month the Fulham branch wrote to the union journal:

'We shall have to work too, with the blackleg and the scat, willy-nilly, if the masters win; so, boys, keep a stout heart, fight and beat the masters, then we will be able to say, 'Oh! yes. We want to return to work, but before we do you have got to send every scat and blackleg on the streets as we have been.'

Both sides stood firm and the dispute dragged on for several months. In June the London Central branch reported the situation:

'We are still in the thick of the fight. After nine weeks struggling for better conditions our boys are as firm and true as in the first few days of the strike and why should they not be? Have not the builders shown us the way to fight for principle? Those brave fellows, the builders' labourers, after 18 weeks of practically no strike pay, still determined to stand out, then, surely we, who are supposed to be more intelligent individuals, are not to be the ones to give in.'

Early in August when war was very close the employers offered 10½d. an hour without the condition that union members should work peacefully with non-unionists. On the day after Britain declared war on 4th August the E.T.U. accepted the offer; and the electricians returned to work along with the builders.

By that time the more militant actions of the E.T.U. had attracted more members; there were now just over 8,000, a big increase over the 702 sixteen years before. Some of this growth probably took place because in 1913 the union formed an auxiliary section to bring in semi-skilled men. There were now more and more of these men working as 'temporary lightmen, arc lamp trimmers, electric crane drivers, accumulator erectors, jointer's mates, dynamo attendants, telephone linesmen and other electrical workers'. Soon there was to be a far quicker growth.

The declaration of war in 1914 was a great shock. Most working men were against Britain entering the war, but once it had begun they were strongly pro-war, until 1917 when there was a great deal of discontent. The E.T.U. was no exception to this. On the day before the declaration it protested strongly against Britain becoming involved in a war which did not concern it. Later in 1914 its executive stated:

'Our opinion that there can be no possible justification for the governments of Europe in setting millions of men – who know nothing of secret diplomacy – against each other to kill, slay, and clear the world of the best of its manhood . . . our deepest regret that in this, the twentieth century, when education was supposed to be making rapid strides, the so-called most civilized nations of the world should have receded back to the methods of barbarism . . .'

All the same when, in 1914, the trade unions announced that there would be a truce between capital and labour in industry the E.T.U. supported it. However, when there were widespread unofficial strikes in the engineering industry for shorter hours and higher wages, the local districts of the union supported them.

The effect of the war was to cause a great expansion in all parts of the electrical industry, to increase the number of men employed, and to make new kinds of work. One important new section of the industry arose from the fact that submarines and tanks were equipped with batteries; the first branch of the E.T.U. for men in accumulator work was formed. There were also many more maintenance electricians because more advanced techniques were used. It was in electricity supply that the union made most progress. The first branch for station engineers started in Manchester in 1916, and by the end of the war there were 2,000 station engineers alone in the union. No wonder that the membership had risen from 8,000 to 31,000 in four years. It had paid to start the auxiliary section for semi-skilled men; it now included unskilled men and numbered nearly a quarter of the total. Wages had not kept pace with the cost of living but the 53-hour week had come down to 47.

The electrical workers employed in the Post Office had no strike funds but they did have a trade union, then called the Engineering and Stores Association. However it first had to win recognition from the Post Office, and this did not happen until 1906 when a Liberal government was in power. Straight away the union presented its claims. It said that the skill required of a maintenance lineman justified higher wages and that the long hours of work should be reduced; it pointed to the danger and hardship in the work of the construction men. For instance the cable jointer's work, in the days of horse transport: 'We wish to point out the disagreeable nature of this duty owing to the accumulation of gaseous matter, water and sweepings from the pavement and roads, and it frequently happens that the foul air which is let out by the raising of the covers causes lengthy illnesses to the men concerned. Some of these covers have to be left off for as long as an hour before it is possible to enter them.' The Post Office replied that the construction men were well looked after: 'The nature of a gang-hand's work is such that he must frequently leave home, but he is not required to walk long distances, since the men are given lodging allowances so that they may remain in the neighbourhood of their work. When the men are employed in sparsely populated districts, where lodgings are unobtainable, it is the department's practice to provide tents for the men's accommodation, together with a cook to prepare meals . . .' For the time being the union gained a 50½ hour week, a higher subsistence allowance, and the issue of protective clothing for linemen and ganghands.

The main change in the pre-war years was that, in 1912, the telephones were completely taken over by the Post Office. Before this much of the telephone network was in the hands of the National Telephone Company and the men and women employed by it had their own union. After this event the unions amalgamated into one, the Post Office Amalgamated Engineering and Stores Association, which took its present name, the Post Office Engineering Union, in 1919 during the period of militancy after the war.

The electrical workers in the Post Office were thus separated from their fellow workers in private enterprise. They were always in a minority. By the end of the 1914–18 war the membership of the Post Office union was less than half that of the E.T.U.

Additional Reading

Sir Ambrose Fleming, *Memories of a Scientific Life*, Marshall, Morgan & Scott, 1934.

Lee de Forest, *Father of Radio*, Chicago, 1950.

Degna Marconi, *My Father, Marconi*, Frederick Muller, 1962.

D. E. Dunlap, *Marconi, the Man and his Wireless*, New York, 1937.

Dunsheath, P., *A History of Electrical Engineering*, Faber & Faber, 1962.

CHAPTER SEVEN

Television and Broadcasting

TELEVISION, seeing at a distance, was first demonstrated by John Logie Baird in 1926 but the idea of television goes back fifty years before that. American, British and French scientists experimented from 1875 onwards with tiny selenium cells electrically sensitive to the influence of light. The main principle of television was known. But nothing practical was possible until after 1897 when the cathode-ray tube, on which modern television depends, was first made. Going further back, it was not possible to make the cathode-ray tube until there was scientific knowledge of the electron. Someone had to prove first that electrons existed and that their behaviour could be measured. Then, after it was known that a continuous stream of electrons was emitted by the cathode, a cathode-ray tube was made. The man who first proved the existence of the electron was J. J. Thomson.

SIR JOSEPH JOHN THOMSON (1856–1940)

Thomson was born at Cheetham Hill, Manchester, a few months after the end of the Crimean War and he died at the time of the Battle of Britain. His ancestors on his father's side were all lowland Scots and, on his mother's, Lancashire people. His family was fairly comfortably off; his father had a business as publisher and bookseller which his father had carried on before him. Through the business the family met men of science and letters. One day his father introduced him to James Prescott Joule, after whom the joule, the unit of work, was named, and said, 'Some day you will be proud to be able to say you have met that gentleman.'

After going for a year or two to a school for little boys and girls kept by two ladies, friends of his mother, Thomson was sent to a private day school for boys near his home. There he had a thorough grounding in Latin, English, mathematics, history and geography. The mathematics did not include any algebra but a great deal of arithmetic, which was well taught. One of his hobbies was gardening in his own small patch, and he thought he would like to be a botanist when he grew up. At another time he said he meant to go in for 'Original Research'. His parents meant him to be an engineer and they arranged for him to be apprenticed to a firm of locomotive makers. There was, however, a long waiting list and so, rather than keep him at school, his father sent him to Owens College in Manchester to have some scientific training. He was then only fourteen, two years younger than was normal. His father died two years later and, as the family could not now afford to pay the high premium for the apprenticeship, he stayed on at Owens College until he was nineteen.

Thomson was lucky in being able to go to Owens College; it was the first step forward in his career. Such a chance could not have happened in any other provincial town. Only Manchester had such a college as Owens. That city, the home of free trade and liberalism, was at the height of its prosperity. Manchester flourished in the age when cotton was king and England was the workshop of the world. It also had a tradition of science, with John Dalton and Joule. The college had been founded by John Owens, a Manchester merchant. Later on it changed its name twice and eventually became the university. At that time there was a brilliant staff of professors and teachers, better than many universities. During Thomson's first two years the college had very overcrowded accommodation in an old house in Quay Street, but one advantage of this was that it brought teachers and students closely together. As he was taking the engineering course he had most to do with the professor of engineering, the brilliant Osborne Reynolds. Thomson has left a picture of him:

'He was one of the most original and independent of men, and never did anything or expressed himself like anybody else. The result was that it was very difficult to take notes at his lectures, so that we had to trust mainly to Rankine's textbooks. Occasionally in the higher classes he would forget all about having to lecture, and after waiting for ten minutes or so, we sent the janitor to tell him that the class was waiting. He would come rushing into the room pulling on his gown as he came through the door, take a volume of Rankine from the table, open it apparently at random, see some formula or other and say it was wrong. He then went up to the blackboard to prove this. He wrote on the board with his back to us, talking to himself, and every now and then rubbed it all out and said that it was wrong. He would then start afresh on a new line, and so on. Generally, towards the end of the lecture, he would finish one which he did not rub out, and say that this proved that Rankine was right after all. This, though it did not increase our knowledge of facts, was interesting, for it showed the working of a very acute mind grappling with a new problem.' Thomson won a scholarship in engineering and a prize for an essay and obtained the college certificate in engineering. But that was the end of engineering for him. About this time he was described as 'wearing a nice brown suit, with a brown tie the bow of which was under one ear, a fact of which I dare say he was quite unaware, and was possibly indifferent . . .'

He had always been interested in mathematics and physics and the professor of mathematics suggested he should try for an entrance scholarship to Trinity College, Cambridge. This attracted him very much; Clerk Maxwell, the great mathematician was at Cambridge and his famous book on electricity and magnetism, on which Thomson had had some lectures, had recently been published. He stayed on at Owens College to work for the Cambridge examinations but he failed the first time and after another year's work he managed to win only a minor scholarship worth £75 a year.

Before he left Manchester he carried out a small piece of research of his own on 'Contact Electricity of Insulators'; it was good enough to be published by the Royal Society. Now aged nineteen he seemed to others 'a rather pallid, boney youth with the air of a serious but happy student, unassuming and modest without diffidence, very approachable and friendly'.

Thomson went to Trinity College, Cambridge, in 1876 and it remained his home until he died there in 1940. He found himself in a different world, a world in which conditions for those who wanted to study were excellent. As there was no room in the college he went into lodgings. 'I found, however, the lodgings so comfortable and my landlady so attentive, that I stayed in them for four years and did not come into College until I became a Fellow. I have never been able to remember, while I was working, to attend to a fire, nor work to any advantage when the room was cold, so I got on much better in lodgings where there was always someone about to look after the fire, than in rooms in College where the bedmaker would be away for the greater part of the day.'

As he had gone to Cambridge to get a good degree in mathematics he worked hard. He took no part in games or sports but he often went for long walks. The final examination lasted nine whole days, in two parts with an interval of ten days between them. 'It was held,' he wrote, 'in the depth of winter in the Senate House, a room in which there were no heating appliances of any kind. It certainly was horribly cold, though the ink did not freeze as it is reported to have once done.' However he came out second from the top in the first-class honours list. He was very soon elected a Fellow of his college for a thesis on the transformation of energy, and this meant leisure for several years' research.

Two years after taking his degree he became an assistant lecturer in mathematics in the University; a year later he was elected lecturer and gave courses on electromagnetism and electrostatics. In addition he took many tutorials and at one time he had eighteen hours of teaching mathematics a week. He was a keen teacher as the following account shows:

'One of my pupils came to me at the beginning of his third year with a very bad record. He was said to be idle, to take no interest in his work, and to have very little chance of getting through the Tripos. At first I agreed with this estimate, but we plodded on until we came to the subject of collision between two elastic spheres. I knew he was fond of billiards, and so I pointed out to him that the rules he used for playing certain shots at billiards followed at once from the mathematics. The result was marvellous. He had never before conceived that there was anything in mathematics that could interest any reasonable being. He now respected it, and began to work like a nigger . . .'

In the meantime Thomson started on the path which was to lead to his discovery of the electron. He began research into the behaviour of cathode rays. 'I was attracted to this,' he wrote, 'by the beautiful experiments on cathode rays which had lately been made by Crookes . . .' His first interest in Maxwell's theories of electromagnetic radiation had led him to cathode rays as a different kind of radiation. At this time there were two different schools of thought about the nature of these rays. This was one of the main problems of physics. The British scientists believed that the rays were made of particles whereas most of the German scientists thought that they were waves. The question was not settled until some years later when Thomson discovered the electron. At this time, however, in 1881, Thomson's research, taking only a first step in that direction, was limited to calculating what effect charged particles would have on each other, in order to prove the theory that cathode rays were composed of particles.

When he was only twenty-eight Thomson was appointed professor of physics and head of the now famous Cavendish Laboratory at Cambridge. Thomson himself was surprised. He wrote '. . . a well known college tutor had expressed the opinion that things had come to a pretty pass in the university when mere boys were made professors . . . I felt like a fisherman who with light tackle had casually cast a line in an unlikely spot and hooked a fish much too heavy for him to land.'

For the next ten years Thomson organized the Cavendish, published two important books, and continued research into cathode rays, but without any startling progress. Then two events led to the great step forward a few years later. In 1895 Röntgen discovered X-rays and one effect of this was that since they made a gas into a conductor of electricity Thomson's research could now be based on much better experiments. In the same year Cambridge University changed its regulations so that graduates from other universities could enrol as research students and gain a higher degree. The first of these students was Ernest Rutherford from New Zealand, the future great scientist who was to split the atom. Others followed and so Thomson had a brilliant team whose work could be directed to the problem in hand.

Thomson and his team in the Cavendish Laboratory started work on the problem in the autumn of 1895. The improvement in vacuum pumps, which had been brought about by the manufacture of electric lamps, meant that he could work with tubes with a very high vacuum. By 1897 he had been able to show that the cathode rays were rapidly moving material particles from a negative pole. Here is a picture of that time by his friend and biographer, Lord Rayleigh:

'In the summer of 1897 J. J. was bubbling over with enthusiasm over his work on cathode rays. The first I heard of it was from himself. I was at the time an undergraduate, but he knew I think from the questions I had asked him after his lectures that I was as eager to hear as he could be to talk, and chancing to meet on King's Parade he began to unfold to me what he had been doing – telling me that the cathode rays had now "turned out" to be particles, and particles quite different from atoms.'

Thomson then went on to measure the speed of the particles and he proved that the particles were far smaller than atoms. In fact he showed that the mass of a particle was about one eighteen hundredth part of that of an atom of hydrogen. Thomson's own words later were:

'I could see no escape from the conclusion that in the cathode rays we had particles far more minute than any hitherto recognized. I think the first announcement of this result was made at a Friday evening meeting of the Royal Institution on 30 April, 1897. Subsequent investigations have shown that these minute negatively charged particles, corpuscles I call them, are very widely diffused and form part of every kind of matter and play an important part in many physical phenomena.'

At the age of forty-one Thomson had brought about a revolution in science. Up to then the chemical atom was believed to be the smallest possible unit of matter. Now there was a more fundamental one, the electron, a particle of electricity which was a part of all chemical atoms. It is not surprising that when Thomson gave the evidence for the electron, at a meeting of the British Association in the autumn of 1899, in a paper entitled 'On the existence of masses smaller than atoms', the chemists present, whose work was based on the atom, were not satisfied. But Sir Oliver Lodge, the great physicist and forerunner of radio, who was to read the next paper at the meeting, said that Thomson's paper was so exciting that he found it difficult to concentrate on reading his own.

In science the discovery of the electron opened up a great new field in atomic theory. In technology the electron became a vital factor in modern engineering and the basis for hundreds of new devices and industries, including television. By 1911 it was possible to focus a beam of electrons on to a viewing screen.

Having accomplished his greatest work, Thomson remained professor at the Cavendish Laboratory until he was appointed master of Trinity College in 1918; he was then succeeded by Rutherford. His whole life centred on the Cavendish; in fact, at the age of thirty-three, he married one of its students. They had a son, an eminent physicist who was awarded the Nobel prize, and a daughter. Thomson was a humorous sociable man, very popular with both teachers and students. Rutherford, who became his close friend, gave a picture of him:

'He is just forty and looks quite young, small, rather straggling moustache, short, wears his hair (black) rather long, but has a very clever-looking face, and a very fine forehead and a radiating smile, or grin as some call it when he is scoring off anyone.'

After about 1914 much of his time was taken by official bodies and committees. He was president of the Royal Society for five years and during the 1914–18 war he was a member and often chairman of the Board of Inventions and Research under the Admiralty. In the meantime the Cavendish Laboratory, under his guidance, produced seven Nobel prize winners and over seventy professors in universities all over the world. Although he had never had any private income in addition to his salaries, he left a large fortune of £82,000 which was due to his business ability and dealings on the Stock Exchange. He died at Trinity College, Cambridge, and his ashes were interred in Westminster Abbey, near the graves of Newton, Kelvin and Rutherford.

Between 1897 when J. J. Thomson discovered the electron and 1926 when Baird gave the first practical demonstration of television a number of scientists each took a step towards the transmitting of living pictures. These two events had, however, no direct connection. Baird's system of television was a mechanical one, quite different from the modern electronic one.

The principle of television was known well before Thomson's discovery; scanning a great number of very small points on the object to be transmitted, turning their brightness or dimness into electrical impulses, sending the impulses and turning them back into light values which are reassembled into the original object. It was a problem of getting the speeds right. As early as 1883 a German student, Paul Nipkow, had invented a simple scanning machine. It was based on a revolving disc pierced with holes in a spiral, through which a strong beam of light shone on the object to be transmitted. Later on Baird's system used the Nipkow discs. Nipkow himself could not do any more because of technical difficulties and this mechanical system got no further until Baird's system appeared.

The discovery of the electron stimulated other scientists to tackle the problems of 'seeing by electricity' from another angle. Germans, Russians and Englishmen developed the method of directing a beam of electrons on to a viewing screen at the enlarged end of a cathode-ray tube. By 1908 the Englishman, Campbell-Swinton had pointed the way to the future. He wrote in a letter to *Nature* in June 1908:

'. . . This part of the problem of obtaining distant electric vision can probably be solved by the employment of two beams of Kathode rays (one at the transmitting and one at the receiving end) synchronously deflected by the varying fields of two electromagnets placed at right angles to one another and energized by two alternating electric currents of widely varying frequencies, so that the moving extremities of the two beams are caused to sweep synchronously over the whole of the required surfaces within the one-tenth of a second necessary to take advantage of visual persistence. Indeed so far as the receiving apparatus is concerned, the moving Kathode beam has only to be arranged to impinge on a sufficiently sensitive fluorescent screen and given suitable variations in its intensity to obtain the desired result. The real difficulties lie in devising an efficient transmitter.'

Three years later a scientist at the St. Petersburg Technological Institute used a cathode-ray tube to receive pictures transmitted over a wire. After that there was no real progress until Baird invented his system, ignoring electronics.

JOHN LOGIE BAIRD (1888–1946)

Baird was born at Helensburgh, Dunbartonshire, the youngest of the four children of the Reverend John Baird, Minister of the west parish of that small town. The Reverend Baird had taken the Master of Arts and Bachelor of Divinity degrees at Glasgow University, had gone to Helensburgh and stayed there all his life. His little church flourished but he himself never advanced to a more important place or position although he was a talented, able man. His unorthodox views and irreverent sense of humour did not make him popular with the dignitaries of the church. 'Now Willie', he said to one of his students of theology, 'you believe the story of Jonah and the whale?' 'I do indeed, sir' Willie said. 'Aye, Willie, you and the whale rival each other in swallowing capacity.' Baird's grandfather on his mother's side was an artist but when he died she was cared for by an uncle, a wealthy Glasgow shipbuilder. Baird left an account of his childhood:

'The home in which we lived was not a manse, but belonged to my father, who had purchased it after his marriage, with the help of my mother's dowry. It was an old stone house called "The Lodge", built in the most inconvenient possible fashion, but with a fair sized garden, in which I spent the greater part of my childhood playing with Willie Brown, the small son of a gardener who lived next door. . . .

'The church dominated my life and the life of those around

me; it was a living force in those days and I was a whole-hearted believer. I thought that God was actually floating somewhere overhead, a stern man with a beard, something like Papa, only of enormous dimensions, infinitely powerful and fearsome . . . By the time I was twenty I knew, or thought I knew, that I was just an animal, a mechanism, a cousin of the arboreal ape. The clergymen who told me I was an immortal spirit imprisoned in mortal clay I regarded as hypocrites and humbugs.'

Baird went first to a small private school where he was happy and learned to read and write easily and then to a preparatory school, ruled with the cane by a middle-aged spinster where he had a miserable time. His third school, in Helensburgh, where he started at the age of ten, was a poor imitation of a public school. Sport came before everything, and Baird was no good at it. There was plenty of Latin, which he disliked, but no science and little mathematics. He was interested in science, however, provided it was practical; as the proud owner of a camera he was president of the school photographic society. He and a friend, inspired by the flights of the Wright brothers, built a glider. He constructed a small working telephone exchange in his bedroom, connected with school friends in their homes, and a small lighting plant, using a home-made dynamo and a water wheel. Later in life he wrote:

'I read a great deal of everything and anything and it is interesting to consider what out of all this I have retained. There is much of Goethe's Faust, something of Tolstoy, much of Voltaire, much of Shakespeare's Macbeth and Hamlet. Not that these classics were my favourites; favourites came and went: Guy Boothby, Max Pemberton, W. W. Jacobs, Jerome K. Jerome and many others. Not one line of any of these has left a trace, whereas even today, after over thirty years, I remember whole passages from the classical authors; their words bit deep. One popular author, however, soars far above all others and takes his place among the classics. In my boyhood and youth he was a demigod; the reading of any new book by him I regarded as a feast. This was H. G. Wells and today he still occupies a high place, although he is no longer a demigod.'

As soon as he left school Baird went to the Royal Technical College at Glasgow. His father wanted him to go into the church but gave way to his son's wishes. Baird's course was in electrical engineering and eventually, after five years, he obtained the College diploma and associateship. It took him so long because his studies were continually interrupted by long illnesses. At the same time as his college course he served an engineering apprenticeship in Hailey's Industrial Motors and the Argyle Motor Works near Glasgow. Hours of work were long: the start at 6.00 a.m. was often followed by overtime. Afterwards he recalled his first job as an apprentice in 1909, chipping grooves in some castings:

'I remember they were called spring housings. Week after week I chipped these little grooves, with all around me the most depressing conditions, and in the winter it was icy cold. The result was that my work was punctuated by perpetual ill health. . . .'

Soon after he finished at the technical college Baird persuaded his parents to let him go to Glasgow University to study for a B.Sc. degree in electrical engineering and physics. This was one of the happiest periods of his life. He enjoyed the social life after the lack of it at the technical college. In fact he was as much interested in his own practical experiments at home as in the university studies. In the kitchen of The Lodge he spent as much time as possible in experimenting with selenium (light-sensitive) cells, talking pictures and even crude attempts at television.

In 1914 the war put an end to his studies when he was in the final year. Everyone thought the war would soon be over, but Germany showed no signs of giving way and Baird went to enlist. He presented himself at the recruiting office.

'The medical examiner, a shrewd-looking old gentleman, examined my skinny form with sad and disapproving eyes, tapped my scanty chest and placed his ear to listen to my wheezy breathing. An assistant ran a tape-measure round me and shouted the paltry inches with contempt. "Do you suffer from colds very much?" asked the doctor. "Yes," said I, "a great deal." "Every winter you are knocked up, I suppose?"

he asked; then grunted: "Aye, aye, umphn. You can dress now." He went to his desk and wrote something on a piece of paper which he endorsed with a large rubber stamp. I examined it and read in large red letters: "Unfit for any service".

Wanting to do something useful rather than go back to the university, he obtained a job as assistant mains engineer in the Clyde Valley Electrical Power company which supplied the shipbuilding yards and engineering and munition works in the district. However the work was too much for his health. He was responsible for repairing breakdowns at any hour of the day or night. He wrote:

'It was a horrible job. My memory conjures up visions of standing the whole night in the rain, cold and miserable, while Stibbs, the chief ganger, and his men dug holes in the road to find faulty cables. Trying to placate a gang of truculent Irish labourers at four o'clock in the morning, when they want to stop the job and go home, is anything but pleasant. Sometimes in the night drunken fights started, . . . Sordid, miserable work, punctuated by repeated colds and influenza. I wanted more money. I received thirty shillings a week and was unable to get a better job because I was always ill.'

Realizing that he could not make a career in engineering Baird decided that he could be a successful businessman. His first commercial venture was with a patent sock which he invented. He had always suffered from cold feet and the special sock which he had manufactured was to cure this trouble for everybody. Advertised as 'The Baird Undersock, Medicated, Soft, Absorbent. Keeps the feet warm in winter and cool in summer. Ninepence per pair, post free', this article sold well thanks to Baird's vigorous salesmanship. He combined with it a shoe cleaner, Osmo Boot Polish, and within a year he had a prosperous little business. Then he was ill again, his business fell away and he decided to go to a warm climate, to Trinidad. In his own words:

'I decided to close down the Baird Undersock Company and try my luck in the Caribbean Paradise. I found when I closed the company that I had made roughly £1,600. That is to say, in twelve months of business on my own I had made more than I would have made in twelve years as Clyde Valley Engineer. I was full of optimism and set out blithely for the West Indies, taking a cheap passage in a cargo boat so as to keep as much as possible of my capital intact. I had three trunks filled with samples and cotton and other goods to sell to the natives.'

Finding before long that the natives did not want his goods, he decided that in view of the plentifulness of fruit and sugar, he would go in for jam making. He started a primitive factory consisting of bamboo huts and copper vats heated by wood fires. As the jam would not sell in Trinidad, and Baird fell ill of malaria, he returned to London, having sold his factory for £5. He was still confident that he could be successful in business but it was a bad time to try. The post-war boom broke in the winter of 1920–21. Baird tried a number of ventures, including trading in honey, coir fibre dust and soap, in the midst of which he was ill for six months. He was beginning to make a success of another product – Baird's Speedy Cleaner – when he had a complete nervous and physical breakdown and he was told he must get out of London for a complete rest. He went to Hastings with what he had left, £200.

At Hastings Baird began experiments with television which were so successful that after two years he moved back to London where before long he was able to give practical demonstrations. He assembled his apparatus on the washstand in his bedroom in the lodgings he shared with a friend. Fortunately for him a good deal of old Government radio stock was available. All the requirements for television were already known, the problem was to combine them in a working model. Baird understood the basic principle of breaking up a picture into small elements of light and shadow and transmitting these in sequence by the action of scanning. His method of scanning was the Nipkow mechanical one, using a rotating disc pierced with holes in two spirals, which was driven by an electric fan motor. A light-sensitive, selenium cell converted the signals into electrical impulses which were fed to a neon lamp. He used a tea chest as a base for the motor, the projection lamp was housed in a biscuit tin and the lens through which it shone was a fourpenny cycle one; the discs were cut from a cardboard hat box. The whole thing was held together with scrap wood, darning needles, string and sealing wax.

One afternoon he at last succeeded in transmitting the flickering image, the coarse shadow, of a Maltese cross cut out of cardboard, over a distance of two to three feet. After this success he put an advertisement in *The Times*; it appeared in June 1923:

> Seeing by Wireless – Inventor of apparatus wishes to hear from someone who will assist (not financially) in making working models.

This led, not to an assistant, but to financial help and to publicity. He sold a one-third interest in his invention for £200 to a businessman, and an article appeared in the *Kinematography Weekly* in April 1924. The writer described the 'Radio Kinema':

> 'Not so long ago I visited one John Logie Baird at his laboratory at Hastings and saw a demonstration which proved that he has proceeded so far along the road to radio vision as to make it almost a commercial proposition, for the whole of the apparatus used in the experiment can be purchased for £40. I myself saw a cross, the letter H, and the figures of my hand reproduced by this apparatus across the width of the laboratory. The images were quite sharp and clear although a little unsteady.'

There was a long way to go before television was a commercial proposition. The development was very nearly cut short completely. Baird tried to increase his voltage with a large number of batteries and through carelessness gave himself a powerful electric shock which nearly killed him. Only the fact that he fell backwards, breaking the circuit, saved his life. In August 1924 he left Hastings and settled in two small attic rooms at 22 Frith Street, Soho.

Baird gradually improved his apparatus until, instead of shadows, he could send from one room to another the outlines of simple objects. His money was running out when he had a windfall. Selfridge's Stores in Oxford Street asked him to give demonstrations to attract customers with this novelty. He was paid £25 a week for three weeks. This was in April 1925. Queues of curious spectators waited to see outlines of shapes sent a few yards by a simple wireless transmitter.

Soon, however, Baird was again so short of money that he was forced to sell pieces of apparatus. Fortunately his ship-builder cousins in Scotland backed him with £500. Two industrial firms wanted to encourage this pioneer work; one gave him £200 worth of batteries, the other £200 worth of valves. 'For hard-headed business men to give £200 worth of goods to a dilapidated and penniless crank in a garret is a phenomenon worth recording,' was Baird's comment. 'It was a bright spot in the darkness of anxious days.' Until then he had been quite on his own.

He could not yet show any detail in the picture. All he could give was a black and white effect; the human face appeared as a white oval in which the open mouth showed as a flickering black spot. Then one day in October 1925, after trying for a long time to improve the light-sensitive element, Baird noticed a big improvement in the picture of his object – a ventriloquist's dummy called Bill. Instead of a white oval with three black blobs as before, he could show the rounding of the head, and the nose, eyes and eyebrows with shading and detail. At once he called in the office boy from the floor below, bribed him to take the dummy's place in the blinding light and heat of the lamps, and looking through the little square opening of the viewer, could see the same effect.

His next step was to get recognition, and publicity, from people whose opinions would carry weight. Baird therefore invited the members of the Royal Institution to see a demonstration. On the evening of Friday, 27th January, 1926, about fifty scientists in evening dress arrived at 22 Frith Street. 'This gorgeous gathering,' wrote Baird, 'found that they were expected to climb three flights of narrow stone stairs and then to stand in a narrow draughty passage, while batches of six at a time were brought into the tiny attic rooms which formed my laboratory.' On the following day *The Times* gave television its first important publicity:

'Members of the Royal Institution and other visitors to a

laboratory in an upper room in Frith Street, Soho, on Tuesday saw a demonstration of apparatus invented by Mr. J. L. Baird.

'For the purpose of the demonstration the head of a ventriloquist's doll was manipulated as the image to be transmitted though the human face was also reproduced. First on a receiver in the same room as the transmitter and then on a portable receiver in another room. The visitors were shown recognizable reception of the movements of the dummy head and of a person speaking. The image as transmitted was faint and often blurred, but substantiated the claim that through the "Television", as Mr. Baird had named the apparatus, it is possible to transmit and reproduce instantly the details of movement, and such things as the play of expression on the face.'

The apparatus used was very similar to that which can be seen in the Science Museum at South Kensington.

Immediately after this success Baird's company, Television Ltd., was granted, two licences for experimental transmissions at stations 2TV in London and 2TW in Harrow. Baird moved to grander premises in Motograph House, near Leicester Square, where he began transmission. A journalist who called on him described him as he emerged from under a bench, a pale-faced man with a shock of tangled light hair, clad in a grey flannel shirt without collar, dusty flannel trousers showing bare ankles, and grubby carpet slippers.

In 1927 the problems were to improve the quality of the picture and the range of transmission, and at the same time to work towards selling the product. There was always a danger from competition; an American company demonstrated a transmission from Washington to New York. Stimulated by this, in May 1927 Baird successfully sent pictures between London and Glasgow over a Post Office cable. The Baird company now began to advertise receivers for sale at 30 guineas. Partly because of this the magazine *Popular Wireless* offered a £1,000 challenge to the company to give a demonstration on its own conditions which included the showing of movement, but Baird was unable to accept it. However he made a sensational advance in the range of transmission when, in February 1928, pictures were sent across the Atlantic, and soon after passengers on a liner received pictures in mid-ocean. Baird was compared with Marconi.

He now became involved in the world of high finance. A second company, Baird Television Development Company, had been formed in 1927 with a capital of £125,000 and the then chairman of the Daimler Company as chairman. Businessmen began to speculate about television. In 1928 a third company, Baird International Television appeared with a capital of £700,000. Baird himself did not take to the financial manœuvres which were going on. He did not enjoy arguing with the directors at the far too numerous board meetings:

'I was busy with my wheels and pulleys and soon came to regard board meetings as analogous to going to church – functions to be slept through. Sometimes I woke up with a start at some of the proceedings at these meetings, but after a few squeaks I relapsed again into dreams of further permutations and combinations of wire and mirror drums and lamps.' (By this time Baird was using the mirror drum, a revolving drum with thirty mirrors set round its rim, instead of the Nipkow disc, for scanning.)

Baird himself was living in comfort for the first time for many years. But he found that his stomach could not stand rich living and his doctor warned him to avoid it.

At this point the future of Baird's television and the profits his backers could make depended on what support he could get from the B.B.C. The Baird Company asked for permission to use a B.B.C. station for experimental transmissions. A demonstration was held but in 1928 permission was refused. The B.B.C.'s attitude was that television was too crude and that without some quite new principle or method it would not be good enough for a service to the public. It would be wrong therefore to use public stations for television as it was. On the medium-wave band used by Baird a television service could be started only by stopping one of the sound broadcasts and Baird's transmissions were too bad to justify that. The B.B.C. pointed out that artists still had to sit or stand rigidly in order to be televised. In fact at this stage the quality of Baird's transmission was poor because he used only 30 lines and 12 frames per second.

Baird's financial backers and publicity men were very anxious to launch his television as it was before any better system came along. They made strenuous efforts to get public support, with continued demonstrations and new devices by Baird. In 1928 he gave a demonstration of colour television in which he used coloured scanning discs. He showed at the National Radio Exhibition a set which combined sight and sound and in which the definition was much better. Early in 1929 he was able to show the movement of boxers in a ring and cyclists riding.

This pressure was successful after questions had been asked in the House of Commons. A group of members of Parliament, after seeing a demonstration recommended that the B.B.C. should reverse its decision made six months earlier. Eventually, transmission from the Baird studios in Long Acre through the B.B.C. station 2LO began on 30th September, 1929. They were made from 11 a.m. to 11.30 a.m. on five days a week. Vision only could be sent, or vision and sound at different times, because only one transmitter was available until the Brookmans Park station was opened. The wave band width was 10 kilocycles. Baird's Televisor, which was used for reception, gave a picture 2 inches x 4 inches in size. It cost 25 guineas and few were sold.

Baird was now so well known that at Hastings the town council placed a plaque on the wall of the house where he had done his first work. It read: 'Television first demonstrated by John Logie Baird from experiments started here in 1924.' Baird was present at the unveiling in November 1929; he said:

'. . . It is interesting to note that the machines now used are, in principle, almost identical with that early apparatus. I need not go into technical details, but there are the same neon tubes, the same disc with its holes, and the same type of motor to drive the disc.'

In 1930 sound and vision were broadcast together. A few months later the first television play was produced, The Man with Flower in his Mouth by Pirandello, but only one figure could be shown at a time. Baird himself had gone off in another direction. This was the showing of television programmes on a big screen to a large audience as if it were in a cinema. The screen was an elaborate arrangement of a honeycomb of over 2,000 cells into each of which a peanut-type filament lamp was placed. At the London Coliseum, 'Television, the New Baird System, British Invention' appeared in the music-hall bill and the thrilled audience saw the faces of celebrities talking to it. These faces included those of some members of the Labour Government in 1930, the first Lord of the Admiralty, the Minister of Transport, the daughter of Ramsay MacDonald, the Prime Minister, Sir Oswald Mosley, the future leader of the British fascists, who had just resigned from the government because it had rejected his schemes for reducing unemployment. There were then over two million unemployed. In June 1931 television scored another triumph when Baird made a sensation by televising from Epsom the finish of the Derby.

Baird television went further ahead in 1932. The B.B.C. equipped a studio with Baird's apparatus, agreed to finance the programmes and started the first official broadcasts. It promised that this arrangement would continue for two years. The programmes went out on Mondays to Fridays from 11.00 p.m. to 11.30 p.m. Typical items in 1932 were: ju-jutsu, fencing, exclusive fashions, Mr. and Mrs. Mollison (*née* Amy Johnson), the aviators, film and stage stars, performing seals, toys, art treasures, ventriloquilism, music-hall turns of the nineties, and Dick Whittington complete with cat. The broadcasts were still regarded as experimental and the B.B.C. was still cautious. It spent only £2,225 on television in 1932 and £7,129 in 1933. There were still only about 500 television sets in use.

All seemed to be going well with Baird television but it was not to last. Baird was still convinced that his mechanical method of scanning was the only practicable one. 'There is no hope for television by means of cathode-ray tubes,' he told the Americans in September 1931. But other television systems developed, the chief of which was electronic. Campbell Swinton had forecast in 1908 the use of the cathode-ray tube for both transmitting and receiving. Very soon after Baird started his experiments with a mechanical system at Hastings in 1924 scientists in America began work on an electronic one. While this work was developed by the giant Radio Corporation of America, E.M.I. continued it in England. By 1934 E.M.I. had developed the Emitron television camera. In that year the Marconi Company and E.M.I. pooled their interests and formed the Marconi E.M.I. Television Company. This meant that the joint system, consisting of the Emitron camera and a Marconi transmitter was now available for television. It was a powerful competitor to the Baird system.

In the same year the experimental period which the B.B.C. had guaranteed to Baird ended. In 1934 the Postmaster General set up a committee which inquired into the future of television. It said that high definition television was good enough for the B.B.C. to start a public service. The B.B.C. was instructed to test the two systems, Baird's and E.M.I.–Marconi's in alternate weeks. Unfortunately for Baird the E.M.I.–Marconi system was on 405 lines with 50 frames per second whereas his was only on 24 lines with 25 frames per second. In addition, in Baird's system a film of the scene had to be made, developed immediately, and then scanned while still wet, instead of the scene itself. This made it inconvenient, cumbersome and expensive. The first regular high definition television service was started by the B.B.C. in November, 1936. It then became necessary to choose one system and the Marconi–E.M.I. system was chosen. Baird and his mechanical system had lost; the big firms with ample laboratories, plenty of money and strong interests in electronics had won.

'The bitter blow – the B.B.C. adopted the Marconi system,' wrote Baird. 'And so, after all these years, we were taken off the air!' But he remained optimistic. 'It seemed to me,' he wrote, 'that now we should concentrate on television for the cinema, and should work hand in glove with Gaumont – British, installing screens in their cinemas and working towards the establishment of a broadcasting company independent of the B.B.C. for the supply of television programmes to cinemas.' So he set to work to show that the future of large screen and colour television depended on the mechanical system he had developed.

When the war came in 1939 television closed down. There were then only about 20,000 receivers in use. Baird was anxious to use his abilities in a government research department but he was never asked to. He spent the war, almost single-handed now, working on his large screen colour system. He had married in 1931 the daughter of a diamond merchant of Johannesburg and they had a son and a daughter. He sent his family away to Devonshire but he could not stay away from his laboratory in a bomb-damaged building at Sydenham and he remained there throughout the bombing of London. He lived on the capital he had saved from the Baird Company which had gone bankrupt and paid his two assistants out of his own pocket.

During the war Baird did produce a greatly improved colour television transmitter which showed a picture 2 feet by 2 feet 6 inches. But he wrote to a friend: 'My position here is very difficult, but I can still carry on for a time on my own.' His health, never good, became worse. When his money was spent he obtained a post as consultant to Cable and Wireless Ltd. This gave him enough money to continue his own experiments while he worked for the firm on applications of television to the transmission of facsimiles by telegraph. In November 1945 he caught another of the severe chills he had always suffered from. He could not recover from it and died at Bexhill on 13th June, 1946. Five years after his death the London County Council placed a memorial plaque on the wall of 22 Frith Street. It reads: 'In 1926 in this house John Logie Baird, 1888–1946, first demonstrated television.'

Baird made a great and unique contribution to television, handicapped though he was by ill-health and lack of money. The B.B.C. gained useful experience from the period of his experimental transmissions with them. His contribution was not so much in the science or technology of television as in his enthusiasm and persistence which created publicity for it. This stimulated others with laboratories and money to do research. If Baird did nothing else he made the electronics industry take television seriously. Unfortunately he was on the losing side in the battle between the two systems of television, as Brunel had been in the conflict between the two gauges on the railways.

THE ELECTRICAL WORKERS (1919–1939)

The electrical workers increased greatly in numbers and in

industrial strength during these years between the wars. There were good reasons for this. The inter-war years were the years of queues of unemployed, idle factories, yards and mines, and hunger marchers. But at the same time there was a great deal of technological advance, new industries developed which partly offset the decline of the old ones, and people who were in work were better off. The electrical workers were fortunate because they were employed as much, or more, in the new industries as in the old such as mining, textiles, general engineering and shipbuilding. The new industries which came to full strength in the inter-war years were electrical engineering, chemicals, rayon, radio, motion pictures, aircraft and motor engineering, and in nearly all of these electrical workers were essential. Therefore they suffered from unemployment far less than most other workers. The electrical workers through their two unions, the Electrical Trades Union for those employed in private enterprise and the Post Office Engineering Union, made full use of their opportunity to raise their standards of living: sometimes their action was through strikes, sometimes by negotiation with the employers' organization or through the new conciliation bodies, the National Joint Industrial Councils. These councils, also called Whitley Councils, composed of representatives of both employers and employees, were meant to discuss not only wages and conditions but also problems of efficiency and management.

The most important of the new industries was electrical generation and supply. It had lagged behind that in other countries until 1920 but now it grew rapidly. At first there were a large number of small power stations but, after the Central Electricity Board was set up under the Electricity (Supply) Act of 1926, the industry was concentrated in a small number of base load stations and new super-stations. The national grid came into operation. Total output increased fourfold between 1925 and 1939. Electricity became cheaper as the price of coal fell. With the 'kitchen revolution' and the growth of all kinds of domestic appliances the demand for electricity grew tremendously. The number of consumers increased twelvefold between 1920 and 1938. Employment rose too and the number of workers in the whole of the electrical industry more than doubled during these years.

In these conditions the trade unions of the electrical workers could not fail to grow. They had their ups and downs, though, as the following figures show:

Year	*Membership* *E.T.U.*	*P.O.E.U.*
1920	57,292	22,282
1923	26,165	15,308
1925	29,241	17,962
1927	25,712	18,662
1932	30,912	15,118
1935	40,270	23,002
1939	70,065	39,446

The figures show for both unions the post-war peak, the effects of the slump of 1921 and, for the E.T.U., of the General Strike of 1926; how slowly the membership crept back to the level of 1920, and how rapid the growth was in the late thirties.

The men in the E.T.U. were more affected by industrial boom and slump than were those in the Post Office Engineering Union. They felt that they were fighting a battle against capitalist employers. In 1923 the union organizer reported:

'We have weathered the greatest storm in the history of the Trade Union movement and defeated the employers in their attempt to smash the organized workers. Let us now go forward and build up an organization that will withstand the onslaught of any federation of employers or capitalist Press.'

By 1926 the membership had recovered to 29,000. In the General Strike of that year the E.T.U. members were in a peculiar position. They were not all affected in the same way. Those in engineering, shipbuilding, and in transport came out on strike but those in power supply often did not. There was much confusion in the ranks. The union leaders criticized the T.U.C.:

'The majority of the T.U.C. General Council felt that a general strike was of such a terrible character and its effects of such a nature that they dared not embark upon it. The result was, of course, that although certain industries stopped other industries continued and as all industries are so much inter-woven and there is no dividing line such a state of chaos was created that in twelve days the strike had to be called off, with disastrous results for those who took part in it. The very conception of a "partial" general strike foredoomed it to failure.'

The response of members to the strike call and the situation in the towns varied in different parts of the country. In Birmingham the local engineering committee was arrested and ten electrical workers there fined £10 each. The union members in G.E.C., Birmingham Small Arms, the Lanchester Motor works, Dunlop Rubber, Cadbury's and the railway carriage works came out, as did those in the tramways and buses. Those in power supply were not called out. In Glasgow 80 per cent of the wiremen and winders and of the traction linesmen in the Corporation tramways came out but they returned to work before the strike was called off. On Merseyside the men in the tramways and in the telephone manufacturing works were solid; those who were in doubt ceased work so as to be sure. In south and west Wales the members were all out. In Bradford the response was described as 'electrical'. When the tram authorities threatened to run a service they themselves were threatened with a strike at the power stations. This is how the Bradford men saw the situation:

'By Tuesday night all but a few men on maintenance in industry not yet called upon were out. What a response! On the Wednesday (what surrender!) news came through by wireless: "Strike called off . . ." It was felt that we had accomplished our object. But the fighters had a bitter pill to swallow, it was to hear that the generals had deserted them. The task had proved too big for the drawing-room and after dinner speech makers. Not only had the miners been deserted but their own members were thrown to the mercy of the employers . . . Mistakes can be allowed for but cowardice, never.'

There were complaints about the vindictiveness of local councils and public bodies in refusing to return men to their jobs but on the whole the E.T.U. was not much affected, except for those members in shipbuilding and manufacture. By the end of 1926 the membership was only 183 down on the previous year. Even when it fell 10 per cent in the following year the E.T.U. did not suffer as much as other unions. By 1929 the union had turned the corner to growth because of the increase in electrification. This increase maintained the membership at around 31,000 during the years of depression when other unions suffered heavily – 1937 was 'the best year yet'. Rearmament had started and there was more Government work for electrical workers.

From the beginning the workers knew that science and technology were on their side. 'Let us realize that scientific progress is forcing on the use of electrical energy and be ready to demand better conditions' was the cry in 1922. The advance of the electrical supply industry brought problems. When the Electricity Supply Act reorganized the industry, men became redundant. Automatic boiler houses and automatic switchgear became more common. These and other labour-saving devices placed more responsibility on the workers; in the superstations the amount of labour per unit generated had fallen by half. Higher wages were therefore demanded. There were also problems of moving men from generation to distribution. Disputes sometimes led to strike action as in the unofficial strike at Fulham power station in 1936. The union debated whether to press for shorter hours or higher wages. In the sub-stations the use of mercury arc rectifiers reduced the number of employees. The claims for compensation for redundancy increased. Therefore the union should demand that shifts should be reduced to six hours.

Throughout these years inventions used in industry created new kinds of work and new skills. In the E.T.U. new branches were continually being opened to cater for these new and growing occupations. For example in 1920 there were five new branches for cinema operators and film workers. The cinema operators were always difficult to organize, and there were more of them. The nineteen-thirties were the greatest years of the cinema, before television came, with grand new Odeons opening all over the country. But the operators were described as 'spineless individuals': sweated labour working seven days a week or 60 hours a week, carrying out electrical maintenance as well as operating, and even cleaning and sweeping. Immediately after the war there were local agreements for a 48-hour week but they broke down, and in 1938 the cinema projectionist members of the E.T.U. in London, Manchester and Hull went on strike for reduced hours. They were successful only in Manchester.

Other new branches were opened to cater for the new and growing occupations. In 1922 there was a new branch for lift engineers, and another for electrical crane drivers; in 1935 in the film industry, the London Studios branch, and new branches for sound technicians – this was, as the union organizers said, 'A new name in our history, but one in which there are great possibilities; they are a very essential part of talking pictures, a very highly trained and highly paid body of men.' In this new industry there was no difficulty in agreeing about conditions of work. Just before the 1939 war work by the union in the big new radio industry resulted in three new branches of radio engineers. In the new aircraft industry low-paid labour was investigated. In the expanding chemical industry, there was a growing body of skilled maintenance men and the E.T.U. found I.C.I. ready to agree on a 47-hour week and a minimum hourly rate.

Contrasted with these advances in the new and expanding scientific industries was the situation in coal mining. Colliery electricians were the worst paid of any. They had to go into the most difficult places in the mines with heavy kits and testing apparatus and for this their wages were little more than those of a 'surface labourer'. Electricity was being used more in the mines and the safety of electrical appliances became a heavier responsibility. The difficulty, though, in getting better conditions was not so much from the mine owners as from the miners, who objected to the E.T.U. poaching on their territory. They themselves were fighting a rearguard action all the time.

The wages and conditions of work of the electrical workers varied a good deal, mainly as the cost of living changed. The reason for this was that the National Joint Industrial Councils were important in the electrical industry, unlike many other big industries. Negotiations on the councils between the two sides resulted in sliding scales of wages, wages moving up or down according to the official cost of living index. From 1919 onwards the E.T.U. took part in the N.J.I.C.s set up for electrical contracting, electrical supply, cable making, and in a number of government departments such as the Admiralty. In manufacture and shipbuilding the electrical workers' wages were linked with those of the engineering workers. Wages fell in the first few years after the war, rose slightly between the General Strike and the Slump of 1931, fell slightly in 1931, started to rise again in 1934 and continued rising until 1939. Sometimes the E.T.U. found the sliding scales were to its advantage, sometimes not. In contracting work they were an advantage during the depression of the 1920's. In 1930 however it gave notice to the N.J.I.C. for electrical supply to end the agreement on the sliding scale because of the reduction in wages it caused. The employers countered with a demand for a reduction of one penny per hour. This claim was referred to the Industrial Court to judge. The result was favourable to the workers; in seven areas of the country there was a reduction of only a halfpenny an hour, and in six areas there was no reduction at all.

There was still the old difficulty of getting employers with government contracts to carry out the fair wages rule laid down by the government in 1891. In 1939 the union organizer wrote:

'We are still troubled with the Jerry Contractor, although due to war circumstances quite a number have been forced out of business. If only the public authorities who place contracts would insist on the fair wage clause being operated more of these unfair firms would be unable to carry on.'

Training became more and more important as the electrical industry grew and became more highly technical. The E.T.U. membership came to have a higher percentage of technically trained young men. The apprentice section of the union had about a quarter of the total membership. On the other hand the union was much troubled about casual boy labour, partly for the sake of the boys themselves, partly because of the danger to wages. The union said it was mainly the small contractor who was to blame:

'There are far too many boys coming into the trade, it is not good for them. The training they get is of no value to them in after-life, and they just become a floating menace to the trade. Certain firms have no regard whatever for the training of boys.

They bring them on to a job and as soon as the job is finished, discharge them.'

In the last few years of peace when Neville Chamberlain was still trying to appease Hitler and Mussolini, and the country drifted towards war the E.T.U. was always firmly opposed to Fascism whether at home or abroad. During the Spanish civil war it sent large sums of money to help the Republican government and the dependants and wounded of the International Brigade. Two thousand men went from Britain to fight against Franco; five hundred were killed.

The labour movement did not trust the Chamberlain government. When the crisis of Czechoslovakia was mounting in 1938, the T.U.C. and the Labour Party declared: 'Whatever the risks involved, Great Britain must make its stand against aggression. There is now no room for doubt or hesitation.' The distrust continued. In 1939, before war began, the E.T.U. declared:

'That in view of the government's recent action in introducing conscription, thereby breaking its pledge to the Trade Union movement we cannot co-operate with the National Government, and therefore the T.U.C. General Council should:

1. Withdraw from the National Service Schemes.
2. Wage a national campaign against the Conscription Bill and the government's foreign policy.'

During the first eight months of war, the 'phoney war' period, this distrust still continued. At the end of 1939 the E.T.U. would not agree to any dilution of labour. Only when Churchill's government replaced Chamberlain's was labour co-operation wholehearted. In May 1940, at the time of the retreat from Dunkirk, the E.T.U. decided to relax the agreed rules of work and admit dilutees.

The history of the electrical workers employed in the Post Office and organized in the Post Office Engineering Union was broadly similar to that of their fellow workers in private enterprise. There were some differences. Being civil servants the members of the P.O.E.U. did not go on strike. Their ability to protect their conditions of work was limited by the fact that they had to rely on influencing public opinion and Parliament. On the other hand, with few exceptions, they had more security from permanent and pensionable employment. Like electrical work in private industry, engineering in the Post Office expanded a great deal, especially in telecommunications. Consequently the trade union membership trebled between 1918 and 1939. One fact which the figures on page 233 do not show is that nearly 80 per cent of the staff were in the union, a far higher proportion than in private industry.

On the whole the Post Office electrical workers had a difficult time during the nineteen-twenties and thirties. Wages were tied to the cost of living on a sliding scale, but in fact real wages, that is money wages related to the cost of living, fell slightly between 1921 and 1939. At times of depression, as in 1921, there was always a public demand to reduce the cost of the civil service. The P.O.E.U. was handicapped in the struggle to improve conditions. It could not join the other unions in the General Strike of 1926 but limited itself to giving financial help and preventing strike-breaking as far as it could. The next year it was still more handicapped under the Trade Disputes and Trade Unions Act. It had been affiliated to the T.U.C. and the Labour Party but under the Act it was forced to cut itself off from both.

The inability of the P.O.E.U. to maintain, let alone improve, real wages caused serious problems. Technical progress made them worse. New techniques and new apparatus continually appeared, particularly in the telephone service. As the work became more complex and more skill was required the skilled men became discontented. This was particularly so in the exchanges:

'Progress was most pronounced in the exchange switch-rooms, test rooms and telegraph instrument rooms. The Baudot and Morkum Teletypes were introduced into the instrument rooms; special valves, frequency filters and impedance adjusters were now found in the telephone repeater rooms, new types of apparatus and circuits were placed in the automatic exchange line finders, registers and selectors.'

As a result, in order to get recognition of their skill, the men on the exchanges broke away and formed their own union, the

Telephone and Telegraph Engineering Guild. They did not go back until the P.O.E.U. changed and improved its organization in 1930.

When the depression and the financial crisis came in 1931 the Post Office engineers, like the rest of the working class, had to take cuts in wages. Pay had fallen all the time, more or less in step with the cost of living; for example, the London pay of the Skilled Workman 1 grade dropped from 100s. in 1921 to 80s. 10d. in 1932. Now in the crisis the government decided to cut the cost of living bonus. This provoked a great demonstration and march of the P.O.E.U. combined with the other civil service unions, culminating in a meeting of 100,000 in Hyde Park. Banners carried the protests: 'Twenty-three cuts since 1920'; '1921–1931 £60 million surplus, 40 per cent wages reduction.'

As the country slowly climbed out of depression, as re-armament began and the cost of living rose, it was possible to press for higher wages. By the outbreak of war wages had risen to the level of 90s. for Skilled Workman 1, 75s. for Skilled Workman 2, and 57s. for Labourer.

Additional Reading

Lord Rayleigh, *The Life of Sir J. J. Thomson*, Cambridge, 1942.

J. J. Thomson, *Recollections and Reflections*, Bell, 1936.

J. G. Crowther, *British Scientists of the Twentieth Century*, Routledge & Kegan Paul, 1952.

S. Moseley, *John Baird*, Odhams Press, 1952.

D. F. Tiltman, *The Life Story of John Logie Baird*, Seeley Service Co., 1933.

S. G. Sturmey, *The Economic History of Radio*, Duckworth, 1958.

J. D. Percy, *John L. Baird*, The Television Society, 1950.

A. Briggs, *The History of Broadcasting in the United Kingdom*, Vol. II, Oxford, 1965.

CHAPTER EIGHT

Radar

RADAR will always be famous in the history of England, because without it the Battle of Britain in the autumn of 1940 could not have been won and England would not have survived. Before radar the politicians said: 'The bomber will always get through.' After it, the fighter pilots of the R.A.F., 'the few', were able to defeat the German air force and save England from invasion.

Radar is short for radio detection and ranging (to get a range on an object is to determine its distance away). Sir Robert Watson-Watt is known as the father of radar but many previous scientists and engineers provided the knowledge which he applied so successfully to the defence of England. In the nineteenth century Heinrich Hertz discovered radio waves (see Chapter Six). He also found that they were reflected from solid objects. His discovery was not developed. Marconi also noted this reflection in his experiments with short-wave transmission, and in 1922 he prophesied that 'it would be able to give warning of the presence and bearing of ships, even should these ships be unprovided with any kind of radio'. But this idea was not followed up at that time.

A few years later scientists in England and the United States were carrying out research into the outside layers of the upper atmosphere of the earth. They were trying to find out the distance between the earth and the ionosphere, a layer near the top of the atmosphere, which reflects radio waves. The technique they used was to send up to the ionosphere very short pulses, or very intense short bursts, of radio energy, and measure the time it took for the reflected pulses to return to earth. This pulse technique became a vital part of radar.

Radar was born in the nineteen-thirties when a number of people in different parts of the world realized that the pulse technique could be used to detect aircraft and ships. Scientists in England, America, Germany and France worked secretly on the problem. In England Sir Robert Watson-Watt found a solution.

SIR ROBERT ALEXANDER WATSON-WATT
(1892–)

Watt was born in the small cathedral city of Brechin in the county of Angus, about twenty-five miles north-east of Dundee. Among his ancestors was James Watt, the great inventor, and the Watson branch of his family included craftsmen and farmers. He was the last of five sons. Watt's father, like his father before him, was a master carpenter and joiner. He was also an elder of the United Presbyterian Church and a Sunday-school teacher for fifty-five years. Watt's mother, Isabelle Watson, was the daughter of a Dundee millwright. Some members of the Watson family rose in the social scale, for, one of them, Watt's godfather, was a minister of the church with a fashionable congregation at Butterburn, Dundee.

With his father Watt had, as he recalled, 'long hours of companionship among the wood shavings, the putty, the screwnails, the smooth, sweet sweep of the plane on the aromatic pitch pine board, the diminuendo and crescendo of the irresistibly terrifying circular saw'. At the elementary school in Brechin Watt was a clever boy. One of his teachers said that he 'very quickly became bored with anything that did not specially interest him' but she gave him freedom to read the books he wanted. At fourteen he won a scholarship to Brechin High School. This was a co-educational State school where some pupils paid fees and some were on scholarships. This is what he thought later on of the subjects taught in the first year:

'English was easy and absorbing. French was interesting and attractive; History and Geography, in their normal form, boring and non-significant; Latin unutterably depressing in its elaborate and over-rational formalism. Geometry was somewhat artificial jugglery, often with the "obvious", algebra relatively easy – but it was a little like gymnastics rather than walking; trigonometry made real sense despite some difficulty. Science wasn't "learning", it was just fun, and endlessly entertaining and curious-making. Physical training, gymnasium, was a stupid waste of time that might so much better have been spent in the lab.'

After two years at the High School Watt decided that science was for him, and he persuaded the headmaster that he should take German instead of Greek which he was due to start. The headmaster had intended him to take classics as a preparation for a career in journalism. Watt went on to win several medals and a scholarship to St. Andrews University. He already had a strong interest in electrical engineering after visits to the city's generating station and had the ambition to become its chief electrical engineer. He entered at the University for the B.Sc. (Engineering). He was interested in politics, and at election times he campaigned for the eminent Liberal statesman, John Morley.

In his first year at University College, Dundee, he studied physics (then called natural philosophy), chemistry, mathematics, engineering and German. Although he did well, gaining several medals and a prize, the pure mathematics taught baffled him. Only when the mathematics became applied mathematics did it interest him. However, the effect of the first year was to turn his interest away from engineering towards physics. . . .

In his second year he was very surprised to be offered a job as assistant to the professor of natural philosophy (physics) at £100 a year. He accepted it, as he greatly admired the professor for his philosophy as well as his science. He was now part-time teacher as well as student. As assistant he had to supervise laboratory work and classes and give one lecture a week on mechanics to first-year students. He concentrated on increasing his knowledge of physics, particularly optics and radio. He set up radio-receiving equipment in his department, and improved his practical skill at setting up experiments. He was still unsettled during these pre-1914 years, for his interest in radiotelegraphy led him to think of sitting the examination for a job in the Post Office Engineering Department. To help him in this his professor gave him a one-man course on the physics of radio-frequency oscillations and wave propagation.

The First World War changed the direction of Watt's life and work. In August 1914 he took the Intermediate examination for the B.Sc. degree of London University in order to get some qualification in science. Then he wrote to the War Office offering his services and a year later he was invited to join the Meteorological Office. There he found that the work was to use radio to give warning of thunderstorms to aircraft pilots. He got leave of absence from the University, and in September 1915 he went down to the Branch Meteorological Office at the Royal Aircraft Factory, Farnborough, Hants, on a salary of £150 a year.

He arrived with the idea of locating thunderstorms by radio direction-finding on atmospherics but he found that the experts at Farnborough had already started to explore this. Most of his work was on watching and reporting the weather. He wrote:

'. . . I lived laborious days. The weatherman's day began with the sending up of a pilot balloon, a toy-size balloon (filled with hydrogen to give it an allegedly known and constant rate of ascent) which was watched by theodolite so that, by assuming its height from the assumed rate of ascent in still air and the lapsed time since its release, and from its exact compass bearing and angle of elevation read by theodolite each minute or half minute, we could compute the wind direction and speed in each thousand foot slab of atmosphere . . . we had to release our balloon about 6.00 a.m. The weather reporting day ends, in general, soon after 6.00 p.m.; Sundays are . . . like other days; the week-days are full of more or less routine work, "the rest of the time was our own", for research, recreation if any, and rest in moderation. It was, mostly, in this "rest of the time" that thunderstorm research had to progress. . . . But of course it was fun.' Soon Watt was promoted to senior professional assistant at £225 a year and in 1917 he was meteorologist-in-charge at Farnborough.

The use of radio to study lightning was not a new idea. Professor Popoff, the Russian scientist, had tried to do this in 1895. Watt worked on the problem from 1916–18, with help from the navy's network of direction-finding stations round the coast of Britain. He achieved some success in locating thunderstorms by means of recording atmospherics but he could not sort out the atmospherics which came from thunderstorms from those which came from other disturbances. So it was necessary to carry out more thorough research into the sources of all atmospherics. It became easier for him to do this when in 1921 he was transferred to the Department of Scientific and Industrial Research which had been set up to bring science closer to military and industrial needs.

Watt spent the years from 1921 to 1935 on research into methods of using radio to get a very thorough knowledge of atmospherics. It was knowledge which became useful for weather forecasting, but it was also a preparation for his work on radar. At first he had to improve the existing means of direction finding and recording. 'I needed a twenty-four-hour watcher,' he wrote, 'undistracted by other duties, immune from fatigue, less discriminating, perhaps, than the human operator, more informative, certainly, than the Popoff-Fenje "lightning recorder" . . . We used a turret clock, of the kind more ordinarily found in the village belfry, to rotate continuously, throughout the twenty-four hours, a vertical indoor frame aerial about six feet square.'

In Watt's first device the atmospherics were picked up by the aerial, amplified, passed to an oscillograph and recorded on a drum. This directional recorder was installed at different points – Aldershot, Lerwick in the Shetlands, Potsdam in Germany, Aboukir in Egypt and Bangalore in India. He then took the important step of using a cathode-ray tube in his directional recorder. Ever since 1916 he had tried without success to get a cathode-ray tube of the high sensitivity and convenience in use which was necessary. In 1919 he had written a memorandum on his 'proposed cathode-ray directional recorder'. Then in 1922, listening to a lecture at the Institution of Electrical Engineers, he heard that the Americans had a new cathode-ray oscillograph and he was able to get one.

He made the first model of his cathode-ray direction finder in 1923, and patented it the following year. With this he could greatly improve his collection and classification of atmospherics. He was trying to classify them according to their shape, that is 'the graph, against time, of the variation of voltage induced in the radio antenna by the atmospheric'. The portrait on the cathode-ray screen was not bright enough to be photographed and so he drew sketches of what he saw on the screen. During three years he drew about 6,000 of these sketches. The place, type and origin of atmospherics were now being pin-pointed. Another method of obtaining information was by getting the help of volunteers who listened to a series of scripted radio talks broadcast by the B.B.C. The listeners, in a network covering Britain and Europe, marked on typescripts of the carefully timed talks the points where atmospherics interfered with reception. A few years later it became possible to make a photographic recording of the direction and wave form of atmospherics. All this work over the years meant that Watt and his helpers could say with increasing accuracy where and how far away had occurred the atmospherics in general and lightning in particular received on his device. It was a big contribution to meteorology and also to the safety of flying.

In 1933 Watt's radio research station was made part of the National Physical Laboratory. This caused problems because the work of the N.P.L. was highly scientific and concerned with very high standards of accuracy. Watt's interests were in more practical problems in which larger tolerances were necessary. He describes here where he wanted to go:

'My own past history showed clearly enough where my sympathies, my enthusiasms and my convictions lay. I had struggled to hold a middle path between fundamental research of a university kind, which I preferred to admire and respect from without rather than from within, and engineering development or *ad hoc* instrument design, which I was glad to be instructed to leave to others. . . . That middle way was the utilization of the principles, methods, techniques and products of fundamental research in a series of scientific investigations, basic to one or another of a wide variety of technological "industries".'

By 1935 Hitler had come to power in Germany and claimed that the German air force was as strong as the R.A.F.

There were sensational reports that Germany had some kind of death ray. Watt was asked by the Director of Scientific Research at the Air Ministry, who was also a personal friend, to inquire into the possibility of using radiation to damage enemy pilots or aircraft. He reported that any such thing was impossible. His report ended thus:

'Meanwhile attention is being turned to the still difficult but less unpromising problem of radio-detection as opposed to radio-destruction, and numerical considerations on the method of detection by reflected radio waves will be submitted if required.'

Fortunately the Air Ministry was interested and did require the calculations Watt promised to give. Watt therefore asked his assistant to work out answers to the following questions.

'Assuming that the wing span of a big bomber can be represented by a simple horizontal wire; (a) what current would be produced in the wire by radio waves of the greatest intensity that we are sure we could play on it, the wavelength used being twice the span, this at a distance of some five or ten miles from our radio sender? (b) what will be the intensity of the radio wave that is sent back, to our sending site, by the wire carrying the current calculated in (a)?'

As a result of these and other calculations Watt sent to the Air Ministry in February 1935 his report on the 'Detection and Location of Aircraft by Radio Methods'. This was the birth of radar. This vital report, about 2,000 words long, explained how it would be possible to detect enemy aircraft up to 200 miles away, by using the methods Watt had used in his cathode-ray direction finder, provided the techniques were improved very greatly. Almost immediately Watt was asked to give a demonstration. It was a demonstration, not of radar, but of the correctness of Watt's calculations, which showed that radio waves would be reflected back from an aircraft strongly enough to show on the cathode-ray screen. Secretly a mobile receiving set was taken to a field ten miles from the powerful short-wave transmitter at Daventry and an R.A.F. Heyford aircraft was ordered to fly at 6,000 feet, shuttling to and fro on a course up and down the centre-line of the radio beam. In this crucial test the aircraft showed as a vertical stub on the screen. Watt wrote:

'The pilot made only a fair job of holding the requested course, no one of his four runs took him right over our heads, but three passed very close. While we waited, now at the screen, an occasional sample of my old raw material, atmospherics from far-off thunderstorms, flicked the little stub of vertical line momentarily to a moderate length, but that was all . . . Then the little stub started to grow steadily, until it was a little over an inch long, then it waxed and waned between a half inch and an inch and a quarter in length; steadied again and waveringly dwindled as we listened to the diminishing drone of the engine.'

Watt and the Air Ministry observer were so pleased with the result that on the way back to London they discussed the possibilities of laying anti-aircraft guns on an invisible target. The official report said, 'It was demonstrated beyond doubt that electromagnetic energy is reflected from the metal components of an aircraft's structure and that it can be detected. Whether aircraft can be accurately located remains to be shown. No one seeing the demonstration could fail to be hopeful of detecting the existence and approximate bearing of aircraft at ranges far in excess of those given by the 200 feet sound mirrors.' (The sound mirrors were great concave walls of concrete intended to catch the whispers of distant aircraft engines and concentrate it on microphones. They were the only warning system Britain had and they could not give much information.) Very soon after this the Air Ministry gave £10,000 to develop Watt's system; it was the first instalment of many millions of pounds. Watt now had to show that radar protection was practicable. Only a few months before the Prime Minister, Baldwin, had said, 'Let us never forget this, since the day of the air the old frontiers are gone. When you think of the defence of England you no longer think of the chalk cliffs of Dover; you think of the Rhine. That is where our frontier lies.' Watt had to show that an air frontier could be put round Britain.

Watt and his team of six began work in disused buildings and laboratories at Orfordness, a remote peninsula on the Suffolk coast. He soon reported that he had been able to detect aircraft fifty miles away and a formation of aircraft as well as a single one. 'Distance was already in the bag; vertical angle was quite another thing and certainly no "piece of cake" ', he wrote. This problem took some time to solve. But the Air Ministry was so pleased with progress that by December, 1935, the government sanctioned a chain of five stations covering the approaches to London, ranging from the South Foreland to Bawdsey, near Orfordness. Bawdsey Manor 'with its spacious lawns, its peaches, its bougainvillaea and its sandy beach below the cliffs', had been bought by the government for Watt's great project; it had the advantage of being 70 feet above sea level.

In these gracious surroundings research went ahead rapidly. It was soon possible to distinguish the number of aircraft up to six by the type of echo received. Under Watt's influence as Superintendent, Bawdsey Manor became a scientific community. He described it:

'. . . a small group of young men, led by one not so young, who set themselves consciously and explicitly the tasks of saving their country from invasion. They were formed into teams and into sub-teams and they did indeed rely on the team aspect. . . . They lived and breathed their enterprise, and they talked about it at breakfast, at lunch, at dinner, in the boat crossing to the Island, and in the hotel sitting-room, until it was time to go to bed.

'The team had no caste spirit. Its pet phrase, "This is a soviet", represents the very real truth of how they should do their work . . . it is not an exaggeration to say it was a dedicated community. It was gay and serious, it was effervescent and painstaking, it was cynical and earnest, it was well-informed and inquiring, it was enthusiastic, tireless and hard-working . . . it was respectful almost of no one and almost of only one thing – professional competence. It saw visions, but it put them aside for immediate production.'

After an R.A.F. exercise in 1937 Watt could report:

'As far as could be judged from the Exercise, accurate plan positions of formations of six or more aircraft at heights of 10,000 feet or more can be effected at ranges of 100 miles or more from the coast, by co-operation of two or more R.D.F. stations under certain conditions. (R.D.F. = Radio Direction Finding.)' Watt felt frustrated by the slow rate of constructing the first five stations. Bawdsey was still the only completed station in June 1937. At this time the Chamberlain government was not much alarmed by Hitler and Mussolini whom it allowed to help Franco crush the Spanish Republic.

As war came rapidly closer, the building of a radar chain was pushed ahead. In March 1938 Hitler entered Vienna and made Austria part of the German state. Churchill warned the House of Commons that Europe was 'confronted with a programme of aggression, nicely calculated and timed, unfolding stage by stage'. By August 1938 when the annual R.A.F. home defence exercise took place there was at last a chain of five radar stations which, however, protected only the Thames estuary and London. The exercise showed, in Watt's words later, 'the true lesson was that we had not yet found the best means of handling so much information as was available on the screen, and even at the plotting-table. There was research to be done in this field, and it was probably even more important than the training of the crews. . . . The Air Staff was not yet prepared to abandon standing patrols, but considered that when the chain was in full going order standing patrols would not be required save in "saturation" conditions. It was, of course, a bit of our job to make the system so good that "saturation" did not occur.' This looked forward to the Battle of Britain when radar made it unnecessary to maintain standing patrols of aircraft so that the pilots could be kept on the ground until enemy aircraft were detected.

During the Munich crisis the short radar chain of five stations was on continuous watch, twenty-four hours in the day; it could give warning of aircraft at 10,000 feet, 80 miles from the coast. The pressure was now on to complete eighteen stations within six months but they were only just finished in time before war began.

In March 1939 Hitler seized what remained of Czecho-Slovakia and on Good Friday the radar chain started a six years' continuous watch. It showed German air formations operating over the North Sea and the English Channel and watched one which flew from Wick to Selsey Bill.

Almost immediately after the announcement of war at 11.00 a.m. on 3rd September, 1939, the air raid sirens wailed for the first time, but there was no raid. Fortunately for radar's reputation the mistake was due to a mistake by a visual observer. The months of the 'phoney' war were used to strengthen the chain; the great fleet base at Scapa Flow was covered. By mid-1940 radar cover stretched from the Isle of Wight, up the east coast and round the Orkneys; it extended into France, Belgium and the North Sea.

On 16th July, 1940, after the evacuation of the British army and its allies from Dunkirk Hitler ordered the invasion of Britain. Invasion was not possible unless the German Luftwaffe first defeated the R.A.F. The Battle of Britain began, according to the Germans, on 13th August. In fact five radar stations between Dover and the Isle of Wight were attacked and damaged on the previous day. Four of them were operational again within a few hours. By that date the chain reached from the Shetlands, down the east coast to Dover, along the south and west to the Lizard, up to the Isle of Man and Northern Ireland.

On 13th August the Germans began their full attack on south-east England, Watt recorded:

'At 5.30 a.m. two large formations began to form over Amiens. The chain, from 110 and more miles away, watched with close interest. A few minutes later an assembly near Dieppe, and another north of Cherbourg, were added to the radar plot. At about 6.30 a.m. they reached the coast where ten squadrons were waiting, also interestedly if less patiently.'

Two days later a harder test came: '15th August was for us The Big Day,' wrote Watt. While the enemy was attacking in the south-east radar reported about midday a formation approaching the Tyneside and Teesside. As the radar operators had not had enough experience of estimating numbers they suggested the formation would be 30 strong; it turned out to be 170. Half an hour later another Luftwaffe formation of about 50 was detected heading for Scarborough. No sooner had these been dealt with than 100 enemy aircraft approaching Bawdsey, 100 over Deal and twenty minutes later 150 over Folkestone were detected. Between 5.00 and 5.20 p.m. radar on the south coast reported 200 to 300 aircraft in seven separate formations. At 6.15 p.m. it reported another 60 to 70 approaching the south-east. Enemy aircraft had tested the radar fence from Portland Bill to the Firth of Forth and had not found a gap anywhere. The R.A.F. squadrons were always waiting for the enemy at the right place. By 18th August the Germans had lost 236 aircraft against 95 British. On that day, however, they began their most dangerous tactic, the attempt to destroy the fighter bases in Kent and Essex. The attack on the fighter bases nearly succeeded; Biggin Hill and North Weald were damaged many times. Then on 7th September the Germans changed their tactic and turned aside to bomb London. This saved the fighter airfields. Watt recorded:

'It was late in the afternoon of 7th September when the radar stations spotted several enemy formations making for Kent and Sussex. The airfields were apparently to be attacked again, and the fighters were dispersed on this assumption, but the Arsenal, the oil tanks at Thameshaven and the Docks instead were bombed by successive waves, and as night fell, provided a beacon on which their successors in turn bombed in an eight hour stream.'

On the 15th September the Luftwaffe made its last great attack. On this occasion their particularly well-organized and concentrated assembly could be detected early and gave the R.A.F. extra time to be in position. Of about 900 enemy aircraft 56 to 60 were shot down during the morning and afternoon to 26 British. At one point Churchill, who was in an R.A.F. operations room, asked 'What reserves have we?' He was told, 'There are none.' But as he recorded:

'Another five minutes passed, and most of our squadrons had descended to refuel. In many cases our resources could not give them overhead protection. Then it appeared that the enemy was going home . . .'

Two days later Hitler postponed the invasion.

After the Battle of Britain radar as well as aircraft went into mass production. Throughout the rest of the war new ways of using radar and new devices were continually being discovered. As each stage of the war developed so radar was called on to help in the operations.

When the night attack on the cities developed the British night fighters were helpless at first. It was essential to equip them with radar. The scientists concentrated on working out ways of using short wavelengths. They found that the shorter the wavelength used the more exact was the location of targets, and the more compact the aerials transmitting the radio beam. When the new Beaufighter planes had radar they could get within a few hundred yards of their targets.

Anti-aircraft fire was also helped. Before the war began it had been decided to produce a gun-laying radar. Watt recorded its development:

'When I found a charming young Ulster territorial officer in charge of an A.A. gun site on a hill-top near Arras on 16th May, 1940, I made slightly apologetic noises in inquiring how he was getting along with his GL MK.1. I was delighted with his reply "It's awfully lonely up here when the GL goes unserviceable" . . . Despite its deficiencies GL MK.1 had to be used, in default of anything nearly as good, in France, in the Middle East, and in Great Britain during the night attacks of September–October 1940, to direct unseen fire. In this night battle over a quarter of a million rounds were fired, and 14 aircraft brought down. 18,500 rounds per bird was in the circumstances a good score. GL. 1 with E-F (Elevation Finding) brought it down during 1941, to 4,100 rounds per bird.'

The battle of the Atlantic to maintain supplies from America reached a climax in April 1941 when 700,000 tons of shipping were sunk. The long battle between enemy submarines and British (and later American) surface and air attack had begun. The first few planes of coastal command equipped with radar were able to detect the submarines as they surfaced to recharge their batteries. The Germans equipped the U-boats with listening sets which could detect the radio beams long before the aircraft was in a position to attack. There was a grim game of cat and mouse, in which the wavelengths were continually changed to prevent the U-boats detecting the aircraft. The answer to the problem was to use very short wavelengths of 10 centimetres and less to defeat the listening sets. This was made possible by research carried out on the magnetron valve by a team at Birmingham University, which resulted in its use as a high-powered generator of short pulses at very short wavelengths. The race for supremacy was won in 1943. In March 477,000 tons of shipping were sunk and only twelve U-boats destroyed; in the last quarter of that year only 146,000 tons were sunk but 53 U-boats.

When D-Day for the invasion of Normandy came on 6th June, 1944, radar played a vital part.

'At 11.00 p.m. on the 5th the paratroop pathfinders, each with his Eureka radar strapped to his knee, took off to mark the dropping zones for the glider-borne air troops, who had to secure intact the bridges on the left flank of the attack. The pathfinders were followed half an hour later by eleven hundred transport aircraft, and, a couple of hours later than that, by the glider force, all equipped with radar assistance principally "Rebecca" sets; "Rebecca" which sought their way to "Eureka" by continuously asking the radar question "Where are you?" to be answered automatically by "Eureka" "I am here" and to be answered only when the question was asked by the right kind of radar set sending and the right kind of signals.'

It was essential that the German radar system should be put out of action. The Germans had 47 radar stations between Calais and Guernsey. They were attacked with rocket-firing aircraft so successfully that not one in six was working.

After the war Watt turned to the peaceful uses of radar and helped to develop it for marine navigation and civil aviation. He left the civil service and became a consultant scientific adviser. He thought that the original team of seven workers in radar was entitled to recognition from the government. After a long inquiry in 1951 the Royal Commission on Awards to Inventors awarded the team £87,950, of which Watt received £52,000. Shortly afterwards he went to live in Canada.

Watt became a Fellow of the Royal Society in 1941 and he was knighted in the following year. He put a hyphen between Watson and Watt. In 1943 he received two honorary degrees, one from his old university, St. Andrews, the other from Toronto. In 1946 he was awarded the U.S.A. Medal of Merit. More recently he has been concerned with the danger to man of the weapons he has invented. Watt attended the Pugwash conference of international scientists on chemical and biological warfare in 1959, and in 1962 he published a book on the control of armaments called *Man's Means to his End*.

THE ELECTRICAL WORKERS (1939–1960)

The 1939–45 war has been called an engineers' war; certainly without the extra efforts from the engineering workers it could not have been fought. The same thing is true of the electrical workers whose skill was vital in the armed forces as well as in the production of arms. In 1944 nearly one-fifth of the members of the Electrical Trades Union were in the forces, in spite of the heavy demand for them in industry. A new corps in the army was created, the Royal Electrical and Mechanical Engineers. Because of the rapid increase in the use of electricity in industry and particularly of electronics in the forces the E.T.U. membership grew from 70,000 to 133,000 during the war.

The main aim of the organized electrical workers during the war was twofold; to increase production as much as possible and at the same time to protect wages and conditions of work. Go To It!, the government's slogan, was printed across the cover of the *Electrical Trades Journal*. The unions had to deal with many problems which arose from this aim. The government issued orders which imposed a strict control of labour, but which at the same time required consultation with the unions and satisfactory welfare arrangements to be made by the employers. The unions accepted willingly the control but they had to make sure that the employers played their part. Dilution agreements, the employment of unskilled and semi-skilled women, as well as men, on skilled jobs, were a continual problem. The Electrical Trades Union frequently had to complain that the local discussions with employers which were part of the agreements were not being held. At different stages of the war it was necessary to move skilled electricians to various parts of the country, the Clyde, the north-east coast and Southampton, and the E.T.U. had to see that proper arrangements for travel and welfare were made. Members in the forces were sometimes not employed properly and the union was able to see that their skill was not wasted in spit and polish. As in the First World War more and more women were employed; soon the E.T.U. had over four thousand women members. The unions' aim was equal pay for equal work.

The great need for more efficient production of arms of all kinds caused a great deal of criticism of muddle and waste in industry. When the government set up joint production committees in the royal ordnance factories and the engineering industry followed suit they were welcomed by the electrical workers. The E.T.U. said:

'The function of management in industry has always been viewed as a privilege of ownership. Workers were mainly "hands", hewers of wood and drawers of water, to be disciplined in the factory and workshop by one of their own kind in the figure of an overlooker or a foreman taking orders from above. The problems of workshop management were considered outside the province of the workers. . . . Now with the establishment of joint works production committees this barrier of exclusive control has been pierced. For the first time in the history of industrial relations in this country the right of labour to participate with the management in matters relating to production has been recognized. The executive council hopes that members will do everything possible to make the committees a success.'

All employers did not welcome the joint production committees, as they seemed to threaten their right to manage their own firms. In the shipbuilding industry some conservative employers resisted the coming of yard committees. At Cammell Laird's yard the E.T.U. received complaints that the supply of electrical materials was badly managed and that the time of the workers was wasted waiting for materials. The E.T.U. decided:

'That the Comptroller of the Admiralty be forwarded the complaints of our members as there is no Yard Committee functioning at Messrs. Cammell Laird to deal with grievances due to the refusal of the firm to recognize same.'

It was however in the shipbuilding industry that the organized electrical workers made their biggest change of policy. In the crisis of the war at sea against the German U-boats the Minister of Labour, Ernest Bevin, appealed to the E.T.U. to agree to the wage system of payment by results in order to speed up the production of naval escort vessels. The union had always been opposed to this system and a ballot vote of the members had rejected it. Now when Bevin explained the necessity of a 30 per cent increase in electrical work and that there was no other way of getting it the E.T.U. agreed to his request. Afterwards Bevin acknowledged the help:

'I suddenly had to find 4,000 electricians. . . . We met the unions, and indeed most of the shipbuilding unions in the various branches. But the E.T.U. – and I pay them this public compliment – agreed with me to take on that pernicious thing, as they always thought it, payment by results, to help us in this task. Now what was the result? The change they made at their delegate conference was worth about 3,000 to 4,000 men to us, and enabled us to put on the campaign against U-boats at the precise date the Cabinet decided it should operate.'

This was one of the reasons why the battle of the Atlantic was won in 1943.

Because of this attitude to war production there were very few strikes or even disputes. But there was trouble at some places. In Vickers Armstrong at Barrow there was a dispute in 1943 about the operation of a premium bonus scheme. But when an agreement was reached it stated that 'it is mutually recommended that each workman shall give output in accordance with his capacity'. In the same year at Manchester there was a strike on contracting work, although strikes were illegal. A demand for an increase in wages of threepence an hour went to arbitration, as was then compulsory. The Manchester men threatened to continue the strike unless the full amount was awarded. The arbitration tribunal awarded an increase of three farthings an hour for some grades of work, the E.T.U. repudiated the Manchester local strike committee, and the men went back to work.

Apprentices and young workers were not a new problem but a bigger one. In spite of recruitment to the forces the number of apprentices as a percentage of all members of the E.T.U. rose from 13 per cent to 21 per cent during the war. In Scotland the contractors refused the union the right to negotiate wages until 1943. In England the union negotiated wages of 16s. 6d. per week in London and 14s. 6d. elsewhere at age fourteen, increasing to 46s. in London and 43s. elsewhere at 21 and over. There had been two unofficial strikes of apprentices because of low wages and there was a threat of legal proceedings against them but the matter was dropped when the E.T.U. intervened. The union also made an agreement with the employers which limited the percentage of unindentured apprentices and other young workers to be employed.

The effect of earlier inventions on the activities of the E.T.U. appeared in various ways. A new branch called Manchester Radio was opened to cater for the hundreds of radio workers in that area. Technical developments with process instrument work at Imperial Chemical Industries led to negotiations between the union and the firm. It was agreed that the instrument men on calibrators should have craft status, whether instrument artificers or instrument attendants. In another modern industry, air transport, the union made an agreement on wages.

As electrical work spread into more and more industries so the E.T.U. was obliged to enter them. While the union maintained its older activity in supply, contracting, engineering and shipbuilding, it also gained the right of negotiating wages and conditions of work for the first time in quite different industries, for instance, flourmilling, papermaking, seed crushing and provender and compound feeds, motor vehicle retail and repair. When the war ended with a Labour government in power for the first time for sixteen years the union called for 'a realistic approach to new processes in industry and to the plans of the government for post-war reconstruction'.

After the war the electrical workers, in private and public enterprise, organized in the E.T.U. became more involved in government policies. This was partly because all governments were forced to deal with the post-war economic problems, but also because in 1945 the Labour government began to control and plan the economy. In addition the union itself was very active in politics as its leadership became communist.

One of the first acts of the government was to nationalize the electrical supply industry in 1947. Twelve years earlier the E.T.U. had demanded this and now it was deeply involved because of the large number of its members employed in the industry. It now wanted the compensation which was to be paid to the shareholders in the electricity companies to be lower than the government's figure, and also workers' representatives to have places on the new boards. Although it did not get either of these demands it was clear that nationalization gave promise of better conditions. The general secretary of the union was appointed to the board of the new British Electricity Authority.

In the same year there was a basic change of policy on wages. This was the change to payment by results. There had always been strong opposition to piecework among the organized electrical workers but now the circumstances were different. It was necessary to help a Labour government which was starting the post-war reconstruction while at the same time having to grapple with serious economic problems caused by the war. If production in industry were increased the export drive would go well, more food could be imported and 'the sooner we can do away with queues'. In the long debate on this issue there was some opposition. One old worker said:

'I have finished work, or shall soon, but I am very concerned about people between 35 and 50, men are too old to work at 35 now . . . I have two reports . . . one bricklayer refusing to work with another man because he was not working quickly enough. I think the reason men are not working quickly is due to material. . . . Pay them a decent wage for the work they are doing, without this Payment by Results.'

Another worker argued that this was not the way to increase production:

'I believe that if workers are given a full share of responsibility to manage industry, for the government to control profits as they should, and to give the opportunity to the workers to say yes or no in management of industry, then I think there will be a full sense of responsibility on the part of the workers which by accepting it they will go forward to increase production as the miners have proved that without any incentive bonus they realize the economic position of the country, and are playing their part to overcome it.'

Others argued that in a capitalist system the workers should press for profits to be shared out instead of working harder for more pay. The reply was that Labour in power must be helped to build a socialist system and that if there were more planning all would be well. At the end payment by results was approved by a large majority. This was partly because the decision only recognized what was already the practice in some industries, partly because it would give the union leadership more scope to push the government towards the left.

By 1948 wage increases and improvements in hours of work had been won in many industries. During the next four years of the Labour government the union always opposed its economic policy. It led the resistance to the government policy of wage restraint as soon as the T.U.C. accepted it in 1948; it said that there should be more control of profits instead of restraint on wages. It claimed that it was necessary to 'continue to press the legitimate claims of our membership for higher wages at the expense of profits'. Finally, in spite of arguments that it was the cost of living which had to be brought down, it was the E.T.U.'s motion against wage restraint which the T.U.C. passed in 1950.

Electrical work continued to spread rapidly into more and more industries. In the past this had frequently meant demarcation disputes with other organized workers. It was particularly important that the electrical workers should have friendly relations with workers in other occupations because there was now hardly any industry which did not include some electrical work. The trade union world as a whole had a great deal of trouble with inter-union disputes during the post-war decades but the E.T.U. tried actively to prevent them. It made agreements with many other unions about recruitment and negotiation with employers; the building operatives, the miners (with whom there had been many disputes about the colliery electricians), the film studio and cinema employees, the radio officers, the railwaymen, the municipal workers, and the health service employees. Electrical technology had become part of an ever-widening range of occupations. By 1960 the membership of the E.T.U., then the seventh largest of the unions, had reached almost a quarter of a million.

In spite of, or partly because of, this growth in size the

union went through its worst crisis since it was formed in 1889. There was a struggle inside the union between the communist leaders and their opponents. In order to keep their power the leaders falsified the results of elections to posts in the union. Consequently in 1960 certain members of the union issued writs against the union and its officers for fraud in the election for the general secretary. In that election John Byrne, a non-communist, stood against the retiring secretary, Frank Haxell, a communist, and was declared to have been defeated although he had a majority of the votes. After a trial which lasted six weeks the judge found that a group of communist leaders, including the president of the union, 'conspired together to prevent by fraudulent and unlawful devices the election of the Plaintiff Byrne in place of the Defendant Haxell as General Secretary of the Defendant Union'. The union was expelled from the T.U.C. and the Labour Party. However, the next elections in the union, supervised by chartered accountants, resulted in a new leadership and the union was restored to the labour fold in 1962.

After this shock the E.T.U. reorganized itself so as to ensure not only the rights of the organized electrical worker but also a new structure for the union more in keeping with industrial and social change. Its economic policy also changed. When the government came forward in the early sixties with a policy for incomes and prices the union supported it. 'We are in favour of an incomes policy,' it stated in 1966, 'because we accept the general proposition that if the gross national product is expanding at a certain rate, increases in income must be contained within the boundaries of that rate of expansion.' But an incomes policy must do more than merely control incomes: 'As well as being the means for keeping income increases within the bounds of gains in overall output, an incomes policy must have two main aims. One, it must further the cause of social justice. Two, it must encourage increases in productivity.'

This statement, made on behalf of 30,000 electrical workers to the Royal Commission on trade unions and employers' associations was a great change, in tune with the times, from the purposes of the union when it was founded seventy-seven years before.

Meanwhile in another province of electrical work, the Post Office, there were also big changes. The Engineering Department of the Post Office (together with factories and cable ships) grew rapidly. By 1960 the number of employees had risen to about 80,000 of whom 90 per cent were members of the Post Office Engineering Union. Its membership had nearly doubled since 1939. The basis of this growth throughout the period was the rapid technological change and automation. The main effort of the workers was to get recognition of the greater technical knowledge and skills required of them.

They did not begin to succeed in this aim until after 1945. During the Second World War they played a great part. The Post Office engineers were determined that telecommunications should be maintained in spite of heavy bombing. In the London blitz they had to work while the bombs were falling. Much of the work in repairing underground cables and circuits in bomb craters was dangerous. Bravery and determination were often needed. At sea two cable ships were sunk, with loss of life. In spite of all this, real wages fell, particularly those of the skilled men, while at the same time their work became more complex.

It was because of this situation that two groups of skilled men in the P.O.E.U. formed breakaway unions, the Engineering Officers' (Telecommunications) Association and the National Guild of Motor Engineers, and did not rejoin until nine years later. For the same reasons the union wanted a change in the name of the skilled workman grade which dated back to 1911. Consequently the two new and more up-to-date grades of technical officer and technician were made.

The period of Labour government from 1945 had two effects. When the Trades Disputes Act was repealed the P.O.E.U. could affiliate to the T.U.C. once again and this it did immediately, thus taking its proper place in the labour movement. Shortly after, when the T.U.C. accepted the government's policy of wage restraint the union gave its support. When however the Korean war brought inflation it pressed for wage increases like most other unions.

Wages were the main concern throughout the post-war years of growing inflation. For many years the union had tried to get wages that compared fairly with those in the electrical industry. At last a Royal Commission accepted the principle that they should so compare and gave a formula which made it possible for the wages to be roughly in line with those in manufacture whereas they had always been liable to fall behind. It seemed that the authorities had now realized that it was necessary to reward knowledge and skill in the public service just as much as in private enterprise. It was, however, quite another thing for the Post Office to operate the principle. When the Post Office refused to negotiate on this basis in 1961, 12,000 members of the union marched in protest from the Embankment to Tower Hill with banners carrying slogans – 'Fair Play, Fair Pay; Negotiation not Dictation; Without Us no TV; Without Us no Phones', and placed a ban on overtime; and when it refused to accept an arbitration award of wages because of the government's current 'pay pause' they resorted to work to rule.

Although there was discontent with pay and conditions of work, the Post Office engineers were always keenly interested in new techniques and new methods of work. This was bound to happen in a service which could make use of the latest technological developments as they appeared and where there was always scope for improvement. In fact it was often the union which pressed the political head of the Post Office, the Postmaster-General, for better services, as with the telephone for example. Here is part of a typical press release from the P.O.E.U. in February 1963:

> *Longer Wait for Telephones*
>
> Average waiting time for a telephone has lengthened throughout the country to just over 13 weeks. In March last year the average wait was just over 11½ weeks. This emerges from studies made by the Research Department of the Post Office Engineering Union which reveals Britain's backwardness as a telephone-using country.

At the back of this public pressure for better services was a long history of participation with the management in production, productivity and the introduction of new methods of work. Ever since 1939 there had been a joint committee of the union and the Post Office to discuss changes in engineering practice, and it was the union which asked for joint production committees in the Post Office. The two sides collaborated in a new method of maintaining automatic telephone exchanges. Together they reviewed engineering methods and organization and thereby improved the ways in which the skills of the workers could be used. The union called for the full use of discoveries by scientists and technologists to improve the public service. It promised support on three conditions: full consultation with it, proper safety rules, and a share in the results of higher productivity in the form of wages and conditions of work.

Additional Reading

Sir Robert Watson-Watt, *Three Steps to Victory*, Odhams Press, 1957.

Radar. A report on Science at War. Published in the U.S.A. by the Government Printing Office. Reprinted by H.M.S.O., 1945.

Index